TEACHER'S ANSWER BOOK
HAYES MODERN GEOMETRY

P9-AOV-855

UNIT I
EXERCISES A - C

1. Point 2. Straight line 3. Curved segment 4. Line-segment
5. Broken line 6. Ray 7. Half-line 8. Plane 9. Curved surface (sphere) 10. Space 11. Plane geometry 12. Solid (space) geometry 13. Plane geometry 14. Solid (space) geometry 15. Line 16. Plane 17. two 18. Three 19. Line-segment MN 20. Line AB 21. Point x 22. Ray OC
23. Broken line RSTX 24. Plane N 25. Curved surface R
26. Half-line xy 27. T 28. X 29. T 30. T 31. X 32. T
33. T

EXERCISES D - F

1. Postulates 2. Infinite 3. Infinite 4. One 5. Three 6. Four
7. One 8. Skew lines 9. Parallel lines 10. A straight line
11. None 12. Parallel 13. No 14. Yes 15. Theorem
16. Yes 17. Yes 18. Yes 19. Yes 20. No 21. Yes 22. No
23. Yes 24. Yes 25. Straight line-segment 26. Odd
27. inductive 28. deductive 29. deductive 30. intuitive
31. intuitive 32. inductive 33. deductive 34. intuitive

EXERCISES G - H

1. Angle 2. Union 3. Vertex 4. Side 5. 3 6. 360° 7. 600'
8. 20° 9. 7200' 10. No 11. Angle-number line
12. Opposite ray 13. Other 14. Acute ∠ 15. Right ∠
16. Obtuse ∠ 17. Straight ∠ 18. Acute ∠ 19. Obtuse ∠
20. Oblique ∡ 21. Supplementary 22. Complementary
23. Yes 24. Yes 25. Yes 26. No 27. Yes 28. No 29. No
30. Yes 31. Yes 32. Yes 33. 130° 34. 30° 35. Acute
36. Obtuse 37. Right 38. Straight 39. Vertical 40. Adjacent
41. Dihedral 42. Edge 43. Faces 44. Supplementary adj.
45. Complementary adj. 46. Line-segment joining them
47. One 48. 45° 49. 120° 50. 30° 51. 75° 52. 30°
53. 45° 54. 90° 55. 30° 56. Between A & C 57. 4
58. Midpoint 59. 3 points 60. Between M and S
61. Betweenness 62. No 63. 3 64. 2 65. 2

EXERCISES I

1. 1 2. 1 3. 1 4. 1 5. Infinite 6. 1 7. 1 8. 1
9. Perpendicular 10. Perpendicular

UNIT II
EXERCISES A

1. Polygon 2. Triangle 3. Quadrilateral 4. Pentagon
5. Hexagon 6. Heptagon 7. Octagon 8. Nonagon
9. Decagon 10. Equilateral 11. Scalene 12. Isoceles
13. Acute 14. Right 15. Obtuse 16. Altitude 17. Base
18. Perimeter 19. Diagonal 20. Interior region 21. Exterior region 22. No 23. X 24. X 25. X 26. T 27. T 28. T
29. X 30. X 31. 1 32. 29 33. 22 34. 3-0-1 35. 4-1-2
36. 5-2-3 37. 6-3-4 38. n — 3 39. n — 2 40. inductive

EXERCISES B - C

1. Real numbers 2. Zero 3. Line of real numbers 4. B
5. Rational 6. Irrational 7. Rational 8. Irrational 9. Zero
10. One 11. Distributive 12. Yes 13. Yes 14. Yes 15. Yes
16. No 17. No 18. Yes 19. Yes 20. No 21. Yes 22. Yes
23. Yes 24. Yes 25. No 26. No 27. Yes 28. Yes 29. No
30. Yes 31. Yes 32. Yes 33. Yes 34. Yes 35. Yes
36. Reflexive 37. Symmetric 38. Substitution 39. Transitive
40. Congruent 41. When = in length 42. When = in measure 43. When they can be made to coincide 44. cscte
45. cacte 46. RA 47. ∠A 48. equal 49. measure
50. Size-shape

THEOREM 17

PROOF 1. Th. 10 2. BC-Reflexive 3. - 4. ASA 5. c.p.c.t.e.
6. c.p.c.t.e. 7. Th. 8 8. Div. Prop. of equality 9. ASA
10. c.p.c.t.e.
Cor. 1: XZ = YZ = XY PROOF 1. Given 2. YZ - Th. 17
3. Given 4. YZ - Th. 17 5. Transitive

THEOREM 19

PROOF 1. Post. 26 2. Post. 24 3. Post. 25 4. - 5. Post. 6
6. ≅ ▲

THEOREM 20

PROOF 1. Post. 26 2. - 3. Given 4. Def. of isos. △ 5. Base ∡ of isos. △ are = 6. HA

EXERCISES D

1. a. s.a.s. = s.a.s. b. a.s.a. = a.s.a. c. s.s.s. = s.s.s.
2. a. h.a. = h.a. b. h.s. = h.s. 3. a. c.p.c.t.e. b. Vert. ∡ are

= c. base ∠s of isos. △ d. comp's of = ∠s e. sup's of = ∠s f. ∠s
= to same ∠ 4. a. = sides of isos △ b. c.p.c.t.e. c. Line-
segment = to same line-segment 5. PROOF 1. Vert. ∠s are =
2. h.a. = h.a. 3. c.p.c.t.e. 6. PROOF 1. h.s. = h.s. 2. c.p.c.t.e.
7. a. s.s.s. = s.s.s. b. ∠5 c. c.p.c.t.e. 8. a. h.a. = h.a.
b. Th. 8 c. given 9. a. a.s.a. = a.s.a. b. c.p.c.t.e. c. Th. 8
10. a. s.s.s. = s.s.s. b. c.p.c.t.e. c. c.p.c.t.e. 11. a. s.a.s. =
s.a.s. b. cacte c. Th. 8 12. a. h.s. = h.s. b. c.p.c.t.e.
c. sides opp = ∠s of a △ are 13. a. s.a.s. = s.a.s. b. c.p.c.t.e.

EXERCISES E

1. 1 2. 0 3. 1 4. 2 5. Infinite 6. 0 7. 3 8. Infinite 9. 1
10. 1 11. 5 & 10 12. 5 & 8 13. 5 14. 5 & 8 15. axis of
symmetry

UNIT III
CONSTRUCTION 1

PROOF -AS-BS:
1. BS-construction 2. RS reflexive Prop. of Equality 3. SBR-
s.s.s. 4. c.p.c.t.e. 5. s.a.s. (or a.s.a.) 6. c.p.c.t.e.
7. c.p.c.t.e. 8. def. of ⊥ ls. 9. def. of ⊥ bisector

CONSTRUCTION 2
PROOF BO:
1. BC-Construction 2. BO-Construction 3. CO-Reflex. Prop. of
Equality 4. AOC-BOC-s.s.s. 5. NCO (or BCO)-c.p.c.t.e.
6. def. of ⊥ ls.

CONSTRUCTION 3
PROOF:
1. RWP-SWP-s.s.s. 2. ROP-SOP-s.a.s. (or ASA) 3. c.p.c.t.e.
4. def. of ⊥ ls.

CONSTRUCTION EXERCISES A

1.

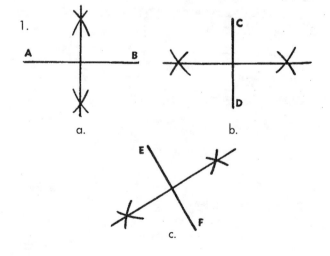

a.

b.

c.

2.

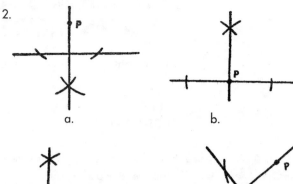

a.

b.

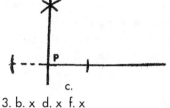

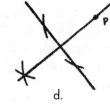

c.

d.

3. b. x d. x f. x

CONSTRUCTION 4
PROOF CO:
1. SO-reflexive Prop. of Equality 2. SC-construction 3. CO-
Construction 4. SOA-SOC-s.s.s. 5. RSO-c.p.c.t.e. 6. def. of
bisector of ∠

CONSTRUCTION 5
PROOF RS:
1. construction 2. DC-RS-construction 3. DOC-RPS-s.s.s.
4. c.p.c.t.e.

CONSTRUCTION EXERCISES B

1.

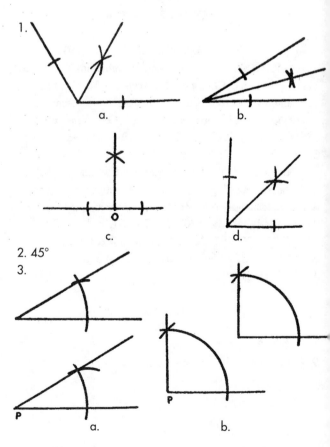

a.

b.

c.

d.

2. 45°
3.

a.

b.

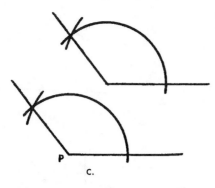

c.

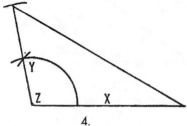

4.

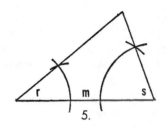

5.

UNIT IV
PRELIMINARY EXERCISES A

1. Parallel-skew 2. Sometimes 3. Never 4. One 5. One
6. Any number 7. Parallel-meet (intersect) 8. Parallel
9. Parallel 10. Parallel

PRELIMINARY EXERCISES B

1. a. transversal b. exterior angles c. interior angles
d. consecutive interior angles e. alternate exterior angles
f. corresponding angles g. alternate interior angles 2. a. MN
b. 2, 3, 5, & 6 c. 1, 4, 7, & 8 d. 2-6, 3-5 e. 1-8, 4-7
f. 1-5, 2-7, 8-3, 4-6 g. 2-5, 3-6

THEOREM 22

PROOF: 3. Reflex. Prop. of Equality 5. c.p.c.t.e. 7. Supp. of
= ∠ area = (Th. 8)
Cor. 1: To Prove: 4 - 7 PROOF 1. 22 2. 6 3. substitution
Cor. 2: 2 To Prove: 8 PROOF 1. Th. 22 2. 4-8-vert. ∠ are =
3. Substitution
Cor. 3: To Prove: 4 PROOF 1. Supp. adj. ∠ 2. 22
substitution

THEOREM 23

2. 22 5. 19
Cor. 1: PROOF 1. Vert. ∠ are = 2. given 3. substitution
4. Th. 23
Cor. 2: PROOF 1. Vert. ∠ are = 2. given 3. substitution or
Prop. of Equality 7 4. Th. 23
Cor. 3: PROOF 1. Def. of supp. ∠ 2. given 3. substitution
or Prop. of Equality 7 4. Prop. of Equality 2
5. Th. 23
Cor. 4: PROOF 2. Th. 23

EXERCISES B

1. a. alt. int. - alt. ext. - corres. b. a pair of int. ∠ on same
side of transversal - 180 c. converse d. parallel e. parallel
f. parallel 2. a. 125° b. 55° c. 55° d. 125° e. 125°
f. 180° 3. a. yes b. yes c. no d. yes e. yes f. no g. yes
h. no i. yes j. no 4. X = 30° and 5X = 150° · Therefore RS is
‖ to TW because the interior ∠ on same side of transversal are
supplementary.

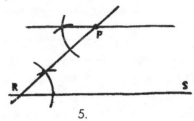

5.

THEOREM 28

PROOF: 1. Post. 7 2. Th. 25 4. Cor. 4 5. Th. 27

THEOREM 29

PROOF: 1. vert ∠ are = 2. Dihed. ∠ is measured by its plane
∠ 3. substitution principle

THEOREM 30

PROOF: 1. Th. 3 2. Th. 11 6. Cor. 4 7. Th. 11 8. Def. of a
plane ∠ of a dihed. ∠ 11. Th. 27

EXERCISES C

1. Perpendicular 2. Parallel 3. equal 4. parallel 5. two
6. parallel (or part of) 7. equal 8. parallel 9. Parallel
10. point

THEOREM 31

PROOF: 1. W - Th. 22, Cor. 1 2. same as 1 3. substitution
or trans. Prop. of Equality

THEOREM 32

PROOF 1. 180 - Th. 22, Cor. 3 2. r - Th. 22 3. substitution

EXERCISES D

1. PROOF: 1. 3 - Th. 32 2. 1 - 2 Th. 31 3. 3 - substitution
2. PROOF: 1. Th. 21 2. Th. 23, Cor. 4 3. Th. 31
3. a. supplementary b. equal

UNIT V
THEOREM 33

PROOF AB: 1. 4 - 1- 5 Post. 14 2. 2 - 3 Th. 22 2. Th. 22
3. substitution
Cor. 1: 1. 180 - supp. adj. ∡ 2. 180° - Th. 33 3. ∠1 + ∠2
+ ∠3 - substitution 4. subtraction 5. Prop. of Equality 5
Cor. 2: 1. 180 - Th. 33 2. obtuse ∠ 3. No. 11 5. Def. of
acute ∡
Cor. 3: 1. To Prove: C - C′ PROOF 1. B - C - 180° - Th. 33
2. B′ - C′ - 180° - Th. 33 3. B - C - A - A′ - B′ - C′ -
substitution or trans. Prop. of Equality 4. Given 5. C - C′
subtraction Prop. of Equality
Cor. 4: To Prove: A - C PROOF 1. A - B - C - Th. 33 2. 90°
- rt. ∠ 3. A - C - 90° - subtraction Prop. of Equality
Cor. 5: PROOF: 1. Post. 27 2. 180 - Cor. 3 3. 180 - Th. 33
5. Post. 27
Cor. 6: PROOF: 1. Post. 27 2. given 3. Cor. 4 4. given
5. Cor. 4 6. hypothesis 7. Post. 27

EXERCISES A

1. a. 3-1-1 b. 180° c. 60° d. 90° 2. 26° 3. 18°-36°-126°
4. 60° 5. 68° 6. 34°

CONSTRUCTION EXERCISES A

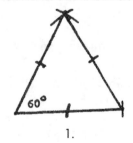

1.

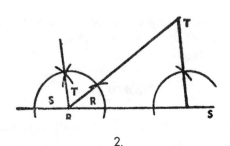

2.

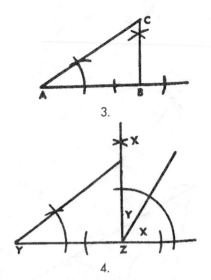

3.

4.

THEOREM 34

PROOF 1. S - Th. 4 2. -3 - 4 - vert. ∡ are = 3. -2 - Cor. 3
Cor. 1: To Prove: 180 PROOF 1. Th. 34 2. 180° - Def. of
supp. adj. ∡ 3. 180 - substitution principle or trans. Prop. of
Equality

EXERCISES B

1. PROOF 1. t - Th. 34 2. t - corres. ∡ of ‖ ls. are =
3. substitution or trans. Prop. of Equality 2. PROOF 1. Given
2. A st. line ⊥ to one of two ‖ s is ⊥ to the other 3. ∡ having
sides ⊥ right to left and left to right are supplementary.

UNIT VI
EXERCISES A

1. a. quadrilateral b. parallelogram c. rectangle d. rhombus
e. rhomboid f. square g. trapezoid h. isoceles trapezoid
i. base j. altitude k. bases l. altitude 2. a. A, B, C, E, F, G
b. D c. B, D d. B, C, D, E, e. F, G f. D g. C, E h. E i. W
j. r, t, m, n k. X, Y, V, Z l. G 3. a. shortest b. straight
c. perpendicular d. perpendicular e. arc of a great circle
4. T 5. X 6. T 7. X 8. X 9. T 10. T

THEOREM 35

To Prove: ZY-XY-Y-Z
PROOF: 1. Post. 3 2. ZY-def. of ▱ 3. Th. 22 4. XY-def.
of ▱ 5. -3 - Th. 22 6. reflex, Prop. of Equality 7. WYZ-
a.s.a. 8. ZY-XY-Z-c. p. c. t. e. 9. 4-3-Y add. Prop. of Equality
Cor. 1: To Prove: BC PROOF: 1. def. of ▱ 2. BC Th. 35
Cor. 3: 1. Def. of ▱ 2. Th. 22, Cor. 3

THEOREM 36

To Prove: YO-ZO
1. Def. of ▱ 2. 2-3 Th. 22 3. Th. 35 4. WOX-YOZ-a.s.a.
5. YO-ZO-c.p.c.t.e.
Cor. 1 PROOF: 1. WO-SO-given 2. 1-2-Vert. ∡s are =
3. SOR-s.a.s. 4. 5-c. p. c. t. e. 5. Th. 23 6. WOS-s.a.s.
7. 7-c. p. c. t. e. 8. Th. 23 9. def. of ▱
Cor. 2 PROOF: 1. given 2. Th. 36 3. div. Prop. of Equality
4. def. of isos. Δ 5. 180 - Th. 33 6. 2-4 Th. 16
7. 2-2-180 substitution 8. div. Prop. of Equality 9. Th. 35
10. Th. 8 11. Def. of rectangle

THEOREM 37

Given: ZY-XY Proof:
1. WYX-s.s.s. 2. s-w-c.p.c.t.e. 3. Th. 23 4. def. of ▱

THEOREM 38
Post. 3
1. Rt reflex. Post. 3 Prop. of Equality 2. 3 - Th. 22 3. WT-
given 4. TWR-s.a.s. 5. ST-c.p.c.t.e. 6. Th. 37

EXERCISES B

1. a. Th. 37 b. Th. 36, Cor. 3 2. a. def. of ▱ b. Th. 36
3. a. Th. 38 b. Th. 35 4. a. Th. 36, Cor. 1 b. Th. 35
5. a. s.s.s. b. c.p.t.e. c. def. of ⊥ ls. 6. a. def. of
parallelogram b. Th. 35 7. a. Th. 23, Cor. 4 b. Th. 35,
Cor. 1 c. HS d. c.a.c.t.e. 8. a. Th. 36, Cor. 1 b. Th. 36,
Cor. 2 9. PROOF: 1. DM = CN Th. 35, Cor. 1
2. AD = BC-def. of isos. Δ or given 3. ΔAMD ≅ Δ BNC-h.s.
4. ∴ ∠ A = ∠ B-c.p.c.t.e. 10. a. parallel
b. equal c. bisect each other d. parallel * & equal *

CONSTRUCTION EXERCISES B

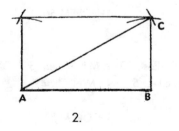

1.

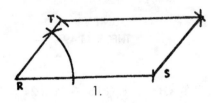

2.

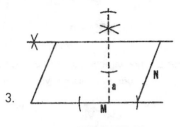

3.

THEOREM 39

To Prove:
PR PROOF: Th. 9
1. construction 2. Th. 21 3. given 4. Th. 35, Cor. 1 5. PH
substitution 6. 2-t Th. 22, Cor. 1 7. 4 Th. 33, Cor. 3
8. a.s.a. 9. PR c.p.c.t.e.
Cor. 1 PROOF: 1. given 2. construction 3. Vert. ∡ are =
4. RSC-MSB-s.a.s. 5. 4-c.p.c.t.e. 6. Th. 23
7. c.p.c.t.e. 8. given 9. BM transitive 10. Th. 38 11. def. of
▱ or opp. sides of ▱ are = 12. Th. 35 13. div. Prop.
of Equality
Cor. 2 to Prove: Th. 9 1. given 2. construction 3. Th. 21
4. MC-given or def. of bisecting line-segment 5. CN-NB
Th. 39 6. $\frac{1}{2}$ AB Th. 39, Cor. 1

THEOREM 40

To Prove:
DB-CD PROOF: Th. 9
1. 1 BR Th. 39, Cor. 2 2. Th. 22, Cor. 4 3. All rt ∡ are =
4. DR reflex. Prop. of Equality 5. DRC-DRB-s.a.s. or H.S.
6. c.p.c.t.e. 7. DB-DC transitive

THEOREM 41

PROOF:
1. Th. 40 2. Th. 16 3. 60° - Th. 33 4. Th. 17

THEOREM 42

PROOF: Post. 3
1. Th. 40 2. given 3. transitive 4. def. of equlat. Δ 5. Th.
16, Cor. 1 6. Th. 33, Cor. 4

EXERCISES C

1. a. equal b. bisect c. $\frac{1}{2}$ the hypotenuse d. equidistant-
vertices e. parallel - $\frac{1}{2}$ 3rd side f. 30° g. $\frac{1}{2}$ - parallel 2. 12
3. 60° 4. 20 5. 20 (Draw MO.) 6. Draw BD. 1. BD-BD Th.
39, Cor. 1 2. BD-BD Th. 39, Cor. 1 3. vw Th. 21 4. vw
substitution 5. Th. 38 8. Th. 39

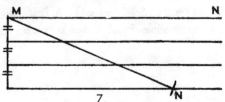

7.

EXERCISES D

1. a. If two angles are not vertical, they are unequal. (false)
b. If two angles are unequal, they are not vertical (true)

UNIT VII
PRELIMINARY EXERCISES A

1. a. 4-4-2 b. 5-5-3 c. 6-6-4 d. 7-7-5 e. 8-8-6 2. a. 13
b. 98 c. 7 d. N-2 3. a. 32 b. 102 4. a. 180 b. 2340
c. 2700 d. (n-2) 180 e. 3600 5. inductive reasoning

THEOREM 43

PROOF:
1. Fundamental Principle I 2. 1 Th. 33 3. multiplication
4. substitution 5. substitution
Cor. 1 PROOF: 1. Th. 43 2. division
Cor. 2 PROOF: 1. def. of supp. adj. $\measuredangle$ 2. n-given (because
there are n $\measuredangle$) 3. add. Prop. of Equality 4. Th. 43
5. subtraction

EXERCISES A

1. 1800°-150°-360°-30° 2. 1080°-135°-360°-45°
3. 6-720°-360°-60° 4. 10-1440°-144-360° 5. 32-360°
6. no: yes 7. yes 8. 100° 9. 4

THEOREM 44

PROOF 3 & 23:
2. Post. 12 3. Prop. of Equality No. 11 4. Cor. 1 5. Th. 16
6. substitution 7. transitive

THEOREM 45 (Direct Method)

1. Post. 15 2. Th. 17 3. substitution 4. betweenness principle
5. mn-substitution

THEOREM 45 (Indirect Method)

1. trichotomy principle 2. M-O Th. 16 3. hypothesis
4. O - Th. 44 5. contradiction of hypothesis 6. elimination of
other possibilities (exclusion)

THEOREM 46

To Prove: N'O'
1. MO'-given 2. MR reflex. Prop. of Equality 3. construction
4. MRO-MRO'-s.a.s. 5. RO'-c.p.c.t.e. 6. Post. 15
7. substitution principle 8. substitution principle

THEOREM 47

To Prove: C-C'
1. trichotomy 2. s.a.s. 3. c.p.c.t.e. 4. contradiction of
hypothesis 5. Th. 46 6. contradiction of hypothesis
7. elimination of all other possibilities (exclusion)

EXERCISES B

1. a. greatest b. greatest c. greater-side d. greater-angle
2. a. AB b. AC 3. a. AC b. AB 4. a. $\angle$ B b. $\angle$A 5. AB
6. AB 7. a. AC b. AB 8. AC 9. a. AC b. Th. 46 c. $\angle$B
d. Th. 44 10. a. $\angle$SMT b. Th. 47 c. acute

UNIT VIII
EXERCISES A

1. a. circle b. radius c. circumference d. diameter e. chord
f. secant g. tangent h. point of tangency i. arc j. semi-circle
k. major arc l. minor arc m. central angle n. inscribed angle
o. sector p. segment q. concentric r. quadrant s. interior
region of a circle 2. a. circumference b. center c. radius
d. diameter e. central angle f. chord g. arc (minor) h. arc
(major) i. secant j. tangent k. point of tangency l. inscribed
angle m. segment n. sector 3. minor one 4. a. r. of = $\odot$ are
= b. r. of same $\odot$ are = c. D. of = $\odot$ are = 5. a. $\odot$ having
= r. are = b. a cent. $\angle$ is meas. by its arc 6. a. a D = sum of
2 r b. D. divides $\odot$ into halves c. pt. outside $\odot$ > r. & pt.
inside $\odot$ < r

THEOREM 48

To Prove:
AB-MN PROOF-No. 3
1. MO-NO Post. 15 2. MO-AO-NO-BO-Post. 30
3. AO-BO substitution

UNIT VIII
THEOREM 49

PROOF:
1. AOB-A'O'B'-s.a.s. 2. c.p.c.t.e. 3. Post. 24 4. Post. 38

THEOREM 50

PROOF:
1. M'O'-N'O'-Post. 30 2. M'N'-given 3. MON-M'O'N'-s.s.s.
4. O-O'-c.p.c.t.e. 5. $\overline{MN}$ - $\overline{M'N'}$-Th. 49

THEOREM 51

PROOF:
1. Post. 39 2. given 3. R-R' substitution 4. Th. 49

THEOREM 52

PROOF:
1. Post. 30 2. given 3. Th. 46 4. Post. 39 5. substitution

THEOREM 53

PROOF:
1. given 2. Post. 30 3. Th. 47 4. $\overarc{AB}$ - $\overarc{A'B'}$-Th. 52

THEOREM 54 (Direct Proof)

1. given 2. O-O'-Post. 39 3. O-O' substitution 4. RS-R'S' Th. 52

THEOREM 54 (Indirect Proof)

1. ∠O > ∠O' or ∠O < ∠O' - Trichotomy Principle of equals 2. then $\overarc{RS}$ must = $\overarc{R'S'}$ Th. 49 3. ∠O ≠ ∠O' - Contradiction of hypothesis 4. then $\overarc{RS}$ must be < $\overarc{R'S'}$ Th. 52 5. this is impossible and so ∠O ≮ O' contradiction of hypothesis 6. elimination of all other possibilities (exclusion principle) 7. RS-R'S' Th. 52

EXERCISES B

1. a. Chords* -Cent. ∡* b. Chords* -Arcs* c. Cent. ∡* -arcs* d. Chord* -Cent ∠* e. Chord* -Minor arc* f. Minor arc* - Cent. ∠ * g. smaller 2. 14 3. 1. $\overarc{MS}$ = $\overarc{RN}$ - Th. 50 2. $\overarc{SN}$ = $\overarc{SN}$ - reflex. Prop. of Equality 3. So $\overarc{MSN}$ = $\overarc{RNS}$ - add. Prop. of Equality 4. ∴ Chord MN = Chord RS - Th. 51 4. ∠1 = ∠2 - and MN = M'N' Th. 51 2. MO = M'O' & NO = N'O' - Post. 30 3. ∴ Δ MNO ≅ Δ M'N'O - s.a.s. or S S S 5. a. less than 2 AB b. equal to 2 $\overarc{AB}$ c. 268

EXERCISES C

1. The path of a point moving so as constantly to fulfill a given condition or the set of all points that fulfill a given condition. 2. loci 3. (1) Prove that every point on the supposed locus fulfills the given condition (2) Prove that every point which fulfills the given conditions lies on the supposed locus. 4. a. A line parallel to the given lines and midway between them b. A plane parallel to the lines and midway between them 5. a. A pair of parallel lines 6 in. apart with the given line midway between them. b. A cylindrical surface of 3 unit radius with the given line along its center. 6. A circle concentric with the given circles and with a radius of 3.5 units. 7. The arc of a circle whose center is at the vertex, whose radius is c, and which is included between the sides of the angle. 8. The bisector of the angle. 9. a. A pair of parallel lines 2 units apart with the given line midway between them. b. A cylindrical surface of 1 unit radius with the given line at

its center. c. A circle having a radius of 1 and its center at the fixed point. d. A spherical surface with a radius of 1 and with the fixed point as its center. 10. a. The perpendicular bisector of the line-segment joining them. b. A plane perpendicular to the line segment joining the points at its mid-point.

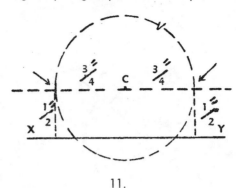

11.

THEOREM 55

PROOF of Part 1:
1. RPM-SPM-s.a.s. 2. c.p.c.t.e.
PROOF of Part 2:
1. RP'M-SP'M-s.s.s. (or s.a.s.) 2. P'MS-c.p.c.t.e. 3. def. of perp. bisector of 1. - segment 4. Th. 11 5. def. of required locus

CONSTRUCTION EXERCISES D

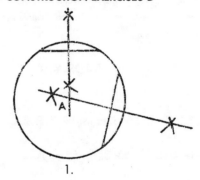

1.

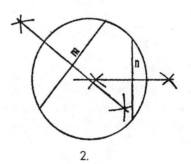

2.

THEOREM 56

PROOF of Part 1:
1. OPR-OPS-h.a. 2. c.p.c.t.e.

PROOF of Part 2:
1. OP'X-OP'Y - h.s. 2. c.p.c.t.e. 3. def. of bisector of ∠
4. Th. 10 5. def. of required locus

THEOREM 57

PROOF:
1. Post. 30 2. Th. 55

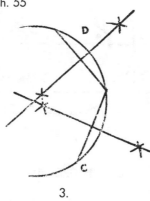

3.

UNIT IX
EXERCISES A

1. a. tangent circles b. tangent internally c. tangent externally
d. common tangent e. common internal tangent f. common
external tangent g. line of centers 2. a. externally tangent
circles b. internally tangent circles c. common internal tangent
d. common external tangent e. common internal tangent
f. line of centers

THEOREM 58

PROOF of Part 1:
1. Cor. 6 2. Th. 55 3. transitive 4. Post. 36
PROOF of Part 2:
1. Post. 30 2. Th. 55 3. Th. 55 4. Post. 6 5. Post. 30
6. Post. 34

THEOREM 59

To Prove
NO-NA-NB PROOF:
1. NC-Post. 30 2. given of def. of ⊥ ls. 3. OC = OC reflex.
Prop. of Equality 4. MOC-NOC-h.s. 5. NO-c.p.c.t.e.
6. NCO-c.p.c.t.e. 7. NA th. 49 8. Post. 32 9. NB
substraction

THEOREM 60

PROOF:
1. MOR-NOR-s.s.s. 2. 1 - 2 c.p.c.t.e. 3. def. of ⊥ ls.

THEOREM 61

PROOF: 3
Post. 3: 1. def. of tangent to a ⊙ 2. Post. 37 3. Post. 22
(20) Cor. 1 PROOF: 1. given 2. Th. 61 3. Th. 11
4. Post. 40

THEOREM 62

PROOF:
1. Post. 22 2. Post. 37 3. def. of tangent to a ⊙

CONSTRUCTION EXERCISES A

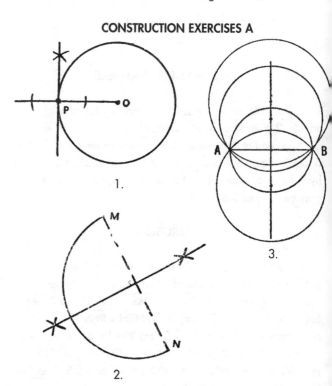

1.

2.

3.

THEOREM 63

To Prove:
PM-2 PROOF: -3
1. N-M Th. 61 2. PO reflex. 3. NO-MO Post. 30 4. △ PON
≅ △ POM-h.s. 5. PM-2-c.p.c.t.e.

THEOREM 64

Case 1: 1. Th. 61 2. Cor. 4 3. 59
Case 2: Th. 9 1. construction 2. Th. 21 3. YP-KP-case 1
4. KY substraction
Case 3: 1. case 1 2. addition

EXERCISES A'

1. circle or triangle 2. bisect-chord-arcs 3. perpendicular-
arcs 4. equal-equal angles-center 5. parallel-equal
6. tangent-tangency-center-circle 7. perpendicular-tangency

8. tangent 9. pass through the center 10. a. 18in. b. 132°
11. 1. AP = CP-Th. 63 2. BP = DP-Th. 63 3. substraction
Prop. of Equality 12. 1. MO = RO-th. 63 2. NO = SO-Th.
63 3. Addition Prop. of Equality 13. a. 70° b. 55°

PRELIMINARY EXERCISES B

1. When all its sides form chords of the circle 2. When all its
sides form tangents to the circle 3. Inscribed in -
circumscribed about 4. Circumscribed about - inscribed in
5. Equidistant-vertices 6. Equidistant-sides

THEOREM 65

1. Th. 58 2. def. of chords and their bisectors 3. Th. 57

THEOREM 66

1. Cor. 5 2. Th. 13 3. Th. 56 4. substitution 5. Th. 56 & 58

EXERCISES B

1. circumcenter 2. constructions:

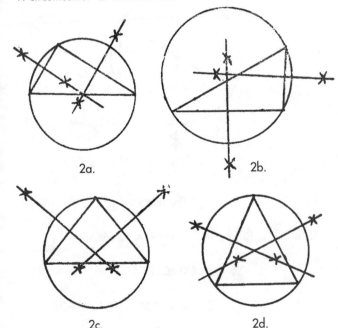

2a.   2b.

2c.   2d.

3. Yes-Yes-Yes-No-No 4. incenter
5. constructions:

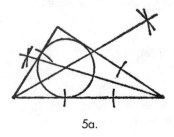   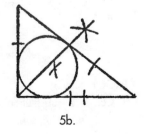

5a.   5b.

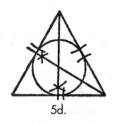

5c.   5d.

6. Yes-Yes-No-Yes-No

THEOREM 67

To Prove:
Th. 9
AR-BM-CS PROOF:
1. Def. of ▭ 2. Th. 35 3. 7 or 8 4. def. of altitudes
5. Cor. 4 6. def. of ⊥ bisector 7. def. of ▭ 8. Prop. of
Equality 7 or 8 9. Th. 22, Cor. 4 10. def. of ⊥ bisector
11. def. of ▭ 12. Prop. of Equality 7 or 8 13. Th. 22, Cor.
4 14. def. of ⊥ bisector 15. Th. 65

EXERCISES B'

1. orthocenter 2. constructions:

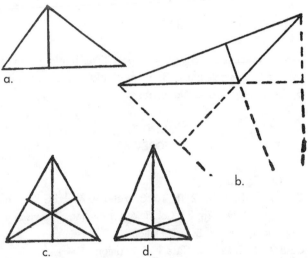

a.

b.

c.   d.

3. A line-segment which connects the vertex of a △ with the
midpoint of the opposite side. 4. Centroid, because it is the
center of gravity of the △. 5. constructions:

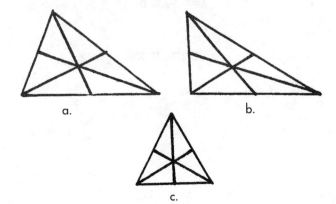

a.   b.

c.

THEOREM 68

Part 1: 1. Post. 27 2. Th. 22, Cor. 3 3. Th. 33 4. 33
5. Post. 27
Part 2: 1. Th. 39, Cor. 1 2. Th. 39, Cor. 1 3. Th. 21 4.
Prop. of Equality 7 or 8 5. Th. 38 6. Th. 36
7. construction 8. substitution
Part 3: 1. part 2 2. substitution or transitive 3. Post. 24

EXERCISES B"

1. Yes-in equilateral △ 2. 12 in. 3. 9 in.

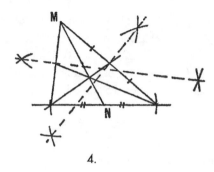

4.

EXERCISES C

1. size, shape, and position (location) 2. Yes b. No c. Yes, if
confined to a single plane 3. a. Yes b. No c. No 4. a. No
b. Yes 5. No. 6. a. No b. Yes

UNIT X
THEOREM 69

PROOF Post. 3:
Case 1: 1. Post. 30 2. Th. 16 3. Post. 39 4. $\frac{1}{2}$ BC Prop. of
Equality 4 5. A-B Th. 33, Cor. 1 6. substitution 7. division
Prop. of Equality 8. BC substitution
Case 2: 1. Case 1 2. Case 1 3. addition
Case 3: 1. BD-Case 1 2. CD-Case 1 3. subtraction
Cor. 1 PROOF: 1. $\angle$ C = $\frac{1}{2}\overarc{AB}$ or 90° - Th. 69 2. $\therefore \angle$ C =
a rt. $\angle$ - Def. of rt. $\angle$
Cor. 2 PROOF: 1. $\frac{1}{2}\overarc{AB}$ - $\frac{1}{2}\overarc{AB}$- Th. 69 2. Substitution or
Prop. of Equality 7

CONSTRUCTION 6

1. Th. 69, Cor. 1 2. Th. 62

CONSTRUCTION EXERCISES A

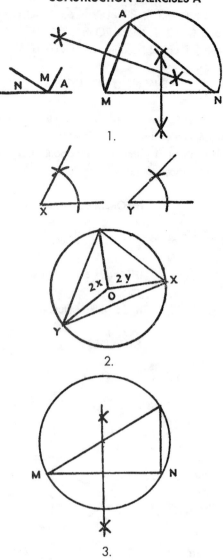

1.

2.

3.

THEOREM 70

1. Th. 22 2. $\overarc{RS}$ Th. 64 3. Th. 69 4. substitution

EXERCISES A

1. 28° 2. 140° 3. 130° 4. 117.5° 5. 100°-30°-50°

THEOREM 71

1. B-R Th. 33, Cor. 1 2. $\frac{1}{2}$ AR - $\frac{1}{2}$ SB Th. 69 3. substitution
Post. 3

THEOREM 72

PROOF Post. 3:
1. Cor. 1 2. substitution 3. Th. 69 4. $\frac{1}{2}\overarc{a}$ Th. 70 5. Th. 69
6. $\frac{1}{2}\overarc{b}$ Th. 70 7. substitution

EXERCISES B

1. 60° 2. 116° 3. a. 95°, 77°, 85°, and 103° b. 68° and
112° 4. a. 20 b. 60° 5. 19° 6. a. 50° b. 70°
c. 40°

THEOREM 73

PROOF Post. 3:
1. O'M' Post. 30 2. Th. 59 3. M'A' division 4. ≅ Δ M'A'O'-
h.s. 5. OA-O'A' - c.p.c.t.e.

THEOREM 74
TO PROVE: MN = M'N'

PROOF Post. 3:
1. MC = M'C' Post. 30 2. given 3. C A M - C'A'M'-h.s.
4. M'A'- c.p.c.t.e. 5. Th. 59 6. substitution 7. multiplication

THEOREM 75

PROOF Th. 13:
1. Th. 73 2. Post. 22 3. Post. 41 4. 6 5. 17 6. substitution
7. substitution

THEOREM 76

1. trichotomy 2. Th. 73 3. contradiction of hypothesis
4. OB-OA Th. 75 5. contradiction of hypothesis
6. elimination of all other possibilities (or exclusion)

EXERCISES C

1-4 (1) equidistant (2) equal (3) unequal (4) greater

UNIT XI
EXERCISES A

1. a. commensurable b. rational c. area d. volume
e. equivalent 2. a. C b. C c. I d. I e. C f. I g. R
3. a. 150 sq. ft. b. 108 sq. ft. (12 sq. yd.) 4. 40 in. 5. 90
in. 6. a. 312 sq. ft. b. 288 cu. ft. 7. 64 cu. in. 8. 75 cu. in.

THEOREM 77

1. bh Th. 77 2. b'h' 3. given 4. multiplication
Cor. 1: 1. def. of rectangle 2. principle II 3. h.s.
4. substitution 5. substitution Th. 77

EXERCISES A'

1. a. 200 b. 68 2. a. 480 b. 128 3. a. 243 b. 90

THEOREM 78

PROOF Th. 9:
1. def. of ▱ 2. ΔRST-STW-s.s.s. 3. a. Th. 77 5. division
Cor. 1: 1. $\frac{1}{2}$ bh - $\frac{1}{2}$ b'h'-Th. 78 2. b'h' multiplication
3. bh-b'h' division 4. substitution 5. substitution
Cor. 2: 1. Th. 77 2. Th. 78 3. substitution 4. multiplication
5. substitution

EXERCISES A"

1. a. 40 sq. in. b. 3 sq. yd. 2. 17 in. 3. 18 √3 or 31.17 +
4. 900 5. Yes. See Th. 78 Cor. 1 6. a. 6 cu. u b. 60 cu. u
c. 132 s.u.

CONSTRUCTION EXERCISES A

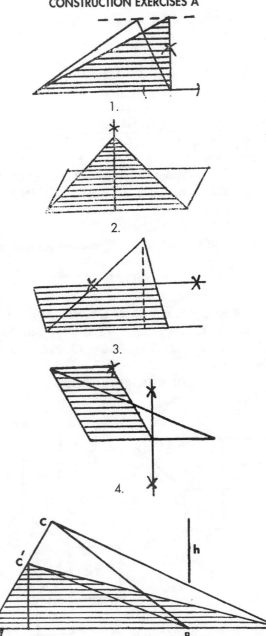

1.

2.

3.

4.

5.

THEOREM 79

PROOF Post. 3:
1. $\frac{1}{2}bh - \frac{1}{2}b'h'$ Th. 78 2. $\frac{1}{2}bh - \frac{1}{2}b'h'$ addition 3. Post. 41
4. $\frac{1}{2}h(b + b')$ substitution
Cor. 1: 1. def. ▱ 2. a.s.a. 3. c.p.c.t.e. 4. division
5. Th. 38 6. Th. 35 7. Th. 77 8. substitution

THEOREM 80

1. Th. 21 2. Th. 39 3. def. of median 4. Post. 18 5. Post. 3
6. Post. 40 7. Th. 39, Cor. 2 8. Post. 17
9. substitution

EXERCISES B

1. 44 2. 880 3. 65 4. 160 s.u. 5. 80° 6. 300 s.i. 7. 400
s.i. 8. 60 s.i.

THEOREM 81

Th. 9 Post. 3:
Part 1: 1. addition 2. s. of ▱ are = of def. of ▱ 3. s. a. s.
4. Supp. Adj. ∠ 5. Th. 78, Cor. 2 6. RO Th. 78, Cor. 2
7. substitution
Part 2: 1. XSR-TSN-s.a.s. 2. same as 4 in part 1 ST-SYT-XSR
3. SXYT XSR Th. 78, Cor. 2 4. SN-SO-SNHO-TSN Th. 78,
Cor. 2 5. XSTY-SNHO
Part 3: 1. Post. 42 2. substitution
Cor. 1: 1. $a^2 - b^2 - c^2$ - Th. 81 2. b^2 reflexive 3. subtraction

EXERCISES C

1. 17 & 60 2. 6 & 4 3. 55. 42 & 13.856 4. 8.66 & 43.3
5. 167.7 6. 128 7. $2\sqrt{5}$ or 4.472 8. 72 9. 240 10. 250
$\sqrt{3}$ or 433+ 11. $400\sqrt{3}$ or 692.8 + 12. 90 s. u.

CONSTRUCTION EXERCISES C

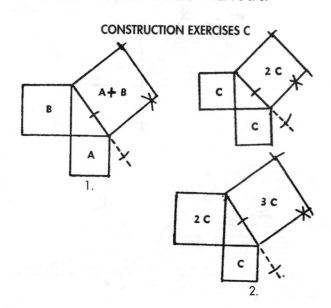

1.

2.

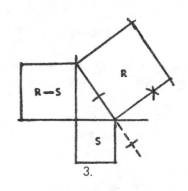

3.

EXERCISES D

1. a. perpendicular-projection b. projections-projection
2. constructions:

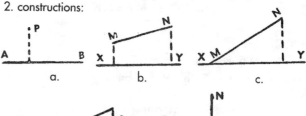

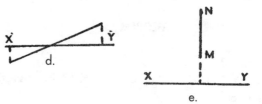

HERO'S FORMULA

1. Th. 81 2. Th. 81, Cor. 1 3. substitution 4. substitution
5. substitution 6. 10 7. Th. 78 8. substitution

EXERCISES D

1. $(x - 2)^2 + (y - 5)^2 = 4$ 2. $(x + 3)^2 + (y + 2)^2 = 9$ 3. $x^2 + y^2$
$= 16$ 4. $(-2,5)$, $r = 6$ 5. $(0,0)$, $r = 5$

EXERCISES D'

1. 6 2. $12\sqrt{2}$ or 16.96+ 3. $150\sqrt{3}$ or 259.8+ 4. $80\sqrt{3}$ or
69.28 5. 6

CONSTRUCTION 7

1. Th. 78, Cor. 1 2. Post. 42 3. substitution 4. Th. 78, Cor. 1
5. Post. 42 6. substitution 7. substitution

CONSTRUCTION EXERCISES E

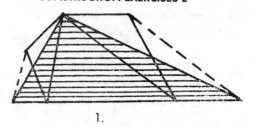

1.

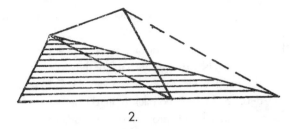

2.

EXERCISES F

Conclusion: $3 - \frac{1}{3} - \frac{1}{3}$ 1. 400 c.u.i. 2. 125 $\sqrt{3}$ or 216.50 + cu.i.

UNIT XII
THEOREM 83

1. Th. 13 2. Th. 23, Cor. 4 3. given 4. Th. 39
5. Substitution principle & Th. 82 6. Add. Prop. of Equality
7. Div. Prop. of Eequality

EXERCISES A

1. 11 2. 7 3. 2 $\sqrt{5}$ 4. 5 5. $\sqrt{34}$, $\sqrt{34}$ 6 6. 5, 10 5 $\sqrt{5}$
7. (8,0) 8. (4,6) 9. (0,6) 10. (2,1)

THEOREM 84
EXERCISES B

1. $\frac{3}{5}$ 2. $\frac{-4}{5}$ 3. 0 4. none 5. +1 6. $+\frac{1}{2}$ 7. $\frac{-2}{3}$ 8. $+\frac{1}{2}$
9. 0 10. no slope

THEOREM 85

1. Construction 2. Th. 13 3. Corres. $\measuredangle$ of $\parallel$ lines are =
4. HA 5. c.s.c.t.e. 6. division 7. Def. of slope 8. Substitution
Principle

THEOREM 86

3. SAS 4. cacte

THEOREM 87

1. Post. 23 2. Th. 13 3. Th. 34 4. HA 5. c.s.c.t.e.
6. division

EXERCISES C

1. parallel 2. slopes 3. negative reciprocal 4. $\frac{3}{5}$ 5. Yes.
Each has a slope of $\frac{4}{5}$ 6. No. They have different slopes.
7. $-\frac{3}{2}$ 8. 2 9. 3 10. -1 11. 3 12. 5 13. no 14. $-\frac{2}{3}$
15. 2 16. 3 17. 2x - 5y = -10 18. +2 19. y = $-\frac{3}{4}$x - 3
20. $-\frac{3}{2}$

UNIT XIII
EXERCISES A

1. a. ratio b. proportion c. antecedent d. terms
e. consequent f. means g. extremes h. mean proportional
i. fourth proportional j. third proportional 2. a. ratio-
numerator denominator proportional-extremes-
b. proportion-terms-antecedents-consequent-fourth
proportional-extremes-means c. mean proportional-third
proportional 3. a. yes b. number of units

B. FUNDAMENTAL THEOREMS OF PROPORTION

90. 1. bd-bd multiplication 91. 1. bd-bd division 92. 1. Th.
90 2. Th. 91 93. 1. Th. 90 2. Th. 91 94. 1. addition
95. 1. subtraction 96. 1. means x means = extremes x
extremes 2. division Prop. of Equality 3. given 4. substitution
5. trans. Prop. of Equality 97. 1. substitution 2. Th. 90
3. br-dr-fr-b-d-f addition 4. division 5. substitution

EXERCISES B

1. s-b Th. 93 2. xy Th. 90 3. $\frac{d}{c}$ Th. 92 4. $\frac{b+d}{d}$ Th. 94 5.
s-c Th. 93 6. $\frac{n-b}{b}$ Th. 95 7. $\frac{m}{a}$ (or $\frac{n}{b}$) - 7 Th. 97 8. y Th.
96 9. 12.5 10. 15 11. 5$\frac{1}{4}$ 12. 2 13. 35° & 55° 14. 30°
& 150° 15. 27 in. & 45 in. 16. a. 15 b. 30 17. a. 36
b. 1$\frac{1}{3}$ 18. a. 12 b. 12

EXERCISES C

1. proportionally - ratio 2. a. yes b. no c. no d. yes 3. a.
internally b. externally c. harmonically 4. a. M-N b. $\frac{1}{2}$ - $\frac{23}{8}$
c. no 5. a. W-T b. $\frac{5}{2}$ (or$\frac{2}{5}$)- $\frac{5}{2}$ (or$\frac{2}{5}$) c. yes

THEOREM 98

2. because MT&RM are commensurable 3. Th. 21 4. x-y-z
Th. 39 6. substitution
Cor. 1 PROOF: 1. Th. 98 2. Prop. by addition Th. 94
3. Post. 17 4. substitution
Cor. 2 PROOF: KW $\parallel$ XY 1. Th. 9 th. 98 2. OM-MG Th. 35,
Cor. 1 3. $\frac{OM}{MG} = \frac{KN}{NH}$ substitution

EXERCISES C'

1. 9 2. 20 3. 10.8

THEOREM 99

PROOF Th. 9:
1. given 2. Th. 98, Cor. 1 3. Th. 96 4. Post. 24 5. Post. 3
6. Post. 40
Construction 8. PROOF 1. Th. 98

CONSTRUCTION EXERCISES C

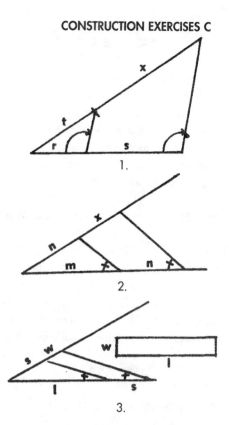

1.

2.

3.

Construction 9. PROOF 1. Th. 98, Cor. 2

CONSTRUCTION EXERCISES C'

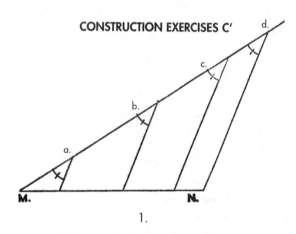

1.

THEOREM 100

1. Th. 9 (CM is ‖ to RA) 2. given or def. of bisector of ∠
3. Th. 22 4. Th. 22, Cor. 1 5. substitution 6. Th. 16 7. Th.
98 8. substitution

THEOREM 101

PROOF Th. 9:
1. given of def. of bisector of ∠ 2. 2 - Th. 22 3. 1 - Th. 22,
Cor. 1 4. substitution 5. TS Th. 16 6. RT-TN Th. 98
7. substitution

EXERCISES C"

1. No. MN and the bisector of ∠ NOR form equal alternate
interior ∡ with NO as a transversal (or they form equal
corresponding ∡ with MR as a transversal.) 2. No 3. 8 4. 4
5. 7-8-18 6. 11.2 7. parallel 8. third side 9. parallel
10. proportionally 11. proportional 12. adjacent
13. transversals 14. proportional 15. isosceles
16. equilateral 17. parallel 18. opposite 19. externally
20. proportional

UNIT XIV
PRELIMINARY EXERCISES A

1. a. Polygons whose corresponding angles are equal and
whose corresponding sides are proportional. b. The sides
which are proportional and similarly placed. c. The ratio of
any two corresponding sides of similar polygons. 2. a. no
b. yes c. yes d. yes 3. ~ 4. a. all b. some c. all d. some
e. some f. all g. some h. all i. some j. some 5. 2, 40° & $\frac{2}{3}$
or $\frac{3}{2}$ 6. 11.2, 8.53 + & 30° 7. 12, 105°, & $\frac{9}{4}$ or $\frac{4}{9}$ 8. 5.6
& 7.2

THEOREM 102

1. proportional 2. Theorem 97

EXERCISES A

1. 210 2. .9

THEOREM 103

1. A 2. Cor. 1 3. Cor. 1 4. substitution 5. substitution
6. A"C'-RT Th. 23, Cor. 1 7. Th. 98, Cor. 1
8. substitution 9. transitive 10. def. of ~ polygons
Cor. 1 Given: A-A'-B-B' To Prove: ABC-A'B'C' 1. A-A'-B-B'-
given 2. C-C' Th. 33, Cor. 3 3. Th. 103
Cor. 2: 1. corres. ∡ of ~ △ are = 2. Same as 1
3. transitive - substitution 4. Th. 103
Cor. 3: 1. corres. ∡ of ~ △ are = 2. Th. 4 3. Th. 103, Cor.
1 4. corres. sides of ~ △ are proportional

THEOREM 104

1. given 2. substitution 3. A'B' Th. 99 4. A' Th. 22, Cor. 1
5. C' reflexive Prop. of Equality 6. AA 7. substitution

THEOREM 105 ABC-A'B'C'

PROOF Post. 3:
1. reflexive Prop. of Equality 2. given 3. substitution 4. MNC
Th. 104 5. corres. sides of ~ △ are proport. 6. given
7. construction 8. Theorem 96 9. MNC-s.s.s. 10. ABC-A'B'C'
substitution

EXERCISES B'

1. I Th. 104 2. L Th. 105 3. H Th. 103 4. N AA or Th. 103, Cor. 1 5. K AA or Th. 103, Cor. 1 6. J Th. 104 or Th. 103

THEOREM 106

1. def. of ~ polygons 2. (n-2) - Fund. prin. 1, unit VII 3. B' - corr. ∠ of ~ polygons are = 4. Corr. sides of ~ polygons are proport. 5. ABC - A'B'C' - Th. 104 6. Corr. sides of ~ △ are proport. 7. corr. sides of ~ polygons are proport. 8. transitive - substitution 9. C' - corr. ∠ of ~ polygons are = 10. 3 - corr. ∠ of ~ △ are = 11. 2-4 substraction 12. ACD-A'C'D' Th. 104 13. corr. sides of ~ polygons are proport. 14. corr. ∠ of ~ polygons are = 15. Th. 104

THEOREM 107

1. B' - corr. ∠ of ~ △ are = 2. 9-10-corr. ∠ of ~ △ are = 3. C' addition Prop. of Equality 4. D' same as 3 5. E' - Corr. ∠ of ~ △ are = 6. A' addition 7. corr. sides of ~ △ are proport. 8. same as 7 9. same as 8 10. substitution or transitive Prop. of Equality 11. same as 9 12. Prop. of Equality of sub. 13. Def. of ~ polygons

CONSTRUCTION EXERCISES C

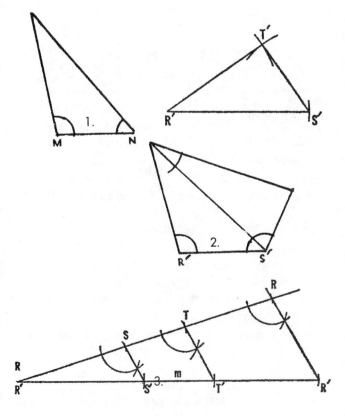

THEOREM 108

1. 2-vert. ∠ are = 2. $\frac{1}{2}$R N - $\frac{1}{2}$RN Th. 69 3. substitution or transitive Prop. of Equality 4. AA 5. SC-RC-NC-cor. sides of ~ △ are proport. 6. Th. 90

EXERCISES C

1. size-proportional - equal - ratio - sides 2. (1) similar to the same △ (2) equilangular (3) angles - angles (4) proportional (5) proportional included - equal 3. sides* - altitudes* - perimeters 4. triangles - similar - similarly 5. product - segments - product - segments 6. 18 7. 30

UNIT VX
THEOREM 109

1. Th. 4 2. reflexive Prop. of Equality 3. AA 4. Z Th. 4 5. Y reflexive Prop. of Equality 6. AA 7. Th. 103, Cor. 2

Cor. 1: 1. Th. 109 2. corr. sides of ~ △ are proport.
Cor. 2: 1. Th. 109 2. corr. sides of ~ △ are proport. 3. Th. 109 4. same as 2

EXERCISES A

1. ADC-BDC 2. 32° 3. 58° 4. AC = 4√5 or 8.944 CD=8, BC = 8√5 or 17.888
Cor. 3: 1. AB-AB-NB PROOF Post. 3 Th. 69, Cor. 1 2. AB-AB-NB Th. 109, Cor. 1

CONSTRUCTION 10 1. TH. 109, Cor. 3
CONSTRUCTION EXERCISES A

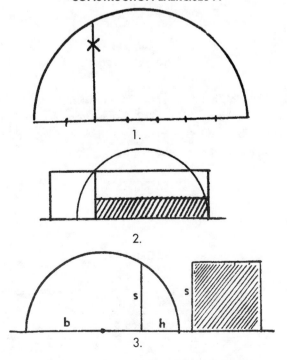

THEOREM 110

1. $b - b^2$ Th. 109, Cor. 2 2. $a - a - a^2$ - same as 1 3. $a^2 - b^2$ 4. addition 5. substitution

THEOREM 111

1. AB-Th. 70 2. AB-Th. 69 3. C-substitution-transitive 4. P-P reflex. Prop. of Equality 5. AA 6. corr. sides of ~ $\triangle$ are proport.

EXERCISE A'. 1. 20
EXERCISES B

1. a. mean-proportional b. shorter- longer-longer
c. extreme-mean d. $l - l - l + W$ 2. $l = 7.41$, w = 4.59
3. 3.06 & 4.94

CONSTRUCTION 11

1. Th. 111 2. proport. by subtraction (Th. 95) 3. construction
4. substitution 5. substitution 6. substitution 7. proport. by inversion (Th. 92)

CONSTRUCTION EXERCISES B

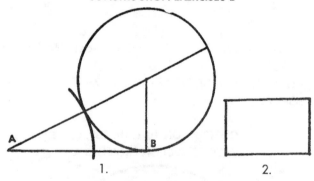

1.   2.

UNIT XVI
THEOREM 112

1. 1. $bh - b'h'$ Th. 77 2. $\dfrac{A}{A'} = \dfrac{bh}{b'h'}$ - division
Cor. 1: To Prove: $\dfrac{h}{h'}$ 1. Th. 112 2. substitution & cancellation
Cor. 2: To Prove: $\dfrac{A}{A'} - \dfrac{b}{b'}$ 1. $\dfrac{bh}{b'h'}$ - Th. 112 2. $\dfrac{A}{A'} - \dfrac{bh}{b'h'}$
$\dfrac{b}{b'}$ - substitution & cancellation

EXERCISES A

1. 25 2. 40 3. 18

THEOREM 113

1. $\dfrac{1}{2}bh - \dfrac{1}{2}b'h'$ - Th. 78 2. $\dfrac{\frac{1}{2}bh}{\frac{1}{2}b'h'}$ division & cancellation

Cor. 1: 1. Th. 113 2. substitution & cancellation
Cor. 2: To Prove: $\dfrac{b}{b'}$ 1. $\dfrac{A}{A'} - \dfrac{bh}{b'h'}$ Th. 113 2. — - $\dfrac{A}{A'}$ -

$\dfrac{bh}{b'h'} - \dfrac{b}{b'}$ subst. & canc.

EXERCISES B

1. 70 2. 50 3. 20

THEOREM 114

PROOF POSTS. 26 & 3
1. Th. 113, Cor. 2 2. same as 1 3. $\dfrac{RC}{RT}$ - multiplication
4. cancellation 5. substitution

EXERCISES B'

1. 90 2. 40

PRELIMINARY EXERCISES C

1. a. 1 to 2 - 1 to 4 b. 1 to 3 - 1 to 9 c. 1 to 2 - 1 to 4
2. the squares of any two corresponding sides 3. Inductive

THEOREM 115

1. Th. 113 2. corr. sides ~ $\triangle$ are proport. 3. Th. 103, Cor. 3
4. substitution $\dfrac{h^2}{h'^2}$
Cor. 1 To Prove: $\dfrac{h^2}{h'^2}$ 1. Th. 115 2. Th. 103, Cor. 3 3. $\dfrac{h^2}{h'^2}$
powers 4. substitution

THEOREM 116

1. $M' - N' O'$ Th. 106 2. $a^2 - N' - a'^2$ Th. 115 3. $\dfrac{N}{N'}$ - substitution 4. $\dfrac{N}{N'} - \dfrac{O}{O'}$ - same as 2 5. $\dfrac{N}{N'} - \dfrac{O}{O'}$ - substitution (step 3) 6. $\dfrac{M}{M'} - \dfrac{N}{N'} - \dfrac{O}{O'}$ transitive or substitution
7. $\dfrac{M + N + O}{M' + N' + O'}$ - Th. 97 on proportion 8. Th. 115 9. subst. or trans. Prop. of Equality 10. Post. 42 11. substitution
Cor. 1: 1. Th. 116 2. Th. 102 3. Prop. of Equality 9
4. substitution
Cor. 2: 1. $\dfrac{b^2}{c^2}$ - Th. 115 2. $\dfrac{a^2 + b^2}{c^2}$ - addition 3. Th. 110
4. substitution 5. multiplication Prop. of Equality or Th. 90.

EXERCISES C

1. a. squares b. square roots 2. a. two b. two c. 4 3. a. $\dfrac{1}{3}$
b. $\dfrac{1}{3}$ c. $\dfrac{1}{3}$ 4. 7 5. 7 6. 3 7. 32 8. 10 $\sqrt{3}$ or 17.32 + 9.
Their volumns are directly proportional to the cubes of their corresponding sides (1 to 8) 10. Their surface areas are directly proportional to the squares of their corresponding sides. (1 to 4)

UNIT XVII
PRELIMINARY EXERCISES A

1. It must be both (1) equiangular and (2) equilateral

2. a. sometimes b. sometimes c. always d. sometimes
e. sometimes f. never 3. regular - center 4. a. center of
polygon b. radius of polygon c. apothem d. central angle
5. a. apothem b. radius of polygon c. center d. radius
e. apothem f. central angle

THEOREM 117

1. given or def. of equilateral p. 2. Th. 50 3. Th. 69
4. arc - add. - Post. 5. transitive 6. def. of reg. polygon

THEOREM 118

1. def. of inscribed polygon 2. Th. 51 3. Th. 117

THEOREM 119

1. Th. 118 2. BC-CD-DE- sides of a regular polygon are =
3. Th. 70 & transitive 4. a.s.a. 5. c.p.c.t.e. 6. c.p.c.t.e.
7. transitive & addition 8. def. of regular circumscribed
polygon

CONSTRUCTION 12

1. Def. of inscribed polygon 2. Th. 4 3. Th. 49 4. Th. 69,
Cor. 1 5. def. of ☐ 6. def. of inscribed ☐

CONSTRUCTION EXERCISES A

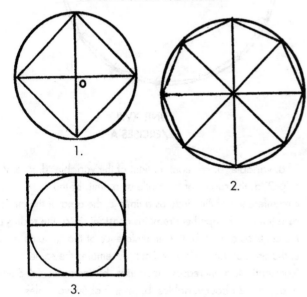

1.

2.

3.

CONSTRUCTION 13

1. def. of inscribed polygon 2. def. of equilateral △
3. equiangular 4. converse of Post. 39 5. def. of regular
hexagon

CONSTRUCTION EXERCISES A'

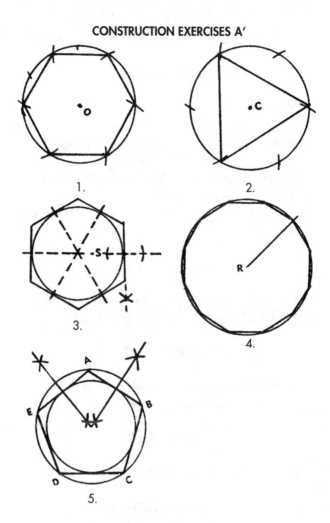

1.

2.

3.

4.

5.

THEOREM 120

1. Th. 58 2. ∡ of a regular polygon are = 3. Post. 30 4. Th.
16 5. substraction Prop. of Equality 6. sides of a regular
polygon are = 7. DOC-s.a.s. 8. c.p.c.t.e. 9. Post. 36
10. same as 2 11. Post. 30 12. same as 4 13. 7-
substraction Prop. of Equality 14. same as 6 15. DOE-s.a.s.
16. c.p.c.t.e. 17. Post. 36 18. def. of an inscribed polygon

THEOREM 121

1. Th. 120 2. equal 3. Th. 73 4. Post. 36 converse 5. Th.
62 6. def. of inscribed ⊙

EXERCISES A

1. 360° - 120° - 180° - 60° - 120° 2. 360° - 90° - 360° -
90° - 90° 3. 360° - 72° - 540° - 108° - 72° 4. 360° - 45° -
1080° - 135° - 45°

THEOREM 123

1. Th. 43, Cor. 1 2. substitution 3. equal 4. division Prop. of
Equality 5. def. of ~ polygon

Cor. 1: 1. polygon R ~ polygon R' 2. $\frac{A}{A'} = \frac{s^2}{s'^2}$ - Th. 116

THEOREM 124

PROOF Post. 3:
1. Th. 123 2. Th. 102 3. Th. 122 4. AOB-A'O'B' - substitution 5. BO - B'O' - radii of a regular polygon are = 6. $\frac{BO}{B'O'}$ division 7. Th. 104 8. corr. sides of ~ polygons are proport. 9. Th. 103, Cor. 3 10. substitution or trans. Prop. of Equality.
Cor. 1: 1. Th. 123 2. Th. 116, Cor. 1 3. Th. 124 4. Powers 5. Substitution

EXERCISES B

1. S' = 10 & a = 6 2. M' = 247.1 + r' = 10 3. 1 to 4
4. 48 √3 or 83.13+ 5. a. $\frac{4}{9}$ b. $\frac{2}{3}$ c. $\frac{2}{3}$ d. $\frac{2}{3}$ e. $\frac{2}{3}$

THEOREM 125

1. Th. 78 2. Addition Prop. of Equality 3. Post. 42
4. perimeter 5. substitution

EXERCISES C

1. a. 7-7-7 b. 49 2. 432 √3 or 750 - 384+ 3. 40

CONSTRUCTION 14

1. construction no. 11 2. substitution 3. reflexive Prop. of Equality 4. Th. 104 5. def. of isos. △ 6. def. of ~ △ 7. def. of isos. △ 8. construction 9. substitution or trans. Prop. of Equality 10. Base ∡ of isos. △ are = 11. corr. ∡ of ~ △ are = 12. same as 10 13. Post. 14 14. O substitution 15. Th. 33 16. substitution 17. division Prop. of Equality 18. Post. 39, converse 19. def. of regular decagon

CONSTRUCTION EXERCISES C

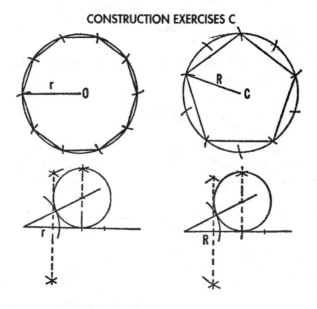

CONSTRUCTION 15

1. construction no. 13 2. construction no. 14 3. subtraction
4. def. of regular pentadecagon

EXERCISES C'

1. a. pentadecagon b. 30-sided c. square d. pentagon
e. decagon f. octagon 2. equilateral 3. circle 4. inscribed
5. circumscribed 6. regular 7. similar 8. apothem* 9. radii*
10. perimeters* 11. squares 12. inscribed 13. circumscribed
14. regular 15. two

CONSTRUCTION EXERCISE C'

1. Directions for making the construction: Draw a circle having radius r and center C. Inscribe a regular pentadecagon in the circle using the method of Construction 15 p. 190.

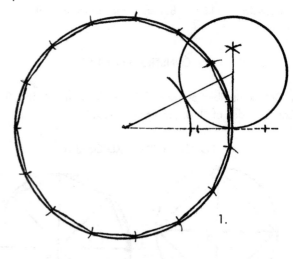

1.

UNIT XVIII
EXERCISES A

1. a. variable b. constant c. limit of the variable d. x e. 7
f. 7 2. a. the radius of the circle as a limit b. the circumference of the circle as a limit c. the area of the circle as a limit d. Its apothem remains constant 3. a. the radius of the circle as a limit b. the circumference of the circle as a limit c. the area of the circle as a limit d. remains the same (constant) 4. a. increases - increases b. decreases - decreases 5. a. prin. 2 about variables b. prin. 2 about variables
6. a. prin. 1 about variables

THEOREM 126

Method 1: 1. Post. 47 2. Th. 124 3. multiplying the numerator and the denominator of a fraction by 2
4. substitution
Method 2: 1. Th. 118 2. 124 3. Th. 90 4. Post. 44

5. prin. 2 about variables 6. prin. 1 about variables
7. Th. 91 on proportion 8. multiplying the numerator and the denominator of a fraction by 2 9. substitution

Cor. 1: 1. Th. 126 2. proportion by alternation

Cor. 2: Since $\frac{C}{D} = \pi$, we have: C = π D, or C = $\pi \cdot$ 2r or C = 2π r

Cor. 3: Since 1° of arc = $\frac{\pi r^2}{360}$, then n° of arc = n $\cdot \frac{2\pi r}{360°}$ or $\frac{n}{360} \cdot 2\pi r$

CONSTRUCTION 16

1. Th. 81, Cor. 1 2. Prop. of Equality 10 3. Post. 17
4. subtraction Prop. of Equality 5. substitution 6. powers of eq. & simplifying 7. Th. 81 8. substitution & simplifying
9. Prop. of Equality 10

EXERCISES B

1. a. 1-6-3 b. .5176-6.2112-3.1056 c. π 2. similar 3. a. A rectangle b. 62.832 sq. in.

THEOREM 127

Method 1: 1. Post. 47 2. Th. 125 3. Post. 47 4. Substitution
Method 2: 1. Th. 125 2. Post. 44 3. Prin. 2 about variables
4. Post. 45 5. Prin. 1 about variables

Cor. 1: 1, Th. 127 2. 2πr - Th. 126, Cor. 2 3 $\frac{1}{2}$r $\cdot$ 2πr - substitution

Cor. 2: To Prove: $\frac{r^2}{r'^2} = \frac{D^2}{D'^2}$ 1. $\pi r^2 - \pi r'^2$ - Th. 127. Cor. 1
2. $\frac{\pi r^2}{\pi r'^2} - \frac{r^2}{r'^2}$ - division Prop. of Equality

Cor. 3: Since a sector of 1° = $\frac{\pi r^2}{360}$ then a sector of n° = $\frac{n \cdot \pi r^2}{360}$ or $\frac{n}{360} \cdot \pi r^2$

EXERCISES B'

1. radii - circumferences 2. squares - radii* - diameters* - circumferences* 3. a. 10a - 25 a$^2\pi$ or 15 an b. 6-18.8496 - 28.2744 c. 10 - 20 - 62.832 4. a. 4 to 25 b. 5,000 sq. in.
c. 6.4 min. 5. 78.54 ft. 6. a. 7.854 in. b. 39.27 sq. in.
7. 25π or 78.53 8. 20.39 9. a. 188.496 sq. in.
b. 245.0448 sq. in. c. 282.744 cu. in.

CONSTRUCTION EXERCISE B

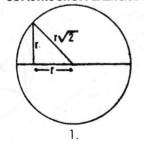

1.

EXPERIMENTAL RESULTS: 3 - $\frac{1}{3}$ - $\frac{1}{3}$
1a. 204.204 i^2 1b. 282.744 i^2 1c. 314.16 i^3 2. 150 i^3
3. 301.593 + i^3

EXERCISES D

EXPERIMENTAL RESULTS: 4 - 4 - 4 - $\frac{2}{3}$ - $\frac{4}{3}$
1. 314.16 i^2 2. 240 i^2 3. $\frac{2}{3}$ 4. 523.6 i^3 5. 500 i^3

UNIT TEST 1

1. One 2. One 3. One 4. The line-segment joining them
5. The perpendicular distance 6. One 7. Infinite 8. Infinite
9. All (infinite) 10. Infinite 11. One 12. No 13. Yes 14. Yes
15. Yes 16. Always 17. Four 18. d 19. its interior region
20. Induction 21. Deduction 22. No 23. Yes 24. Obtuse
25. Adjacent $\measuredangle$ 26. A line-segment 27. The angle bisector
28. Space (or solid) geometry 29. Right angle 30. A straight angle 31. Mid-point 32. Complementary angles 33. An angle 34. 5° 35. 95° 36. 22.5° 37. 120° 38. 22.5°
39. 90° 40. 90°

UNIT TEST 2

1. Polygon 2. Pentagon 3. Octagon 4. Scalene 5. Isosceles
6. Equilateral 7. Perimeter 8. Diagonal 9. Interior region
10. Altitude 11. 4 12. Infinite 13. 6 14. 4 15. 3 16. 1
17. 7 18. 8 19. 2 20. 9 21. 12 22. 11 23. 70° 24. 10
25. SSS 26. c.p.c.t.e. 27. Vert $ are = 28. ASA
29. c.p.c.t.e. 30. SAS (LL) 31. SSS 32. ASA 33. HA
34. HS (HL) 35. SAS (LL) 36. 30 37. 10 38. SAS
39. c.p.c.t.e. 40. Base $\measuredangle$ of isos. $\triangle$ are =

UNIT TEST 3

2. s.s.s. 3. s.a.s. 4. c.p.c.t.e. 5. c.p.c.t.e. 6. Def. of $\perp$ ls.
8. s.s.s. 9. c.p.c.t.e. 11. s.s.s. 12. s.a.s. 13. c.p.c.t.e.
14. Def. of $\perp$ ls. 16. s.s.s. 17. c.p.c.t.e. 18. Def. of $\perp$ ls.
20. s.s.s. 21. c.p.c.t.e.

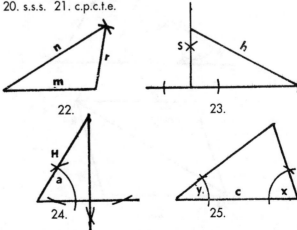

22. 23. 24. 25.

UNIT TEST 4

1. S 2. A 3. A 4. A 5. A 6. S 7. S 8. N 9. N 10. A
11. S 12. A 13. S 14. A 15. A 16. S

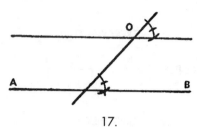

17.

18. corresponding 19. adjacent interior 20. int. ∠ on same side of trans. 21. alternate exterior 22. alternate interior
23. 5 24. 3 25. 8 26. 3 27. 1 28. 9 29. 130° 30. 140°
31. 115° 32. 36° 33. 144°

UNIT TEST 5

1. N 2. N 3. A 4. A 5. S 6. S 7. N 8. A 9. A 10. S
11. A 12. A

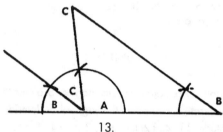

13.

14. 9 15. 9 16. 10 17. 2 18. 4 19. 45° 20. 33° 21. 60°
22. 18° 23. 127° 24. 35° 25. 52°

UNIT TEST 6

1. S 2. A 3. A 4. S 5. A 6. A 7. N 8. A 9. A 10. S
11. S 12. A 13. A 14. A 15. 24″ 16. 132° 17. 27-18-15
18. 14.8 19. born free 20. syllogism 21. converse
22. Inverse 23. contrapositive 24. true 25. true 26. true
27. 8 28. 2 29. 3 30. 7 31. 5

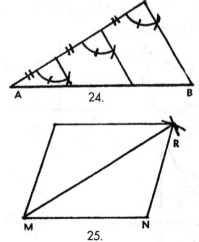

24.

25.

UNIT TEST 7

1. yes 2. no 3. yes 4. no 5. no 6. BC 7. A 8. N 9. A
10. A 11. S 12. 36 13. 4 14. 70° 15. 3,600° 16. 150°
17. 13 18. 12 19. 45° 20. 8 21. 9 22. 10 23. 7 24. 2
25. 9

UNIT TEST 8

1. 6 2. 11 3. 13 4. 7 5. 13 6. 10 7. 2 8. 3 9. 9 10. 5
11. 12 12. cent. ∠ 13. chord 14. radius 15. tangent
16. secant 17. minor arc 18. sector 19. segment
20. inscribed ∠ 21. 9 in. 22. locus

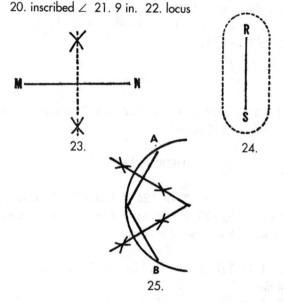

23.

24.

25.

UNIT TEST 9

1. N 2. A 3. A 4. A 5. A 6. S 7. 6 or 5 8. 3 9. 3
10. 16 11. 14 12. 13 13. 12 14. centroid 15. line of
centers 16. circumcenter 17. incenter 18. orthocenter
19. 27 20. 10 21. 38°

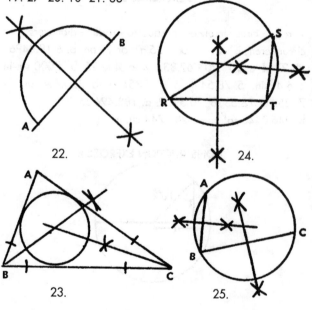

22.

23.

24.

25.

UNIT TEST 10

1. greater 2. obtuse 3. right 4. longest 5. shortest
6. central 7. inscribed 8. equal 9. equidistant 10. the
center 11. equal 12. 110° 13. 220° 14. 120° 15. 130°
16. 62.5° 17. 14.5° 18. 43° 19. 122.5° 20. 18° 21. 6
22. 11 23. 10 24. 12 25. 17 26. 16 or 15 27. 15 or 16
28. 17 29. 8 30. 5 31. 9 32. 17

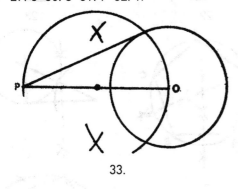

33.

UNIT TEST 11

1. equivalent 2. area 3. commensurable 4. median 5. A
6. A 7. S 8. A 9. A 10. A 11. N 12. 12.5 s.f. (1800 s.i.)
13. 73.5 s.f. 14. 96 s.u. 15. 500 s.u. 16. 120 cu. in.
17. 544 s.in. 18. 1280 cu. in. 19. 20 20. 1800 s.u.
21. 30 s.u. 22. 13 units 23. 56 s.u. 24. 420 25. 120 $\sqrt{3}$ or
207.8 + 26. 12$\sqrt{6}$ or 29.3 + 27. 98 28. 8 29. 60

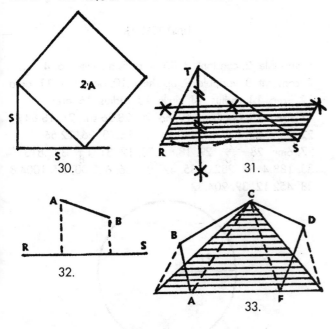

30.

31.

32.

33.

UNIT TEST 12

1. 15 2. $\frac{3}{4}$ 3. 0 4. x-axis 5. x = -6 6. None 7. 5 8. (3,4)
9. (3, -2) 10. $\frac{-4}{7}$ 11. .35 12. Origin 13. $\frac{-2}{3}$ 14. 2 15. 3
16. 4 17. $x^2 + y^2 = 49$ 18. (0, 0) 19. 3 20. (2, -3)
21. Slope 22. Slope 23. -1 24. Positive (+) 25. Negative (-)

UNIT 13 TEST

1. ratio 2. proportion 3. parallel 4. proportionally
5. externally 6. internally 7. 10 & x 8. 5 & y 9. 5 & x
10. 10 & y 11. yes 12. yes 13. no 14. yes 15. yes
16. yes 17. yes 18. yes 19. 10 20. $\frac{1}{4}$ 21. 36 22. 20
23. 30 24. 27° 25. 100° 26. 10 in. 27. 5 28. 6$\frac{3}{4}$
29. 3.2 30. 3.5 31. 10.5

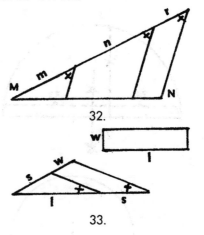

32.

33.

UNIT TEST 14

1. A 2. A 3. S 4. A 5. S 6. N 7. A 8. A 9. A 10. S
11. S 12. A 13. A 14. A 15. N 16. A 17. A 18. A
19. A 20. N 21. 12 & 16 22. 20 23. 8 in. 24. 1 to 5
25. 15 26. 6 27. 12 28. 4 29. 2 30. 1 31. 7 32. 3

33.

UNIT TEST 15

1. tangent 2. mean proportional 3. secant 4. external
5. mean proportional 6. diameter 7. right 8. triangles
9. similar 10. triangle 11. larger 12. shorter 13. 12
14. 40° 15. 50° 16. 50° 17. 10 18. 5 $\sqrt{5}$ 19. 10 $\sqrt{5}$
20. 3 21. 7.416 +

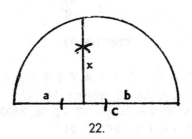

22.

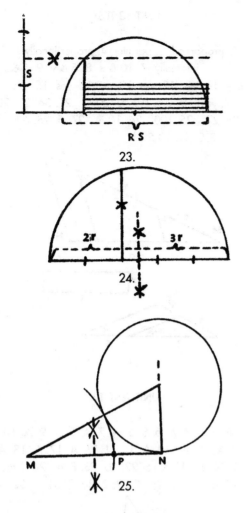

23.

24.

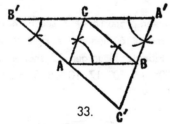

25.

UNIT TEST 16

1. N 2. A 3. N 4. A 5. N 6. S 7. A 8. S 9. A 10. S
11. $\frac{1}{9}$ 12. $\frac{4}{9}$ 13. median 14. $\frac{4}{25}$ 15. 10 16. 30 17. 5
18. 32 19. 16 20. 36 21. 4 $\sqrt{10}$ or 12.64+ 22. 25 23. 2
24. 1 25. 4 or 7 26. 1 27. 4 28. 4 or 7 29. 3 30. 6
31. 1 32. 7 or 4 Make $\angle A' = \angle A$ and make $\angle B' = \angle B$

33.

UNIT TEST 17

1. S 2. A 3. A 4. N 5. A 6. A 7. S 8. S 9. A 10. A
11. cent. $\angle$ 12. radius 13. apothem 14. 72°
15. 135° 16. 20 $\sqrt{3}$ or 34.64+ 17. 12 18. 2400 $\sqrt{3}$ or
4151.8+ 19. 1 to 4 20. $3\frac{3}{4}$ 21. 24

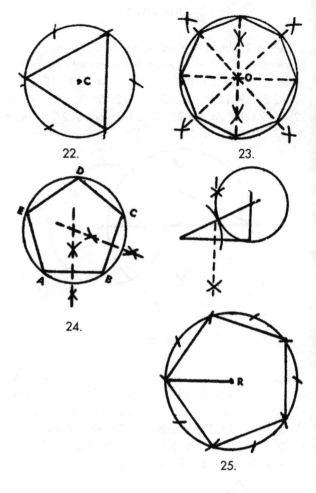

22.

23.

24.

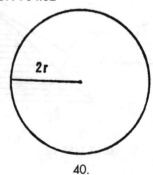

25.

UNIT TEST 18

1. variable 2. constant 3. 35 4. n 5. diameter 6. 4
7. constant 8. variable 9. apothem 10. perimeter 11. area
12. area 13. radius 14. circle 15. radius 16. area
17. area 18. apothem 19. no 20. 28.26 s.i. 21. 18.84 i
22. 3 in. 23. 5 to 9 24. 3.14 25. 15.70 26. 12.56
27. 6mn 28. $\frac{625}{16}$ 29. 18.84 30. 12 31. $1\frac{1}{8}$ 32. .813
33. 188.4 34. 282.6 35. 427.04 36. 628.00 37. 1004.8
38. 452.12 39. 904.32

40.

BENTON'S TEXT-WORKBOOK

IN

NEW MODERN GEOMETRY

A Complete Text-Workbook for Students' Use in High Schools

By

LEROY W. SHRODE

Central High School

Evansville, Ind.

Now Published by Hayes School Publishing Co., Inc., Pittsburgh, Pennsylvania

CONTENTS AND INDEX

ESSENTIAL FEATURES OF THE BENTON'S TEXT-WORKBOOK
IN NEW MODERN GEOMERTY

This is a TEXT-WORKBOOK in Modern Geometry, and it has been prepared for use in high school classes in that subject. The content includes the entire year's work in Geometry as it is usually given in any present-day standard textbook or course of study in the subject.

Some of the essential features of this Workbook-Text are as follows. Teachers and students should familiarize themselves with these features before beginning the use of this Workbook-Text.

1. THE TEXT-WORKBOOK IS UP TO DATE AND COMPLETE IN ITSELF. No additional textbook, reference material, or scratch paper will be needed.

2. HOWEVER, THE TEXT-WORKBOOK MAY BE USED IN CONJUNCTION WITH ANY STANDARD TEXTBOOK IN MODERN GEOMETRY. It will serve as an excellent geometry notebook and guide, since provision has been made for the student to do his work directly in the book itself.

3. The material of this book is organized into EIGHTEEN UNITS with new ideas to conform with the trend of the times. Included are a number of basic concepts of SOLID GEOMETRY and COORDINATE GEOMETRY which now frequently appear in the first year course in Geometry. These ideas may be omitted without destroying the continuity of the program.

4. There is complete TEXTUAL MATERIAL for each unit in subject-matter which is new and unfamiliar to the students. This information is presented to students exactly at the time when it is needed.

5. There is a pad of eighteen UNIT TESTS designed to accompany the BENTON TEXT-WORKBOOK IN MODERN GEOMETRY. These tests are easy to check, and each can be administered in twenty-five to thirty-five minutes.

6. THE UNIT TESTS CAN BE USED ENTIRELY INDEPENDENTLY OF THE WORK-BOOK-TEXT, and, therefore, can be obtained from the publishers without ordering the workbook-text.

Additional features of this book are given below:

7. Provision is made for student-discovery of the steps in proofs. Very seldom are *reasons* given outright. Instead, hints like this one are given in the REASONS COLUMN: "Unit 3, Th.?" The student is here required to determine which theorem in Unit 3 applies to the situation.

8. A great many auxiliary lines required in proofs are explained (where necessary), but they are seldom actually drawn for the student. This approach tends to keep the student mentally alert all the way through the development of a proof.

9. The amount of material is sufficient to meet the requirements of any class in Geometry. An abundance of carefully arranged drill material and exercises gives the teacher an opportunity to select his subject-matter in accordance with student ability and the length of the school year.

10. The amount of help that is given to the student has been carefully selected on the basis of usual student difficulties. The hints to these difficulties are given in ways that encourage the student to exercise his own judgment in arriving at the answers.

11. THE STUDY OF THE MEASUREMENT OF THE CIRCLE IS PRESENTED BY TWO DIFFERENT METHODS. METHOD I develops the relationships involved with a minimum use of the principles of limits. METHOD II treats the same relationships fully upon the basis of the theory of limits. Teachers, therefore, have the choice of using either method.

SUGGESTIONS TO THE STUDENT FOR THE USE OF THE BENTON'S TEXT-WORKBOOK IN MODERN GEOMERTY

The mastery of the truths of Geometry is not the chief purpose for taking this course. The chief purpose of your Geometry course is to teach you HOW TO THINK LOGICALLY.

The author offers the following suggestions to students who are going to use this Workbook-Text:

1. Study the textual material of the unit with which you are working. Refer to this material as often as you find it necessary to do so in the preparation of your assignment.

2. Refer to the material of those units which you have already studied that applies to your problem.

3. Try to get as much of your assignment as you possibly can by yourself.

4. In writing out statements in abbreviated forms, use the symbols and abbreviations. This will not only save time in writing, but will also avoid the crowding of your work.

5. You will find on page 6 of this book a list of symbols and abbreviations for your use. Refer to this list whenever you are in doubt about an expression of this kind.

6. In reviewing the vocabulary of a unit, cover with a sheet of paper the terms which you have written in the corresponding answer-spaces. Then see whether you can recall correctly the terms from their definitions, and conversely. Similarly in reviewing a proof or an exercise, cover the reasons which you have written in the answer-spaces, or which you have underlined, and then see whether you can figure them out.

THE AUTHOR

SYMBOLS AND ABBREVIATIONS
USED IN THIS BOOK

SYMBOLS

=   equals, or is equal to

≐   is equal in number of degrees to

≠   is not equal to, or does not equal

>   is greater than

<   is less than

≮   is not less than

+   plus, or added to

−   minus, or subtracted from

×   times, or multiplied by

·   times, or multiplied by

÷   divided by

~   similar, or is similar to

≅   congruent, or is congruent to

⊥   perpendicular, or is perpendicular to

⊥s   perpendiculars

‖   parallel, or is parallel to

‖s   parallels

⌒   arc

∠, ⩘   angle, angles

△, ⧍   triangle, triangles

▱, ⑤   parallelogram, parallelograms

▭, ⑤   rectangle, rectangles

□, ⑤   square, squares

⊙, ⑤   circle, circles

∟   right angle

→   approaches, or approaches as a limit

∴   therefore

⏢   trapezoid

∪   union

∩   intersection

⊂   is a proper subset of

⊆   is an improper subset of

φ   the empty (or null) set

{ }   the set whose members are

∈   is an element (or member) of

$\overrightarrow{AB}$ ray AB

$\overleftrightarrow{AB}$ line AB

$\overline{AB}$ line-segment AB

AB distance AB (or length of line-segment AB, or length of side AB according to context.)

ABBREVIATIONS

Add.   addition

adj.   adjacent

a.   angle

Div.   division

cor.   corollary

def.   definition

ex.   exercise

fig.   figure

h.   hypotenuse

l.   line, or limit

Mult.   multiplication

prin.   principle

Prop.   property

pt.   point

Post.   postulate

r.   radius

rt.   right

Reflex.   reflexive

s.   side

Subtract.   subtraction

Sym.   symmetric

Th.   theorem

v.   variable

6

Unit I.

FUNDAMENTAL CONCEPTS OF GEOMETRY

A. PROPERTIES OF POINTS · LINES · LINE-SEGMENTS · HALF-LINES · RAYS

We shall classify points, lines, planes, and space as UNDEFINED ideas or terms because it is easier to understand them from a description of their properties than it is to attempt to give precise definitions of them.

We may regard a geometric *point* as a *sizeless dot* that holds a specific location or place of its own in space. Every point, then, is *a place-holder in space*. Points are unique (the only things of their kind) in the sense that (in combinations of two or more) they form each of the other basic geometric ideas and figures. We represent (or draw) points as dots and we name them with adjacent capital letters in this manner: · A, read: *"Point A"*. Points which are in alignment with each other (like these three dots: . . .) are called *collinear points*. Those which are out of alignment (like these three dots: ∴) are called *non-collinear points*. Do we see that any TWO points are ALWAYS collinear?

We may regard a *straight line* as an *infinite set* of collinear points that extends WITHOUT LIMIT in opposite directions. The only property of a line is that of INFINITE LENGTH, which may be indicated as a series of collinear dots with arrowheads at the ends that point away from each other:

Do we see that the points forming a straight line run so close together that they tend to blend into each other to form a solid mark? Hence to

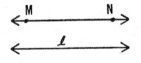

A Straight Line Expressed as Points

designate (or to draw) a straight line in our work, we make a straight solid mark with arrowheads at the ends pointing away from each other. We shall name lines with two capital letters placed near the arrowed ends or with one lower case letter near the center or near one end:

Expressed in symbols, we have: $\overleftrightarrow{MN}$, which is read: *"Line MN."*

This is read: *"Line l"*.
Straight Lines Expressed As a Solid Marks

Do we see that the two *marked* points M and N in the above illustrations are in no way different from the countless *unmarked* points that help to form the line? It requires *two points* to establish (or to locate) a line.

A geometric *curved line* is a figure formed by a set of non-collinear points which follows a bent or curved pattern or path. We shall regard a curved line as an infinite set of non-collinear points that follows a bent course whose ends may or may not eventually meet, depending upon the nature of the curve:

Curved Lines Expressed As Points   Curved Lines Expressed As Solid Marks

The points of a curved line are too close together to permit us to see between them. So we shall indicate a particular curved line as a solid curved mark with arrowheads and name it with capital letters near the arrowed ends or with a lower case letter near the middle:

 This is read: *"Curved line RS"*.   This is read: *"Curved line l"*.

7

We may regard a geometric *line-segment* as a part or piece of a straight line. The only property of a line-segment is that of finite (fixed) length. So it is an infinite set of collinear points of finite length. We shall represent (or draw) a line-segment as a straight solid mark without arrowheads, of course, using capital letters at its ends or a lower case letter its center, to name it:

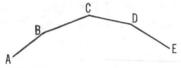

LINE-SEGMENTS

Expressed in symbols, we have: $\overline{RS}$, which is read forwards or backwards in this manner: *"Line-segment RS"*. Or: *"Line-segment SR"*.

Expressed in symbols, we have: l, which is read: *"Line-segment l"*.

Of course, the two *end-points* by which we name a line-segment are in no way different from the rest of its points. Do we see that a line-segment may be regarded as being established in position and direction by any two of its points? Its end points establish a line-segment completely.

A geometric *broken line* is a figure formed by two or more coplanar line-segments whose end-points are successively joined but not collinear. So do we see that we may regard a broken line as the figure formed by the *union* of coplanar line-segments joined end to end?

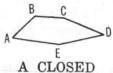

AN OPEN BROKEN LINE

This is read: *"Broken line ABCDE"*.

A CLOSED
BROKEN LINE

This is read: *"Closed broken line ABCDE"*

Do we see that we may separate a straight line into two half-lines by any point of that line?

We will observe that the point of separation (point M) is not included as a part of either half-line:

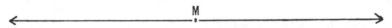

At the right we have *"half-line RS"*: We will observe that one end of a half-line is fixed and the other endless. We will also note that point R is chosen near but NOT AT the fixed end of the half-line RS.

A *ray* is a half-line with a point of separation included:

At the right we have *"ray MN"*.

Expressed in symbols, we have: $\overrightarrow{MN}$

Just below ray MN we have ray SR, expressed

in symbols as: $\overrightarrow{SR}$

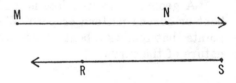

We will observe that end-point M represents the FIXED POINT of ray MN and point N represents ANY one of the other points of the ray.

B. PLANE AND CURVED SURFACES · PLANE FIGURES

We should consider a geometric *plane* as an infinite SET of points that form a boundless and perfectly FLAT surface. This means that the surface of a plane is such that if a straight line touches any TWO of the plane's points, then every point of that line touches the plane also. In short, the line is then a part of the plane and hence a subset of it. (See line m in the accompanying drawing.) So we may regard a plane as a set of points that form a flat surface of infinite extension without thickness. So the properties of a plane are these: perfect flatness, infinite extension and no thickness. Points that lie in the same plane are said to be *coplanar*. Points that form a curved surface are *non-coplanar*.

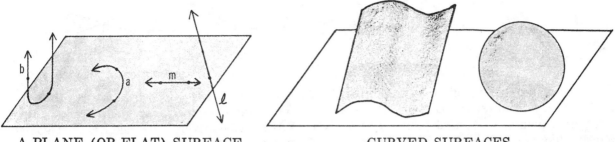

A PLANE (OR FLAT) SURFACE   CURVED SURFACES

If a straight line touches a plane in one and only one point, then the line will pass through the plane. (See line 1 above.) Obviously a curved line (a line with "bow" in it) may or may not lie entirely within a plane with which it comes in contact, depending upon whether it lies "flatwise" or "edgewise" in the plane. (See lines *a* and *b* in the above plane).

A flat sheet of paper, a desk top, a chalkboard, and the walls and ceiling of a room are physical examples of plane surfaces. Geometric figures like straight lines, angles, and circles, which require a plane (but not any space) for their existence, are called *plane figures*. The branch of Geometry which deals with plane figures only is called *plane Geometry*.

It is customary to represent planes as RECTANGLES with heavy front edges, viewed to give them pleasing, oblique appearance. We name planes by means of capital letters at opposite corners, or by one capital letter, or by a lower case letter in one corner.

Any line in a plane separates the plane into two *half-planes*. In plane AC that follows, line l SEPARATES the plane into two half-planes, M and N. The separation line l is not a part of either half-plane. Do we see that ANY straight cross-section of a plane is a straight line? In adjacent plane AC, the line of separation, l, is known as the *edge* of the shaded and the unshaded half-planes.

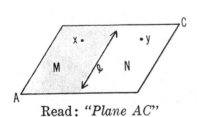

Read: *"Plane AC"*

Point x lies in half-plane M.
Point y lies in half-plane N.

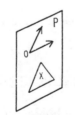

Read: *"Plane P"*

Angle O and triangle X lie in plane P.

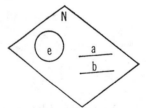

Read: *"Plane N"*

Line-segments *a* and *b* and circle *e* lie in plane *N*.

C.   SPACE AND SPACE FIGURES

Geometric *space* is the infinite SET of ALL points everywhere. So space is infinite and open in all directions. EVERY POINT IN SPACE HOLDS A UNIQUE POSITION OF ITS OWN THERE. *Spacial figures* are called THREE-DIMENSIONAL figures because they possess length, width, and thickness and hence require space for their existence. Boxes, spheres, cylinders, and pyramids are practical examples of spacial figures. They constitute *"space-segments"* or parts of space. The branch of Geometry that deals with figures which occupy space is called *solid*

9

Geometry (or *space Geometry*). Do we see that we may separate space into two *half-spaces* by means of any plane?

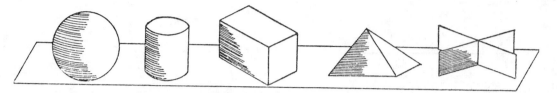

We should bear in mind that the "dots", "marks" and "figures" we draw on paper and the chalkboard to represent geometric ideas are drawings and symbols for these things. REAL Geometric points, lines, and planes occupy NO SPACE whatsoever, whereas REAL Geometric objects, like boxes, spheres, and cyclinders, are filled with parts of space.

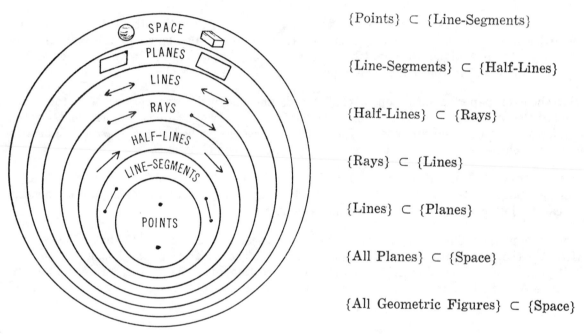

{Points} ⊂ {Line-Segments}

{Line-Segments} ⊂ {Half-Lines}

{Half-Lines} ⊂ {Rays}

{Rays} ⊂ {Lines}

{Lines} ⊂ {Planes}

{All Planes} ⊂ {Space}

{All Geometric Figures} ⊂ {Space}

Sets and Subsets of Basic Geometric Ideas Shown by Venn Diagrams

EXERCISES A - C

1. Name the idea which exists as a place-holder in space but which has no size .... _____

2. Name the idea which exists as a set of collinear points extending endlessly in opposite directions .... _____

3. Name the idea which exists as a set of points that follows an endless curved pattern .... _____

4. Name the idea that exists as an infinite set of collinear points which has a finite length as a part of a straight line .... _____

5. Name the idea that exists as the union of two or more non-collinear, coplanar line-segments joined end to end. .... _____

6. Name the idea that exists as a set of collinear points with one end fixed and the other end endless, if the fixed end is a point of separation of a line into half-lines. .... _____

7. Name the idea that exists as a set of collinear points with one end fixed and the other end endless, if the fixed end is NOT a point of separation of a line into half-lines. .... _____

8. A set of points that form a perfectly flat and boundless surface is called a(n) .... _____

9. A set of points that form a ball-like surface is called a (n). .... _____

10. Name the idea that exists as the set of all points everywhere. .... _____

11. Name that branch of Geometry that deals with figures which require only a flat surface for their existence. .... _____

12. Name that branch of Geometry that deals with figures that require space for their existence. .... _____

13. Name that branch of Geometry that deals with only triangles, circles, squares, lines, and the like. .... _____

14. Name that branch of Geometry which deals only with spheres, pyramids, cubes, cylinders, and the like. .... _____

15. Name the thing it takes to separate a plane into two half-planes. .... _____

16. Name the thing it takes to separate space into two half-spaces. .... _____

17. How many dimensions does a rectangular figure have? .... _____

18. How many dimensions does a rectangular box have? .... _____

Name in the appropriate space provided at the right each of the figures at the left.

19. .... 19. _____

20. .... 20. _____

21. .... 21. _____

22. .... 22. _____

23. .... 23. _____

24. .... 24. _____

25. .... 25. _____

26. .... 26. _____

Answer each of the following true statements with a T and each false statement with an X.

27. Every line-segment is a subset of exactly one line. .... _____

28. Every point is a subset of exactly one line. .... _____

29. Every point is a subset of space. .... _____

11

30. Every line is a subset of an infinite number of different planes. .... _____

31. Every ray is a subset of a half-line. .... _____

32. A basketball is a subset of space. .... _____

33. Every Geometric figure and body is a subset of space. .... _____

D. POSTULATES PERTAINING TO POINTS · LINES · PLANES · SPACE

So far our list of basic ideas in Geometry has been confined to UNDEFINED ideas and terms. Now let us add to the list several self-evident Geometric truths called *postulates*. The geometric facts expressed in postulates are so simple and obvious that we ACCEPT them WITHOUT PROOF. Postulates are used as *"tools"* in establishing the proofs of a great many geometric truths. Our first list of postulates deals essentially with points, lines, planes, and space.

POSTULATE 1. **In space through a given point there exists a line (or linear pair) for EVERY POSSIBLE pair of opposite directions in space.**

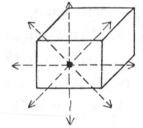

REMARK: Do we see that there are an infinite number of lines passing through a given point in space and that collectively these lines extend in ALL directions?

POSTULATE 2. **Through a given point in a plane, there exists one line (or linear pair) for EVERY POSSIBLE pair of opposite directions within the plane.**

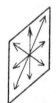

REMARKS: Do we see that there are an infinite number of lines that pass through a given point in a given plane and that collectively these lines extend in ALL directions WITHIN the plane?

POSTULATE 3. **It requires exactly TWO distinct points to establish (or locate) a straight line (or a line-segment).**

REMARKS: This is known as the *line postulate*. Of course, any line l contains a limitless number of points. According to Postulate 3, any two points on line l (such as points A and B) determine the direction and location of that line. Do we see that any one point alone (such as point A) cannot locate a particular line? Do we see how a surveyor uses the principle of Postulate 3 in establishing boundary lines?

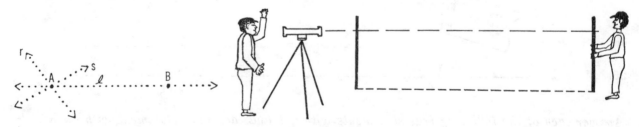

POSTULATE 4. **It requires exactly THREE distinct non-collinear points to establish (or locate) a plane.**

REMARKS: This is known as the *plane postulate*. Of course, any plane contains a limitless number of coplanar points. According to Postulate 4, any three non-collinear points (such as points R, S, and T) determine the position and the direction of plane MN. Do we see how the stability of a three-legged stool depends upon the principle of Postulate 4?

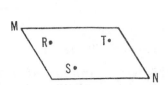

POSTULATE 5. It requires exactly FOUR distinct points (no three of which are collinear) to establish a region of space.

REMARKS: This is known as the *space postulate*. Space, of course, contains ALL points. According to Postulate 5, any four "co-spacial" points (such as those forming triangular pyramid RST — O require a part of space for their existence.

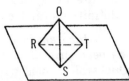

POSTULATE 6. Two distinct straight lines can intersect in exactly ONE point.

REMARKS: One or both lines would have to be curved or broken to intersect in two or more points. Of course, two straight lines, need not intersect at all. This is true when two straight lines are either *parallel* or *skew*. Two or more lines are parallel when ANY TWO of them lie in the same plane and none of them intersect. Two or more lines are *skew* when no two of them lie in the same plane. Do we see that straight streets which run in the same direction are like parallel lines, whereas streets which overpass and underpass each other are like skew lines?

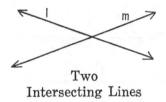

Two
Intersecting Lines

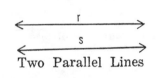

Two Parallel Lines

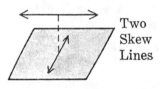

Two
Skew
Lines

POSTULATE 7. The intersection of any two distinct planes is a straight line.

REMARKS: Do we see how the intersection of two walls of most rooms and the intersection of a wall with the ceiling of a room depend upon the principle of Postulate 7?

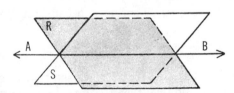

POSTULATE 8. An infinite number of planes may be passed through ONE straight line.

REMARKS: Do we see that planes R and S in the above figure are JUST TWO of an infinite number of planes that may be passed through line AB? A straight line does NOT establish a plane.

POSTULATE 9. If a straight line does not intersect a plane at all, then the line is parallel to that plane; and (conversely) if a straight line is parallel to a plane, then the line does not intersect the plane at all.

REMARKS: A line and a plane are parallel if they never meet regardless of their extension.

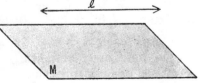

POSTULATE 10. If a straight line intersects a plane in exactly ONE point, then the line does not lie in the plane.

REMARKS: Do we see that a straight line that intersects a plane in two points becomes a part of the plane?

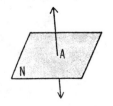

13

POSTULATE 11. If a straight line intersects a plane in more than one point, then the line lies entirely in the plane.

REMARKS: Do we see that this relation must be true because of the properties of a plane and the properties of a straight line?

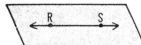

E. THEOREMS PERTAINING TO THE ESTABLISHMENT OF A PLANE

There is a basic rule in Geometry that may be stated in this way: *"Any fact of Geometry that we have already ACCEPTED or PROVED may be used in establishing NEW facts which follow it."*

So the facts that we may use AT THIS TIME in establishing a proof are undefined terms, definitions, and postulates.

A *theorem* is a basic principle in Geometry which is established by proof. After a theorem has been proved, it may be accepted as a "tool" in the proof of other theorems. The theorems which follow deal with the ESTABLISHMENT OF A PLANE.

THEOREM 1. A plane is determined by a straight line and a point outside that line.

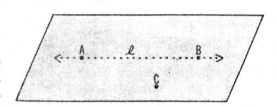

REMARKS: Do we see that the truth of Theorem 1 follows from the fact that a straight line l may replace two of the three non-collinear points in Postulate 4 (such as points A and B)? So Theorem 1 turns out to be a modification of postulate 4.

THEOREM 2. A plane is determined by two intersecting straight lines.

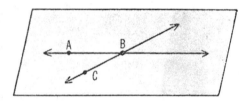

REMARKS: Do we that the truth of Theorem 2 follows from the fact that two intersecting straight lines may replace the three non-collinear points (A, B, and C) in Postulate 4? Do we see that we may *erase* line AB and line CB, retaining only points A, B, and C of Postulate 4? Therefore, Theorem 2 becomes a modification of Postulate 4.

THEOREM 3. A plane is determined by two parallel lines.

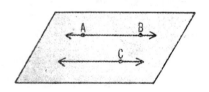

REMARKS: Do we see that two parallel lines may replace the three non-collinear points (such as points A, B, and C) in Postulate 4? Or de we see that we may *erase* lines AB and C, retaining only points A, B, and C? So Theorem 3 too becomes a modification of Postulate 4.

F. THE NATURE OF GEOMETRIC REASONING AND PROOF

A. Examples Involving *Inductive* Thinking:

(1) If every rabbit with which we in this class have ever come in contact (directly and indirectly) has been gray, then it would be natural for us to draw this general conclusion about the color of rabbits: *ALL rabbits are gray.*

(2) If we multiplied several odd numbers by even numbers like these combinations: $2 \times 3 = 6$, $4 \times 5 = 20$, and $6 \times 7 = 42$, then we would obviously draw this general conclusion about their products: *The product of an even number and an odd number is ALWAYS an EVEN number.*

(3) In the science laboratory, we can establish the *Law of the Lever* by an experiment in which we balance a simple lever by placing a comparatively light weight and a compara-

tively heavy weight on opposite sides of the fulcrum (the balancing edge) at distances that will permit the lever to balance. From the specific data collected from a number of trials, we can draw this general conclusion, called the *Law of the Lever*:

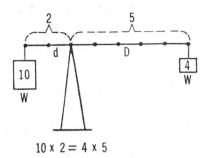

$$10 \times 2 = 4 \times 5$$

The weight on the left side of the fulcrum $\times$ its distance from the fulcrum = the weight on the right side $\times$ its distance from the fulcrum.

Or expressed as a formula, we have: $W\, d = w\, D$

Drawing a general conclusion on the basis of one or more specific supporting facts or cases is called *inductive reasoning* or *inductive proof*. Drawing conclusions by inductive methods are NOT always reliable. For example, conclusion above about the color of rabbits is not always true because there are black ones, white ones, spotted ones, etc.

B. Examples Involving *Deductive* Thinking

(1) If we accept this general fact: *Two-legged creatures having feathers, wings, and beaks are birds*, then if we should find a peculiar-looking creature sitting on our door steps that meets this description, we would be justified in drawing this specific conclusion about it: *The creature is a bird.*

(2) According to Postulate 3, *it takes two distinct points to establish a straight line.* Therefore, we may safely draw this conclusion about drawing lines through points A and B. *We can draw exactly one straight line through points A and B.*

(3) In Algebra, we became familiar with the *Multiplication Property* of *Equality,* which we shall apply here:

$\dfrac{x}{5} = 15$ Find x. Solution: $\dfrac{5\,(x)}{5} = 5\,(15).$ $x = 75$

In the solution of the above equation, we multiplied both members of the equation by 5, which we were justified in doing on the basis of the Multiplication Property of Equality.

Hence we were using a deductive process.

Drawing a specific conclusion on the basis of a general, accepted or assumed principle is called *deductive reasoning* or deductive proof. Deductive reasoning is ALWAYS reliable in Geometry, provided the principles on which we base our conclusions are true.

C. Examples Involving *Intuitive* Thinking:

(1) During a basketball game, a player with the ball suddenly decided to shoot for the basket rather than to pass the ball to a nearby companion because he *"felt"* that he himself could make the basket.

(3) In the accompanying figure, one can *"sense"* that the shortest distance from M to N is along the straight line-segment MN, rather than by way of MR and RN or by way of MS and SN.

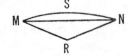

Intuition (or intuitive thinking) is the kind of thinking in which the thinker *"feels"* or *"senses"* the conclusion or outcome of a set of conditions.

15

EXERCISES D - F

Answer each of the following questions correctly with the best answer.

1. What are those basic principles of Geometry called whose truths are so obvious that they are accepted or assumed without proof? .... _____

2. How many lines may be passed through a given point and be confined to a given plane? _____

3. How many lines may be passed through a given point in the freedom of space? _____

4. How many lines may be passed through two distinct points? ...... _____

5. How many distinct points does it take to establish a plane surface? _____

6. How many distinct points does it take to establish a region of space? _____

7. In how many points can two distinct straight lines intersect? .... _____

8. What are two non-intersecting straight lines called which lie in different planes? _____

9. What are two non-intersecting straight lines called which lie in the same plane? _____

10. What Geometric thing is formed by two intersecting planes? .... _____

11. How many planes are determined (established) by a single straight line? _____

12. If a straight line and a plane never intersect, the line and the plane are said to be? _____

13. Can a straight line intersect a plane in exactly two points only? .... _____

14. Can a straight line intersect a plane in exactly ONE point only? .... _____

15. What is a basic principle of Geometry called which requires proof for its acceptance? _____

16. May we use previously accepted postulates to prove a theorem? ...... _____

17. May we use previously accepted definitions in proving a theorem? .... _____

18. May we use previously accepted undefined terms or ideas in proving a theorem? _____

19. May we use a previously proved theorem in proving a theorem? ...... _____

20. May we use a theorem that has not yet been proved or accepted in proving another theorem that follows it? _____

21. Is a plane determined by a straight line and an outside point? .... _____

22. Is a plane determined by two skew lines? _____

23. Is a plane determined by two parallel lines? _____

24. Is a plane determined by two intersecting straight lines? .... _____

25. The distance between two points is measured along the ? joining them. _____

26. $2 + 1 = 3$; $4 + 1 = 5$; $6 + 7 = 13$; $8 + 9 = 17$
Conclusion: *An even number plus an odd number = an ? number.* _____

27. In question 26, we arrived at the answer by ? thinking. .... _____

    STATEMENTS   REASONS
    1. 3x — 7 = 20 ....Given
    2. 3x — 7 + 7 = 20 + 7 ....Addition Property of Equality
    3. 3x = 27 ....Simplifying step 2
    4. ∴ x = 9 ....Division Property of Equality

28. In the above problem, we arrived at step 3 by ? reasoning .... _____

29. In the above problem, we arrived at step 4 by ? reasoning .... _____

30. Suppose we have the choice of catching a standard baseball or a
    steel ball of the same size when each is pitched with exactly the same
    speed and in exactly the same way. We would decide to catch the
    standard baseball by ? thinking. .... _____

31. The selection of a business manager solely on an applicant's appear-
    ance involves the reliance upon ? thinking .... _____

32. Drawing general conclusions on the basis of specific supporting facts
    is called ? reasoning .... _____

33. Drawing specific conclusions on the basis of generally established
    principles is called ? reasoning .... _____

34. The kind of thinking involved in which the thinker "feels" or
    "senses" outcomes or conclusions that result from his decisions. .... _____

G. THE NATURE OF ANGLES · THE KINDS OF ANGLES · THEIR MEASURE

A *plane angle* is the figure formed by two distinct rays that have a COMMON end-point.
The rays are called the *sides* of the angle and the common end point is
called it *vertex*. (See Fig. 1a)

An *angle* may be regarded as the figure formed by the *union* of two
distinct rays that have the same end point. So in Fig. 1a we have:

$\overrightarrow{OA} \cup \overrightarrow{OB} = \angle AOB$

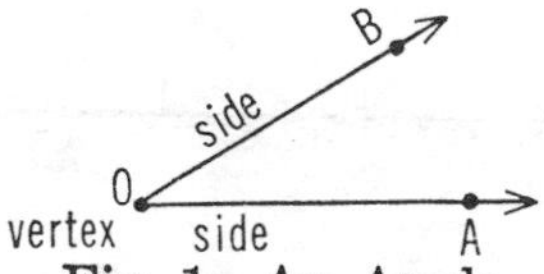

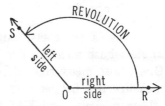

Fig. 1a An Angle

Do we see that an extension of the sides of an angle would form
two intersecting lines, which makes this kind of an angle a PLANE
figure in accordance with **Theorem 2**?

Let us NOT CONFUSE an angle with its MEASURE. The *measure*
of an angle is the minimum number of units of revolution required for
one side to rotate about the vertex of the angle to the position of the

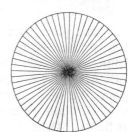

Fig. 1b An Angle

other side.(See Fig. 1b) The Measure of ∠ ROS is greater than than that of ∠ AOB because the ro-
tation from side OR to side OS is greater than the rotation from side OA to side OB. As we view
∠ ROS inward from its vertex, side OR appears at our right and side OS appears at our left.
Hence OR is known as its *right (or initial) side*, while OS is known as its *left (or terminal) side*.

The common unit of *angular measure* is called a *degree* (°), which
is one of the 360 equal units of revolution about a point. (See Fig. 1c).
A degree is subdivided into 60 equal angular parts called minutes ('), and
a minute, in turn, is subdivided into 60 equal angular parts called seconds
(") : $1° = 60' = 60 \times 60'' = 3600''$

Because of the circular nature of angular measure, the *angle number line*
takes the form of a semi-circular CURVED SCALE, ranging from 0°
through 180° (See **Fig. 1d**).

Fig. 1c.
Each ∠ is 6°

17

Based on the definition of angular measure, we have Postulate 12:

In Geometry, an angle may vary in angular measure from any real value greater than 0° to and including 180°.

(Angle-Measurement Postulate, or $0° < x \leq 180°$) *

The facts just stated in Postulate 12 lead us to the so-called Protractor Postulate 13:

Either side of an angle (which is less than 180°) and its opposite ray ALWAYS divides the plane of that angle into TWO HALF-PLANES in such a way that the angle lies in that one of the half-planes which contains the other side of the angle.

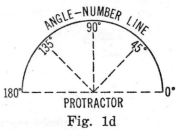

Fig. 1d

POSTULATE 14. If one ray (or more than one ray) lies between two outside rays, all with the same end-point, the measure of the angle formed by the outside rays is equal to the sum of the measures of the angles that appear between the outside rays. (ANGLE-ADDITION POSTULATE).

EXAMPLE: $\angle ABC = \angle 1 + \angle 2 + \angle 3$

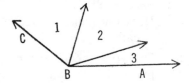

The following drawings illustrate the meaning of the Protractor Postulate. We will observe that in each angle, a side and its opposite ray divides the plane of the angle into a shaded half-plane and an unshaded half-plane. We will note that each angle here appears in an unshaded half-plane.

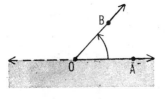

An Acute Angle
Fig. 2a

A Right Angle
Fig. 2b

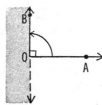

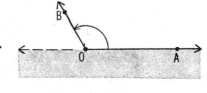

An Obtuse Angle
Fig. 2c

A Straight Angle
Fig. 2d

Angles are classified and named according to their size expressed in angular measure. An angle whose measure lies between 0° and 90° is called an *acute angle*. One whose measure is EXACTLY 90° is called a *right angle*. One whose measure lies between 90° and 180° is called an *obtuse angle*, and one whose measure is EXACTLY 180° is called a *straight angle*. We will notice (Fig. 2b) that the sides of a right angle intersect to form a SQUARE CORNER. Such a pair of lines are said to be *perpendicular lines*. We will also notice that the sides of a straight angle (Fig. 2d) form opposite rays or a straight line. Acute angles and obtuse angles are also said to be *oblique angles* because in each case the sides form slanting rays with respect to each other.

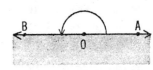

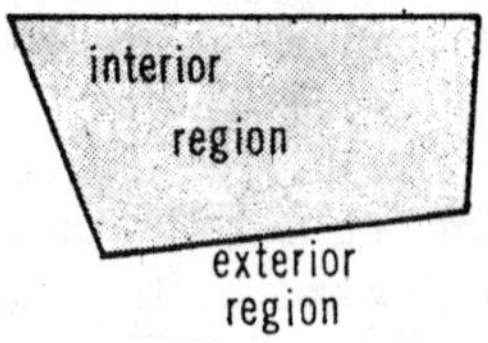

Fig. 3

The plane surface within the boundary lines of a plane geometric figure is called its *interior region*, while the plane surface outside its boundary is called its *exterior region*. (See Fig. 3). The figure itself SEPARATES the two regions and hence does NOT belong to either region. We will observe that points X and R lie in the interior region of $\angle O$, while points Y and Z lie in its exterior region. Points A and B lie *on* $\angle O$.

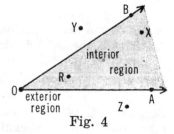

Fig. 4

*Do we see that according to definition, an angle in geometry cannot have a value of 0°?

18

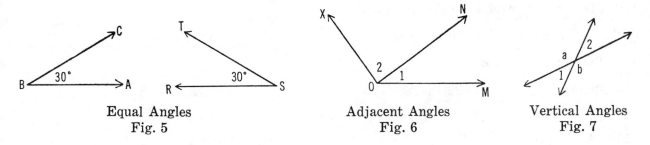

Equal Angles	Adjacent Angles	Vertical Angles
Fig. 5	Fig. 6	Fig. 7

Two angles which have the same angular measure are said to be *equal* (See Fig. 5). Two angles (like those in Fig. 6) which have a common vertex (O) and a common side between them (ON) are called *adjacent angles*. In Fig. 5 ∠ABC and ∠RST are classified as *non-adjacent* angles because they do not have a common side between them. A pair of opposite angles like ∠1 and ∠2 in Fig. 7, formed by two intersecting lines are called *vertical angles*. ∠a and ∠b are also vertical angles. Vertical angles are always non-adjacent.

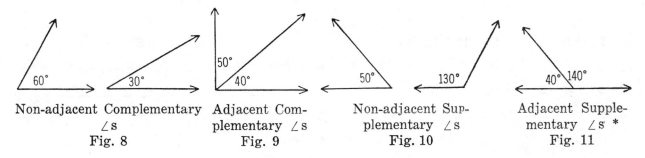

Non-adjacent Complementary ∠s
Fig. 8

Adjacent Complementary ∠s
Fig. 9

Non-adjacent Supplementary ∠s
Fig. 10

Adjacent Supplementary ∠s *
Fig. 11

TWO angles the sum of whose measure is 90° are called *complementary angles*. (See Figs. 8 and 9.) TWO angles the sum of whose measure is 180° are called *supplementary angles*. (See Figs. 10 and 11).

Just as two rays may intersect to form a *plane angle*, so two planes may intersect to form a *space angle*. A space angle formed by two intersecting planes is called a *dihedral angle*. The dihedral angle in Fig. 12 is read: "dihedral ∠M — RS — N" or " dihedral ∠RS".

A dihedral angle may be regarded as the figure formed by the *union* of two half planes that contain the same edge. In Fig. 12 the intersection RS is called its *edge* and the half planes M and N are called its *faces*. The measure of a dihedral angle is the measure of its *plane angle*, which is any one of the plane angles formed by two rays (one in each face) that meet the edge at right angles. In Fig. 12, a plane angle of the dihedral angle is ∠ABC.

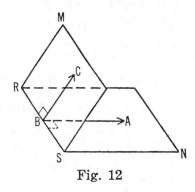

Fig. 12

THEOREM 4: **All right angles are equal.**

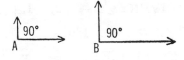

GIVEN: A = 90° and B = 90° TO PROVE: ∠A = ∠B

PROOF	STATEMENTS	REASONS
1. ∠A = 90° and ∠B = 90°		1. Definition of a right angle
2. ∠A = ∠B		2. Substitution Principle

*We will observe that a property of adjacent supplementary angles is that their exterior sides form a straight line (sometimes called a *linear pair*).

THEOREM 5: All straight angles are equal.

GIVEN: $\angle A = 180°$ and $\angle B = 180°$

TO PROVE: $\angle A = \angle B$

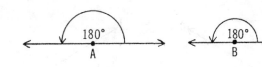

PROOF STATEMENTS	REASONS
1. $\angle A = 180°$ and $\angle B = 180°$	1. Definition of a straight angle
2. $\angle A = \angle B$	2. Substitution Principle

THEOREM 6: Vertical angles are equal.

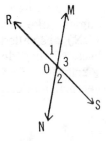

GIVEN: $\overleftrightarrow{MN}$ and $\overleftrightarrow{RS}$ intersecting at point O, forming $\angle 1$ and $\angle 2$ as one pair of vertical angles.

TO PROVE: $\angle 1 = \angle 2$

PROOF STATEMENTS	REASONS
1. $\angle 1 + \angle 3 =$ a st. $\angle$	1. Definition of a st. $\angle$ ....
2. $\angle 2 + \angle 3 =$ a st. $\angle$	2. Why? ....
3. Hence $\angle 1 + \angle 3 = \angle 2 + \angle 3$	3. Why? ....
4. $\therefore \angle 1 = \angle 2$	4. Why? ....

Of course, $\angle 3$ and its vertical $\angle$ can be proved to be equal in like manner.

THEOREM 7: Complements of the same angle or complements of equal angles are equal.

GIVEN: $\angle 1 = \angle 2$, $\angle 1 + \angle a = 90°$ and

$\angle 2 + \angle b = 90°$

TO PROVE: $\angle a = \angle b$

PROOF STATEMENTS	REASONS
1. $\angle 1 + \angle a = 90°$ and $\angle 2 + \angle b = 90°$	1. Given
2. $\angle 1 + \angle a = \angle 2 + \angle b$	2. Substitution Principle
3. $\angle 1 = \angle 2$	3. Given
4. $\angle a = \angle b$	4. Why? ....

THEOREM 8: Supplements of the same angle or supplements of equal angles are equal.

GIVEN: $\angle 1 = \angle 2$, $\angle 1 + \angle x = 180°$ and

$\angle 2 + \angle y = 180°$

TO PROVE: $\angle x = \angle y$

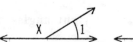 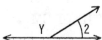

PROOF STATEMENTS	REASONS
1. $\angle 1 + \angle x = 180°$ and $\angle 2 + \angle y = 180°$	1. Why? ....
2. $\angle 1 + \angle x = \angle 2 + \angle y$	2. Why? ....
3. $\angle 1 = \angle 2$	3. Why? ....
4. $\angle x = \angle y$	4. Why? ....

20

H. DISTANCE BETWEEN TWO POINTS · BETWEENNESS

In the measure of lengths of line-segments, we regard them to be SIGNLESS, i.e., we consider only their absolute values of length. This means that the distance from A to R is the same as the distance from R to A. Or AR = RA, in the accompanying figure:

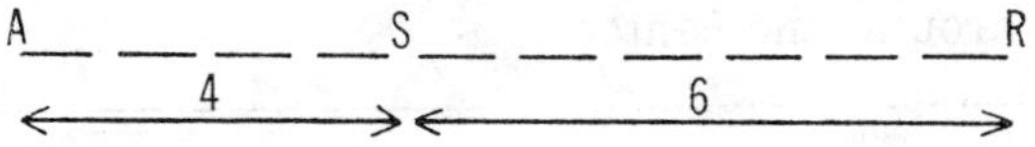

A _ _ _ _ S _ _ _ _ _ _ R   AS + SR = 4 + 6 = 10
  <——— 4 ———> <——— 6 ———>

When we wish to refer to line-segment RS, we write it thus: $\overline{RS}$. But when we wish to refer to the distance between POINTS R and S (of line-segment RS), we write it: RS. In the above figure RS = 6. We may also say: "The length of line-segment RS is 6".

POSTULATE 15: The shortest distance between two points is the measure of the length of the line-segment joining those two points. (The distance postulate)

REMARKS: The distance between any two points is understood to mean the SHORTEST distance between them. For example, the shortest distance between accompanying points A and C is the distance along line-segment AC rather than by way of AB and BC. This can be shown in the following manner: Fasten the two ends of a piece of *stretched rubber band* to points A and C with thumb tacks. At some point between A and C pull the stretched piece of band AC to any position B. When released, the band will always return to its position along AC because this is shorter than distance AB + distance BC.

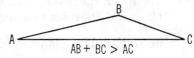
AB + BC > AC

POSTULATE 16: If AB + BC = AC, then points A, B, and C must be COLLINEAR and point B must lie some place BETWEEN points A and C.

REMARKS: Postulate 16 is known as the *Principle of Betweenness*, which is illustrated in the accompanying diagram. We will observe that when B is not in alignment with A and C, or when B does not fall between A and C, then the relationship expressed in this equation does NOT hold true.

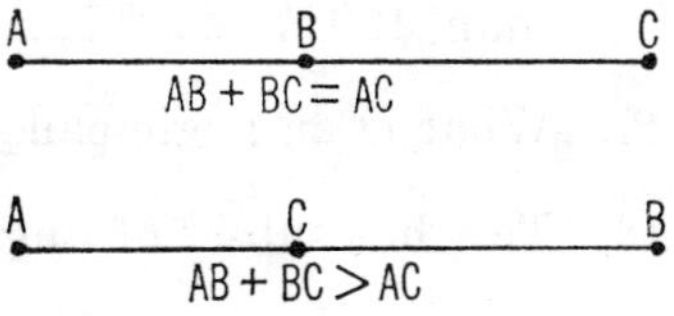

A———B———C
  AB + BC = AC

A———C———B
  AB + BC > AC

POSTULATE 17: (The Converse of Post. 16) If points A, B, and C are collinear and if point B lies between points A and C, then AB + BC = AC (Length-Addition Postulate)

POSTULATE 17A: The length of an entire line-segment is greater than any one of its parts.

POSTULATE 18: A line-segment can have exactly one midpoint.

REMARKS: The midpoint of a line-segment is half-way between its end points and it separates the line-segment into two equal line segments. Obviously, only one such point can exist. When B is the midpoint of line-segment AC, then we have: AB + BC = AC AND AB = BC.

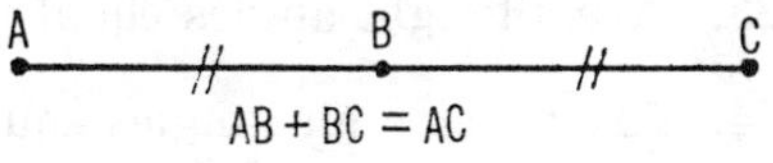

A———//———B———//———C
  AB + BC = AC

Also AB = BC

EXERCISES G - H

Answer each of the following questions correctly with the best answer.

1. What is a figure called that is formed by two distinct rays that have a common end-point? .... _____

2. In the accompanying figure, ∠ROB may be regarded as the ? of rays OR and OB.

.... _____

3. What part of ∠ROB is point O called? .... _____

4. What part of ∠ROB is ray OR called? .... _____

5. The size of an angle is measured by (1) the length of its sides (2) its vertex (3) its number of degrees of revolution (4) the measure of its interior region (5) none of these .... _____

6. How many degrees are there around a point or around the center of a circle? .... _____

7. How many minutes are there in 10°? .... _____

8. How many degrees are there in 1200′? .... _____

9. How many seconds are there in 2°? .... _____

10. In geometry, may an angle have a value of 0°? .... _____

11. What is the mathematical name of the scale which contains the numbers we apply to angular measurements? .... _____

12. - 13. When the plane of an angle has been divided into two half-planes by one of its sides and the extension of its ?, the angle will always _____

    lie in that half-plane which contains the ? side. .... _____

14. What is an angle called whose measure is greater than 0° but less than 90°? .... _____

15. What is an angle called whose measure is exactly 90°? .... _____

16. What is an angle called whose measure is greater than 90° but less than 180°? .... _____

17. What is an angle called whose measure is exactly 180°? .... _____

18. To what subset of angles does a 40° angle belong? .... _____

19. To what subset of angles does a 150° angle belong? .... _____

20. To what subset of angles do acute angles and obtuse angles belong? _____

21. What are two angles called whose sum is 180°? .... _____

22. What are two angles called whose sum is 90°? .... _____

23. Are all right angles equal in angular measure? .... _____

24. Are all straight angles equal in angular measure? .... _____

25. In geometry, can an angle of 80° have a complement? .... _____

26. In geometry, can an angle of 90° have a complement? .... _____

27. In geometry, can an angle of 90° have a supplement? .... _____

28. In geometry, can an angle of 180° have a supplement? .... _____

29. In geometry, can an angle of 100° have a complement? .... _____

30. Are the complements of equal angles equal? .... _____

31. Are the supplements of equal angles equal? .... _____

32. Are vertical angles equal? .... _____

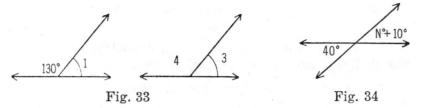

Fig. 33   Fig. 34

33. In Fig. 33, ∠1 = ∠3, how many degrees are there in ∠4? .... _____

34. In Fig. 34, how many degrees are there in N? .... _____

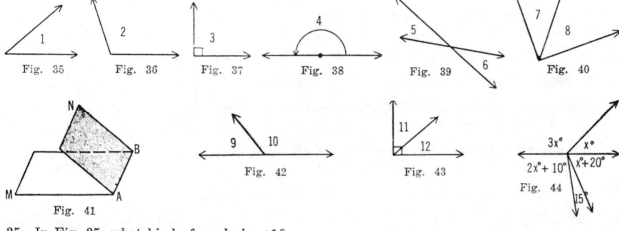

Fig. 35   Fig. 36   Fig. 37   Fig. 38   Fig. 39   Fig. 40

Fig. 41   Fig. 42   Fig. 43   Fig. 44

35. In Fig. 35, what kind of angle is ∠1? .... _____

36. In Fig. 36, what kind of angle is ∠2? .... _____

37. In Fig. 37, what kind of angle is ∠3? .... _____

38. In Fig. 38, what kind of angle is ∠4? .... _____

39. What is the pair of non-adjacent angles 5 and 6 above called? .... _____

40. What is the pair of angles 7 and 8 above called? .... _____

41. What kind of angle is ∠M — AB — N above called? .... _____

42. In ∠M-AB-N above, what is part AB called? .... _____

43. In ∠M-AB-N above, what are parts M and N called? .... _____

44. What kind of angles is the pair of angles 9 and 10 above called? .... _____

45. What kind of angles is the pair of angles 11 and 12 above called? .. _____

46. What is the shortest distance between two points? .... _____

47. How many midpoints can a line-segment have? .... _____

Solve the following numerical exercises.

48. In Fig. 44 how many degrees does ∠x contain? .... _____

49. What is the supplement of an angle of 60°? .... _____

50. What is the complement of an angle of 60°? .... _____

51. A certain angle is 5 times as large as its complement. How large is
    this angle? .... _____

52. A certain angle is 5 times as large as its supplement. How large is
    its supplement? .... _____

53. A certain angle is equal to its complement. What is its measure? .... _____

23

54. A pair of vertical angles are supplementary. How many degrees does each angle contain? _____ _____

55. Three times an angle plus twice its complement is equal to 60° more than its supplement. How many degrees does this angle contain? .... _____

56. Suppose A, B, and C represent points. Then where is B with respect to A and C if AB + BC = AC? _____ _____

57. GIVEN: X   Z   Y Which one of the following expressions is true?: (1) XZ + ZY > XY (2) XZ + ZY = XZ (3) XY + ZY = XZ (4) None of these _____ _____

58. If XY = YZ and XY + YZ = XZ, where is point Y with respect to points X and Z? _____ _____

59. If MR + RS = MS, then what do the letters M, R, and S represent? _____

60. In question 59, where is R with respect to M and S? _____ _____

61. In the expression MR + RS = MS, what mathematical principle is involved and illustrated? _____ _____

62. Is the principle illustrated in the expression AB + BC > AC the same as that involved in question 61? _____ _____

63. Which one of the following choices expresses the meaning "*line segment AB*"?: (1) AB (2) $\overset{\bullet\rightarrow}{AB}$ (3) $\overline{AB}$ (4) $\overleftrightarrow{AB}$ (5) $\overset{\frown}{AB}$ _____

64. Which one of the following choices expresses the meaning "*the distance or number AB is 5*" or "*the distance from A to B is 5*"?: (1) $\overline{AB} = 5$ (2) AB = 5 (3) $\overset{\frown}{AB} = 5$ (4) $\overleftrightarrow{AB} = 5$ (5) $\overset{\bullet\rightarrow}{AB} = 5$ _____

65. How many end-points does a line-segment have? _____ _____

I. SOME BASIC FACTS PERTAINING TO PARALLEL LINES · ANGLES · PERPENDICULAR LINES

THEOREM 9: **Through any given point outside a given line, there exists exactly one line that is parallel to the given line.**

GIVEN: $\overleftrightarrow{MN}$ and any point P outside $\overleftrightarrow{MN}$.

TO PROVE: (1) that one line (such as l) that passes through point P is ∥ to $\overleftrightarrow{MN}$.

(2) Any other line (such as l′) that passes through point P is not ∥ to $\overleftrightarrow{MN}$.

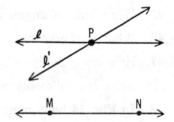

PROOF OF PART 1.   STATEMENTS   REASONS

1. Through point P there exists one line, l, that has the same direction as $\overleftrightarrow{MN}$. .... 1. Postulate 1

2. ∴ l is parallel to $\overleftrightarrow{MN}$. .... 2. Definition of parallel lines.

This proves that *one line* can be passed through point P parallel to $\overleftrightarrow{MN}$.

PROOF OF PART 2.   STATEMENTS   **REASONS**

1. Any line through point P other than l (such as l') will have its own unique direction, which is different from that of l.   1. Postulate 1

2. ∴ l' will intersect $\overleftrightarrow{MN}$ *or* l' will become skew with $\overleftrightarrow{MN}$. .... 2. Definition of non-parallel line. This proves that *only one line* can appear through point P parallel to MN.

POSTULATE 19: With a given ray as one of the sides of an angle of a given measure, exactly one other ray can exist as the other side of that angle ON THE SAME SIDE of the given ray.

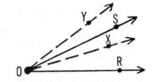

REMARKS: Suppose we examine ∠ROS which has ray OR as one side and ray OS as the other side, and a measure of r°. Then obviously, OR with some other ray like $\overrightarrow{OX}$ will form an angle < r°, while $\overrightarrow{OR}$ with another ray like $\overrightarrow{OY}$ will form an angle > r°.

THEOREM 10: An angle can have exactly one bisector.*

GIVEN: ∠ROS

TO PROVE: (1) *One* ray (such as $\overrightarrow{OX}$) can bisect ∠ROS.

(2) No other ray than $\overrightarrow{OX}$ can bisect ∠ROS.

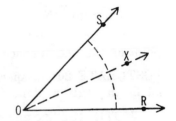

PROOF   STATEMENTS   REASONS

1. Let the measure of ∠ROS = r° .... 1. Every angle has a measure.

2. Then ½ ∠ROS = ½ r° Or ∠ROX .... 2. Division property of equality

3. ∴ $\overrightarrow{OX}$ is a bisector of ∠ROS, which proves than an angle has a bisector .... 3. Definition of an angle-bisector

4. In ∠ROX, $\overrightarrow{OX}$ is the only ray that can exist as the side of ∠ROX besides $\overrightarrow{OR}$ ....   Postulate 19

This proves that an angle cannot have more than one bisector.

THEOREM 11: In a given plane, through a given point on a line, there exists exactly one line that is perpendicular to the given line.

GIVEN: $\overleftrightarrow{MN}$ with point O on $\overleftrightarrow{MN}$, all in plane R.

TO PROVE: that one line and only one line (such as l) can be drawn through point O ⊥ $\overleftrightarrow{MN}$ in plane R.

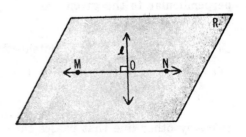

PROOF   STATEMENTS   REASONS

1. We may regard figure MON as straight ∠MON with its vertex at point O .... 1. Definition of a st. ∠

2. ∠MON has exactly *one* bisector, l .... 2. Theorem 10

*The ray that divides the measure of an angle into two angles of equal measure is called the *bisector* of that angle.

25

This proves that in a given plane, there exists one and only one line that is perpendicular to a given line at a given point on the line.

THEOREM 12: **In space, through a given point on a line, there exists an infinite number of lines that are perpendicular to that given line.**

GIVEN: $\overleftrightarrow{MN}$ with point O on $\overleftrightarrow{MN}$ in space.

TO PROVE: that an infinite number of lines may be drawn through point O, each perpendicular to $\overleftrightarrow{MN}$.

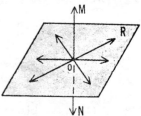

PROOF STATEMENTS	REASONS
1. There exists an infinite number of planes passing through $\overleftrightarrow{MN}$.	1. Postulate 8
2. For each plane that passes through $\overleftrightarrow{MN}$, there exists at any point O on $\overleftrightarrow{MN}$ a perpendicular to $\overleftrightarrow{MN}$.	2. Theorem 11

This proves that an infinite number of perpendiculars can be drawn to a line at a given point on the line in space.

POSTULATE 20: **In space, the perpendiculars to a given line through a given point on the line all lie in a given plane that is perpendicular to the given line.**

NOTE: If a line and a plane intersect in one point, then, by definition, their point of intersection is called the *foot* of the line.

Also by definition, a given line (such as $\overleftrightarrow{MN}$) and a given plane (such as R) are *perpendicular to each other* when the given line is perpendicular to EVERY LINE of the plane which passes through the *foot* (O) of the given line.

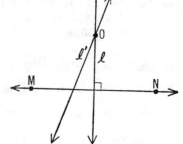

POSTULATE 21: **Through any point in a plane (as well as through any point outside a plane) there exists exactly one perpendicular to that plane, and conversely.**

REMARKS: Do we see that the existence of TWO or more perpendiculars to a plane through any one of its points would nullify Theorem 11?

THEOREM 13: **Through a given point outside a given line, there exists exactly one line that is perpendicular to the given line.**

GIVEN: $\overleftrightarrow{MN}$ with point O outside $\overleftrightarrow{MN}$.

TO PROVE: (1) that one line (such as l) that passes through $\overleftrightarrow{MN}$ is $\perp \overleftrightarrow{MN}$.

(2) Any other line that passes through O is not $\perp$ to $\overleftrightarrow{MN}$.

PROOF OF PART 1. STATEMENTS	REASONS
1. Through point O there exists one line, l, whose direction is $\perp$ to MN.	1. Postulate 1
2. $\therefore$ l is $\perp$ to $\overleftrightarrow{MN}$.	2. Definition of $\perp$ lines

26

PROOF OF PART 2.   STATEMENTS   REASONS

1. Any line other than 1 (such as 1') will have
   its own unique direction, which is different
   from that of 1. .... 1. Postulate 1

2. ∴1' is not ⊥ to $\overleftrightarrow{MN}$. .... 2. Definition of non-perpendicular lines.

   This proves that only one line can appear

   through point O perpendicular to $\overleftrightarrow{MN}$.

POSTULATE 22: The shortest distance from an outside point to a line is measured along the perpendicular from that point to the line.

NOTE: If we fasten one end of a string OB in length
to point O and swing the other end from point B toward
point A and then toward point C, we shall find that the string
will be *too short* to reach line MN EXCEPT at point B, since
the loose end must follow arc XY.

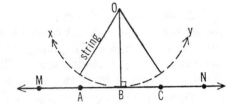

POSTULATE 23: A line-segment may be extended to any required length in either or in both of its directions.

EXERCISES I

Answer each of the following questions correctly with the best answer.

1. Suppose point x lies 1 inch above line MN. How many lines may be
   passed through point x which will be parallel to line MN? .... _____

2. If ∠ROS contains 50° and side OR is in a horizontal position, in how
   many positions may side OS appear ABOVE side OR? .... _____

3. In question 2 above, in how many positions may side OS appear
   BELOW side OR? .... _____

4. How many bisectors may an angle have? .... _____

5-6. Suppose point O lies within line 1

5. How many perpendiculars to line 1 may be drawn through point O
   in space? .... _____

6. How many perpendiculars may be drawn through point O in a
   given plane? .... _____

7. Each perpendicular to a line at a given point on that line lies (1)
   in the same plane (2) in a different plane (3) some in the
   same plane and others in different planes. .... _____

8. Suppose point C lies ABOVE line 1. How many perpendiculars may
   be drawn through point C to line 1? .... _____

9. If a given line passes through a given plane in such a manner that
   every line of the plane that passes through the foot of the given
   line is perpendicular to the given line, then the given line is said to
   be ? to the plane. .... _____

10. The shortest distance from a point outside a line to the line is the ?
    distance from that point to that line. .... _____

Unit II.

NATURE OF POLYGONS ● CONGRUENT TRIANGLES ● SYMMETRY
A. THE NATURE OF POLYGONS · THE KINDS OF TRIANGLES · ALTITUDES

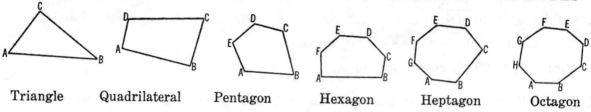

Triangle   Quadrilateral   Pentagon   Hexagon   Heptagon   Octagon

EXAMPLES OF CONVEX POLYGONS

A *polygon* is a closed plane geometric figure formed by three or more coplanar line-segments joined end to end without crossing each other. Hence a polygon may be regarded as a closed figure formed by the *union* of coplanar line-segments WITHOUT CROSSING each other. *Convex polygons* are those whose extended sides will never pass into their interior regions. *Concave polygons* are those of which at least two extended sides will pass into their interior regions.

Do we see that *every polygon has the same number of angles as it has sides?*

A polygon with three sides is called a *triangle*. Of course, no polygon can have fewer than three sides. A distinctive property of all triangles is their regidity. This means that their parts will not shift into new positions under stress or strain.

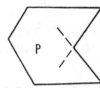

Not a Polygon   A Concave Polygon

That is why the framework of gates, bridges, and the like frequently have triangular designs. A polygon with four sides is called a *quadrilateral;* one with five sides, a *pentagon;* one with six sides, a *hexagon;* one with seven sides, a *heptagon;* one with eight sides, an *octagon;* one with nine sides, a *nonagon;* one with ten sides, a *decagon;* and one with n sides, an n-gon.

Any polygon is composed of its sides and its angles only, or the boundary.

In the "EXAMPLE OF POLYGONS" above, △ABC refers to $\overline{AB}$ ∪ $\overline{BC}$ ∪ $\overline{AC}$. The region (or points) inclosed within the boundary of the triangle is known as the *interior* of the triangle. The union of a triangle with its interior is called a *triangular region*. The region (or points) outside the boundary of a triangle is called its *exterior*.

In the accompanying figure, polygon ABCDEF ∪ its interior = a *polygonal* (pô-lĭg′-ô-năl) *region*. The region outside the boundary is called the *exterior* of the polygon.

The *perimeter* of a polygon is the sum of the lengths of its sides. In the accompanying hexagon, the perimeter is:
10 + 4 + 6 + 12 + 4 + 5 or 41

A triangle is classified and named according to the comparative lengths of its sides as well as the kinds of angles it has. This is illustrated in the chart that follows:

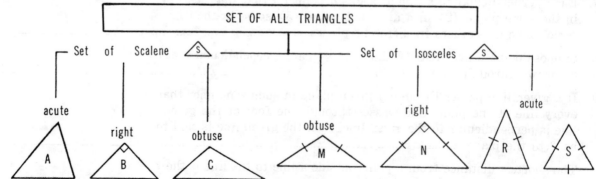

* Do we see why figure X may not be classified as a polygon?

28

From the chart, we will observe these things from the standpoint of the SIDES in the naming of triangles:

1. *Scalene triangles* are those triangles whose sides are all DIFFERENT in length. See triangles A, B, and C in the chart.

2. *Isoscles triangles* are those triangles which have at least TWO EQUAL sides. See triangles M, N, R, and S.

3. We will observe that △S has ALL sides equal, which makes it a SPECIAL CASE of an isosceles triangle. Such triangles are called *equilateral triangles*.

From the standpoint of ANGLES, we will observe these things in the naming of triangles:

1. Triangles having each of their angles acute are called *acute triangles*, regardless of the sizes of their sides. See triangles A, R, and S.

2. Triangles having an obtuse angle are called *obtuse triangles*, regardless of the sizes of their sizes. See triangles C and M.

3. Triangles having a right angle are called right triangles, regardless of the relative sizes of their sides. See triangles B and N.

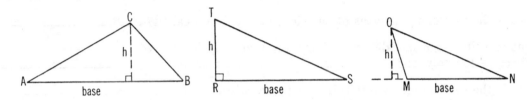

The perpendicular distance from any vertex of a triangle to the opposire side (a base) is called an *altitude* of that triangle. In each of the above triangles, the distance h represents an altitude. In △ABC, the altitude h is the perpendicular distance from vertex C to base AB. In △RST, the altitude h is the perpendicular distance from vertex T to base RS, which makes the altitude the same as side RT. In △MNO, we had to EXTEND side (base) MN toward the left to determine the altitude (or height) from point O to base MN. *Do we see that every triangle has three altitudes and three bases?*

The vertex of each angle of a polygon is also called a *vertex* of that polygon. The vertices of the polygon at hand are A, B, C, D, E, and F. A line-segment that joins any two non-adjacent vertices of a polygon is called a *diagonal* of that polygon. In the polygon at hand AC, AD, AE, and BD are diagonals. *Is it possible for a TRIANGLE to have a diagonal?*

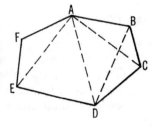

EXERCISES A.

Give the best answer to each of the following questions.

1. What is a closed geometric figure called that is formed by the *union* of three or more coplanar line-segments. .... _____

2. What is a closed geometric figure called that is composed of three sides? .... _____

3. What is a closed geometric figure called that is composed of four sides? .... _____

4. What is a 5 sided polygon called? .... _____

5. What is a six-sided polygon called? .... _____

6. What is a 7 sided polygon called? .... _____

7. What is an 8-sided polygon called? .... _____

8. What is a 9-sided polygon called? .... _____

9. What is a 10-sided polygon called? .... _____

10. What are triangles called that have all sides the same in length? .... _____

11. What are triangles called that have all sides different in length? .... _____

12. What are triangles called that have at least two sides equal in length? _____

13. What are triangles called that have all acute angles? .... _____

14. What are triangles called that have a right angle? .... _____

15. What are triangles called that have an obtuse angle? .... _____

16. What is the perpendicular distance from a vertex of a triangle to the opposite side (extended if necessary) called? .... _____

17. What is a side of a triangle called in relation to the altitude upon it? .... _____

18. What is the sum of the lengths of the sides of a polygon called? ...... _____

19. What is a line-segment called that joins any two non-consecutive vertices of the polygon? .... _____

20. What is the surface inclosed within a polygon called? .... _____

21. What is the surface outside a polygon called? .... _____

22. Is the surface inside a polygon regarded to be a part of the polygon itself? .... _____

Answer each of the following true statements with T and each false statement with X.

GIVEN: A = {All acute ⚹} E = {All equilateral ⚹}
I = {All isosceles ⚹} S = {All scalene ⚹}

23. I ⊂ A _____ 25. A ⊆ 3 _____ 27. E ⊂ A _____ 29. A ⊂ S _____

24. A ⊂ I _____ 26. I ∩ S = φ _____ 28. E ⊂ I _____ 30. S ∪ I = A _____

31. The sum of the lengths of two sides of a triangle is (1) always (2) sometimes (3) never greater than the third side. _____

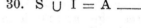
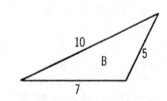

32. What is the perimeter of polygon A? _____

33. What is the perimeter of triangle B? _____

In polygons I - IV draw all possible diagonals from each vertex V. Then fill each of the answer spaces that follows.

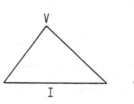

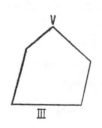
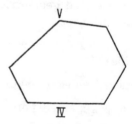

I   II   III   IV

	No. of Sides	No. of Diagonals from one Vertex	No. of Triangles formed
34. Polygon I	_____	_____	_____
35. Polygon II	_____	_____	_____
36. Polygon III	_____	_____	_____
37. Polygon IV	_____	_____	_____

38. Expressed in terms of n, the number of diagonals that can be drawn from a single vertex of a polygon of n sides is .... _____

39. Expressed in terms of n, the number of triangles that will be formed by drawing all possible diagonals from a single vertex of a polygon of n sides is .... _____

40. What kind of reasoning was involved in answering questions 38 and 39? .... _____

B. REVIEW OF PROPERTIES OF REAL NUMBERS

REVIEW OF PROPERTIES OF EQUALITY AND INEQUALITY

Let us briefly review the properties of real numbers that we dealt with in algebra because we shall be using real numbers in geometry too. Each real number is a member of the set of real numbers, which may be represented as points on the *real number line*, which follows:

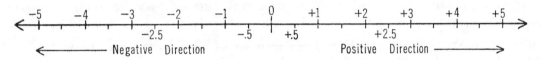

THE LINE OF REAL NUMBERS

We will observe that the set of real numbers is a system of *directed* numbers. If we let **R** represent the set of real INTEGERS, then we have:

$$R = \{ \ldots -4, -3, -2, -1, 0, +1, +2, +3, +4 \ldots \}$$

We will observe that 0 is a *signless* number. For each real number in existence, there is a corresponding point on the real number line, and for each point on the real number line there is a corresponding real number too. This relationship between the points and real numbers is known as a *one-to-one correspondence*.

We will observe that *any point to the right of a given point on the number line represents a greater number than any point to the left of the given point.* EXAMPLES: $+2>0$ and $0> -2$.

Real numbers contain both rational numbers and irrational numbers. A *rational number* is a number that can be expressed as a ratio (or indicated quotient) of two integers. Examples: $5 = 5$ to 1, or $5 \div 1$. $3.65 = 365$ to 100, or $365 \div 100$. $2/3 = 2 \div 3$, or 2 to 3.

$3\frac{1}{2} = 7 \div 2$. An *irrational number* is one like $\sqrt{2}$, $\sqrt{3}$, and π, which cannot be expressed as the ratio of two integers.

Here we have a summary of the principal properties of real numbers:

1. The Closure Property of Addition: **The sum of two real numbers is always a unique real number.** EXAMPLES: (1) $5 + 2 = 7$ (2) $-2 + -3 = -5$

2. The Closure Property of Multiplication: **The product of two real numbers is always a unique real number.** EXAMPLES: (1) $4 (5) = 20$ (2) $-3 (5) = -15$

3. The Associative Property of Addition: **Addends may be grouped in any order.** EXAMPLE: $(4 + 2) + 3 = 4 + (2 + 3) = 9$

4. The Associative Property of Multiplication: **Factors may be grouped in any order.** EXAMPLE: $(3 \cdot 5) \cdot 2 = 3 \cdot (5 \cdot 2) = 30$

5. The Commutative Property of Addition: **Addends may be arranged in any order.** EXAMPLE: $5 + 3 = 3 + 5 = 8$

6. The Commutative Property of Multiplication: **Factors may be arranged in any order.** EXAMPLE: $5 \cdot 3 = 3 \cdot 5 = 15$

7. The Distributive Property of Multiplication over Addition: **The entire product of two factors in which one factor appears as addends is equal to the sum of their partial products.** EXAMPLES: $3(5 + 2) = 3 \cdot 5 + 3 \cdot 2 = 15 + 6 = 21$

8. Zero is the **additive identity** of every number. EXAMPLE: $0 + 15 = 15$

9. One is the **multiplicative identity** of every number. EXAMPLES: (1) $1 \cdot 5 = 5$ (2) $a \cdot 1 = a$

10. The product of any number and zero is zero. EXAMPLE: $0 \cdot 15 = 0$

11. The quotient obtained by dividing 0 by any number (except 0) is 0. EXAMPLE $0 \div 5 = 0$ because 0, the quotient, $\times$ 5, the divisor, $= 0$, the dividend.

12. Division by zero is meaningless (or undefined).

We shall now briefly review the *properties of equality* with which we worked in algebra because we are going to find use for them in geometry.

1. The Addition Property of Equality: **The same real number may be added to each member of an equation.** EXAMPLE: GIVEN: $x - 3 = 7$. $x - 3 + 3 = 7 + 3 \therefore x = 10$

2. Subtraction Property of Equality: **The same real number may be subtracted from each member of an equation.** EXAMPLE: GIVEN $n + 4 = 10$. $n + 4 - 4 = 10 - 4 \therefore n = 6$

3. Multiplication Property of Equality: **Each member of an equation may be multiplied by the same real number (except zero).** EXAMPLE: GIVEN:

$$\frac{x}{5} = 3 \quad 5\left(\frac{x}{5}\right) = 5(3) \therefore x = 15$$

4. Division Property of Equality: **Each member of an equation may be divided by the same real number (except zero).** EXAMPLE: GIVEN: $6n = 42 \cdot \quad \frac{6n}{6} = \frac{42}{6} \cdot \therefore n = 7$

5. The Reflexive Property of Equality: **Any number is equal to itself.** EXAMPLES: $5 = 5$. $n = n$.

6. The Symmetric Property of Equality: **The sides of an equation may be reversed.** EXAMPLE: GIVEN: $n = 4$. Then $4 = n$

7. The Transitive Property of Equality: **If the first of three numbers equals the second, and the second equals the third, then the first equals the third.** EXAMPLE: If $n = 7$ and $7 = x$, then $n = x$

8. The Substitution Principle (or Property): **Any part of an equation may be replaced with an equal part.** EXAMPLE: GIVEN: $x = 5$ and $x + y = 15$. Then $5 + y = 15$

9. Powers of Equality: **The same powers of equal numbers are equal.** EXAMPLE: GIVEN: $n = 2$ Then $n^2 = 4$ and $n^3 = 8$

10. Roots of Equality: **The same roots of equal numbers are equal.** EXAMPLES: GIVEN: $n^2 = 25$ Then $n = 5$ GIVEN: $X^3 = 27$ Then $X = 3$

11. The Substraction of an Inequality from an Equality: **If an inequality is substracted from an equality, the resulting inequality will be in reverse order.** EXAMPLE: $12 = 12$ and $8 > 5$. So $12 - 8 < 12 - 5$. Or $4 < 7$.

The four basic properties of EQUALITY which we have just reviewed may be applied to the solutions of algebraic INEQUALITIES too, with these two exceptions: The multiplication and the division of inequalities by NEGATIVE real numbers REVERSE the symbols $>$ to $<$ and $<$ to $>$.

1. The Addition Property of Inequality: **The same number may be added to each member of an inequality.** EXAMPLE: GIVEN: $n - 3 > 5$. Then $n - 3 + 3 > 5 + 3$ ∴ $n > 8$.

1A. GIVEN: $-5 > -8$. Then $-5 + -2 > -8 + -2$. Or $-7 > -10$.

2. Subtraction Property of Inequality: **The same number may be subtracted from each member of an inequality.** EXAMPLE: GIVEN: $n + 3 > 5$. Then $n + 3 - 3 > 5 - 3$ ∴ $n > 2$

2A. GIVEN: $-5 > -8$. Then $-5 - -2 > -8 - -2$. $-5 + 2 > -8 + 2$. Or $-3 > -6$.

3. Multiplication Property of Inequality: **Each member of an inequality may be multiplied by the same positive real number.** EXAMPLE: GIVEN: $x - 3 > 5$. Then $2(x - 3) > 2(5)$. $2x - 6 > 10$. $2x - 6 + 6 > 10 + 6$. $2x > 16$ ∴ $x > 8$.

3A. **Each member of an inequality may be mulutiplied by the same negative real number, provided its inequality symbol is reversed.** EXAMPLE: GIVEN: $-x > -10$. $-1(-x) < -1(-10)$. ∴ $x < 10$.

4. The Division Property of Inequality: **Each member of an inequality may be divided by the same positive real number.** EXAMPLE: $2x = -10$. $\dfrac{2x}{2} = \dfrac{-10}{2}$ So $x = -5$

4A. **Each member of an inequality may be divided by the same negative real number, provided its inequality symbol is reversed.** EXAMPLE: $-2x < -10$. $\dfrac{-2x}{-2} > \dfrac{-10}{-2}$ ∴ $x > 5$

5. The Transitive Property of Inequality: **If the first of three numbers is greater than the second and the second is greater than the third, then the first is greater than the third.**

EXAMPLE: GIVEN: $7 > 5$ and $5 > 2$, then $7 > 2$.

6. The Addition of an Inequality to an Inequality: **If the members of one inequality are added to the members of another inequality IN THE SAME ORDER, the resulting inequality will be in the same order.** EXAMPLE: $7 > 3$ and $8 > 6$ So $7 + 8 > 3 + 6$ Or $15 > 9$

C. THE NATURE OF CONGRUENT FIGURES · RELATED POSTULATES

Congruent geometric figures are those which can be made to *coincide* (i.e. to fit exactly on each other. The symbol for "*is congruent to*" is $\cong$. Here are examples of pairs of congruent figures:

a. Line-segments of equal length such as $\overline{AB}$ and $\overline{CD}$: $\overline{AB} \cong \overline{CD}$. This is read: "*Line-segment AB is congruent to line-segment CD*". In practice, we often write $\overline{AB} = \overline{CD}$ for $\overline{AB} \cong \overline{CD}$.

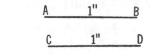

b. Angles of equal measure such as $\angle R$ and $\angle S$. $\angle R \cong \angle S$. This is read: "*Angle R is congruent to angle S*". In practice, we often write $m \angle R = m \angle S$ for $\angle R \cong \angle S$, which means the measure of $\angle R$ is equal to the measure of $\angle S$.

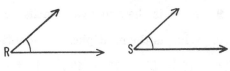

c. Triangles that can be made to fit together exactly such as $\triangle ABC$ and $\triangle RST$. $\triangle ABC \cong \triangle RST$.

This is read: "*Triangle ABC is congruent to triangle RST.*"

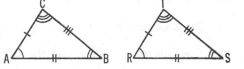

33

The parts of congruent triangles (sides and angles) that are in similar positions and EQUAL are called *corresponding parts*. The expression *"Corresponding sides of congruent triangles are equal"* is usually designated by the abbreviated expression *c s c t e*. The expression *"Corresponding angles of congruent triangles are equal"* is usually designated by the expression *c a c t e*.

Referring to the above pair of triangles again, we have:

Side AC of △ABC corresponds to side RT of △RST.   ∠A of △ABC corresponds to ∠R of △RST

Side AB of △ABC corresponds to side RS of △RST.   ∠B of △ABC corresponds to ∠S of △RST

Side BC of △ABC corresponds to side ST of △RST.   ∠C of △ABC corresponds to ∠T of △RST

We will observe that corresponding sides of congruent triangles are indicated with the same number of short straight marks, called *ticks* across the sides, while corresponding angles are designated by the same number of short *arcs* drawn across the angles.

POSTULATE 24: Equal line-segments can be made to coincide.

POSTULATE 25: Angles of equal measure can be made to coincide.

POSTULATE 26: A geometric figure can be moved about in any way without affecting its size or shape.

EXERCISES B - C

Give the best answer to each of the following questions:

1. What is that set of numbers called of which 0, +1, +2, —1, —2, √2, +π, +2/3, and —3/4 are members? .... _____

2. Which one of the numbers in the set of **real** numbers is signless? .... _____

3. What is the name of the number scale on whose points all these numbers may be represented? .... _____

4. If point B appears to the right of point A on the scale referred to, which point (A or B) represents the greater value? .... _____

5. What is the special name of that subset of real numbers whose members may be expressed as ratios of integers? .... _____

6. What is the special name of that subset of real numbers whose members cannot be expressed as ratios of integers? .... _____

7. In which of the above two classifications of real numbers does 4.7 fall? .... _____

8. In which of the above two classifications of real numbers does √5 fall? .... _____

9. What is the additive identity of 24? .... _____

10. What is the multiplicative identity of 24? .... _____

11. 5(3 + 8) = 15 + 40 illustrates the *?* *property* of real numbers. .... _____

Answer each of the following questions correctly with YES or NO.

12. Does closure apply to the operation of addition of real numbers? .... _____

13. Does closure apply to the operation of subtraction of real numbers? .. _____

34

14. Does closure apply to the operation of multiplication of real numbers? _____

15. Does closure apply to the operation of division of real numbers? .... _____
GIVEN: Set A = {1, 0}

16. Is set A closed under *addition?* _____ _____

17. Is set A closed under *subtraction?* _____ _____

18. Is set A closed under *multiplication?* _____ _____

19. Is set A closed under *division?* _____ _____

20. Is –6>–2? _____ _____

21. Is 0>–1? _____ _____

22. Does the commutative property of numbers refer to switching addends in addition and switching factors in multiplication? .... _____

23. Does the commutative property work in the addition of real numbers? _____

24. Does the commutative property work in the multiplication of real numbers? _____ _____

25. Does the commutative property work in the subtraction of real numbers? _____ _____

26. Does the commutative property work in the division of real numbers? _____ _____

27. Does the associative property work in the addition of real numbers? _____ _____

28. Does the associative property work in the multiplication of real numbers? _____ _____

29. May we divide a real number by zero? _____ _____

30. May we ever multiply a real number by zero? _____ _____

31. May we ever divide zero by any real number besides zero? .... _____

32. May we add the same real number to each member of an equation? .. _____

33. May we subtract the same real number from each member of an equation? _____ _____

34. May we multiply each member of an equation by the same real number? _____ _____

35. May we divide each member of an equation by the same real number (except zero)? _____ _____

Give the best answer to each of the following questions.

36. Which property of equality is illustrated by: "10 = 10"? .... _____

37. Which property of equality is illustrated by: "If x = 20, then 20 = x"? _____ _____

38. Which property of equality is illustrated by: "GIVEN a = 7 and c = 2. Also a + b = c. Then 7 + b = 2"? .... _____

35

39. Which property of equality is illustrated by: "If a = 3 and 3 = b, then a = b"? _____ _____

40. What are geometric figures called that can be made to coincide? .... _____

41. When are line-segments congruent? .... _____

42. When are angles congruent? .... _____

43. When are two triangles congruent? .... _____

44. What is the abbreviated expression for: *Corresponding sides of congruent triangles are equal?* .... _____

45. What is the abbreviated expression for: *Corresponding angles of congruent triangles are equal?* .... _____

GIVEN: △MON ≅ △ARB

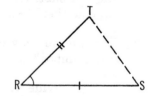

46. Which side in △ RAB corresponds to side MO in △ OMN? .... _____

47. Which angle in △ RAB corresponds to angle M in △ OMN? .... _____

Fill in the missing blanks with the best answers.

48. *?* line-segments can be made to coincide. .... _____

49. Angles of equal *?* can be made to coincide. .... _____

50. Geometric figures may be moved about in space without affecting their *?* or their *?*. .... _____ _____

D. CONGRUENT TRIANGLES
THEOREM 14

If two triangles have two sides and the included angle of the one equal to the two sides and the included of the other, then the triangles are congruent. (S.A.S.)

GIVEN: △ ABC and △ RST with side AB = side RS, side AC = side RT and ∠ A = ∠ R

TO PROVE: that △ ABC ≅ △ RST

PLAN OF PROOF: Let us show that the △ can be made to coincide (or fit together).

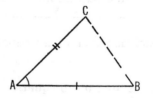

PROOF:

1. We may place △ ABC upon △RST so that ∠ A falls upon ∠ R with vertex A falling upon vertex R, side AB coinciding with side RS, and side AC coinciding with side RT. REASONS: Post. 24 and Post. 25.

2. Then (since point B coincides with point S and point C coincides with point T) side BC will coincide with side ST. REASON: Post. 15.

3. Therefore, the triangles coincide throughout and are congruent. REASON: Definition of congruent triangles.

THEOREM 15

If two triangles have two angles and the included side of the one equal to the two angles and the included side of the other, then the triangles are congruent. (A.S.A.)

GIVEN: △ ABC and △ RST with side
AB = side RS, ∠A = ∠R, and ∠B = ∠S.
TO PROVE: that △ ABC ≅ △ RST.
PLAN OF PROOF: Let us show that the triangles can be made to coincide.

PROOF:

1. We may place △ ABC upon △ RST so that side AB falls upon side RS, ∠ A coinciding with ∠ R and ∠ B coinciding with ∠ S, which makes side AC coincide with side RT and side BC coincide with side ST. REASON: Post. 24 and Post. 25

2. The vertices C and T must coincide. REASON: Post. 6

3. Therefore, the triangles coincide throughout and are congruent. REASON: Definition of congruent triangles.

THEOREM 16: If two sides of a triangle are equal, the angles opposite those sides are equal.

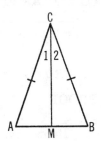

GIVEN: △ ABC with side AC = side BC.

TO PROVE: ∠A = ∠B

PROOF STATEMENTS	REASONS
1. Draw $\overrightarrow{CM}$, the bisector of ∠C	1. Th. 10
2. 1 ∠ = ∠ 2	2. Def. of angle bisector
3. CM = CM *	3. Reflective property of equality
4. AC = BC *	4. Given
5. △ AMC ≅ △ BNC	5. S.A.S.
6. ∴ ∠ A = ∠ B	6. c.a.c.t.e.

Sometimes a theorem is so closely connected with a more comprehensive theorem that it requires a little proof. Such a theorem is called a *corollary*.

COROLLARY 1: An equilateral triangle is also equiangular.

GIVEN: △ ABC with AB = BC = AC.

TO PROVE: ∠ A = ∠ B = ∠ C

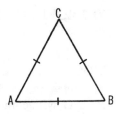

PROOF STATEMENTS	REASONS
1. ∠ A = ∠ B and ∠ B = ∠ C	1. Th. 16
2. ∴ ∠ A = ∠ C	2. Transitive property of equality
3. ∴ ∠ A = ∠ B = ∠ C	3. Substitution principle

* Here we do NOT write $\overline{CM}$, $\overline{AC}$, and $\overline{BC}$ because we are referring to measures or length of these line segments, which are the distances between their end points. In step 4 above, we say: "The length of side AC is equal to the length of side BC".

37

THEOREM 17: If two angles of a triangle are equal, the sides opposite the equal angles are equal.

GIVEN: △ ABC with
  ∠ B = ∠ C

TO PROVE: that side
  AB = side AC.

PROOF   STATEMENTS   REASONS

1. Draw $\overline{BS}$ and $\overline{CR}$ bisecting ∡ B and C re-
   spectively. ....   1. Unit 1. Th.? ....
2. BC = ? .... 2. .... Property of Equality
3. ∠ 1 = ∠ 5 ....   3. Division Property of Equality
4. Hence △ BCR ≅ △ CBS ....   4. Why? ....
5. So BS = CR ....   5. Why? ....
6. And ∠ 4 = ∠ 2 ....   6. Why? ....
7. Hence ∠ 7 = ∠ 8 ....   7. Th.? ....
8. ∠ 3 = ∠ 6 ....   8. Why? ....
9. ∴ △ BSA ≅ △ CRA ....   9. Why? ....
10. ∴ side AB = side AC ....   10. Why? ....

COR. 1. An equiangular triangle is equilateral.

GIVEN: Equiangular △ XYZ with ∠ X =
∠ Y = ∠ Z

TO PROVE: that _____ = _____ = _____.

PROOF   STATEMENTS   REASONS

1. ∠ X = ∠ Y   1. ....
2. Hence XZ = _____   2. Th? ....
3. ∠ X = ∠ Z   3. ....
4. Hence XY = _____   4. Th? ....
5. ∴ _____ = _____ = _____   5. ? .... Property of Equality

Therefore _____

THEOREM 18

If two triangles have the three sides of the one equal to the three sides of the other, then the triangles are congruent. (S.S.S.)

GIVEN: △ ABC and △ RST with AB = RS, BC = ST, and AC = RT.

TO PROVE: △ ABC ≅ △ RST

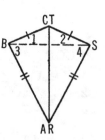

PROOF   STATEMENTS   REASONS

1. Place the ▵ together as shown at the right.   1. Post. 26
2. AC will coincide with its equal RT   2. Post. 24
3. Draw $\overline{BS}$.   3. Post. 3
4. BT = ST and BR = SR   4. Given
5. Hence △ BST and △ BSR are isosceles   5. Def. of isos. ▵
6. Hence ∠ 1 = ∠ 2 and ∠ 3 = ∠ 4   6. Base ∠ s of isos. △ are =
7. Hence ∠ 1 + ∠ 3 = ∠ 2 + ∠ 4   7. Addition property of equality
8. Or ∠ B = ∠ S   8. Substitution principle
9. ∴ △ ABC ≅ △ RST   9. S. A. S.

38

THEOREM 19

Theorems 19 and 20 deal with two special ways of proving RIGHT triangles congruent.

Two right triangles are congruent if the hypotenuse and an acute angle of the one are equal to the hypotenuse and an acute angle of the other. (H.A.)

GIVEN: Rt. $\triangle$ I and Rt. $\triangle$ II in which hypotenuse BC = hypotenuse B'C' and $\angle$ B = $\angle$ B'.

TO PROVE: $\triangle$ I $\cong$ $\triangle$ II

PROOF   STATEMENTS

1. Place $\triangle$ I upon $\triangle$ II so that BC will fall along B'C' and so that $\angle$ A and $\angle$ A' will fall on the same side of B'C', as shown in $\triangle$ III.
2. Hence side BC will coincide with side B'C', point C falling on point C'. ....
3. Side AB will fall *along* side A'B' ....
4. Side CA will fall *along* side C'A' ....
5. Hence point A will coincide with point A' ....
6. $\therefore$ $\triangle$ I $\cong$ $\triangle$ II

REASONS

1. Why permissible? ....
   ....
2. Why? ....
3. Why? ....
4. Theorem 13? ....
5. Post. ? ....
6. Why? Def. of ? ....

THEOREM 20

Two right triangles are congruent if the hypotenuse and a side of the one are equal to the hypotenuse and a side of the other. (H.S.)

GIVEN: Rt. $\triangle$ I and Rt. $\triangle$ II in which hypotenuse AC = hypotenuse A'C', and side BC = side B'C'.

TO PROVE: that $\triangle$ I $\cong$ $\triangle$ II

PROOF   STATEMENTS

1. Place $\triangle$ I and $\triangle$ II along side each other as shown at the right so that BC will coincide with its equal B'C'.
2. ABA' forms a straight line. ....
3. Side AC = A'C' ....
4. Hence figure AA'C becomes a(n) ? _____$\triangle$
5. Hence $\angle$? _____ = $\angle$ _____ ....
6. $\therefore$ $\triangle$ I $\cong$ $\triangle$ II ....

REASONS

1. Why permissible? ....
   ....
2. Exterior sides of adjacent supplementary $\angle$ s
3. Why? ....
4. Why? ....
5. Why? ....
6. Why? ....

EXERCISES D.

Express in abbreviated form:

1. The three general theorems we have used to prove triangles congruent: a. _____
   b. _____   c. _____

2. The two special theorems we have used to prove right triangles congruent:
   a. _____ b. _____

3. Five or more ways we have used to prove angles equal:
   a. _____ c. _____ e. _____
   b. _____ d. _____ f. _____

4. Two or more ways we have used to prove line-segments equal:
   a. _____ b. _____ c. _____

5. Given: In Fig. 1 two line-segments mn and rs intersecting at point o. or = on, and ∠ m = ∠ s = 90°.

To prove: that mr = sn and ∠ r = ∠ n

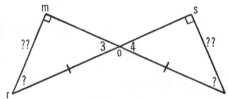

Fig. 1

PROOF   STATEMENTS   REASONS

1. ∠3 = ∠4   1. _____
2. △ mor ≅ △ son   2. _____
3. ∴ mr = sn and ∠ r = ∠ n   3. _____

6. Given: In Fig. 2 $\overline{AB}$ and $\overline{CD}$ ⊥ to each other at O. AO = BO and AD = CB.

   To prove: that DO = CO.

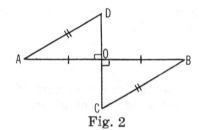

Fig. 2

PROOF   STATEMENTS   REASONS

1. △ AOD ≅ △ BOC   1. _____
2. ∴ DO = CO   2. _____

7. Given: In Fig. 3 AD = DC, and AB = BC

Fig. 3

                                                          Answers
a. Why is △ ABD ≅ △ CBD?   a. _____
b. What angle is equal to ∠ 6? b. _____
c. Why are these ∡ equal?   c. _____

8. Given: In Fig. 4 XZ = YZ, RZ = SZ, and $\overline{RM}$ and $\overline{SN}$ each ⊥ to $\overline{XY}$.

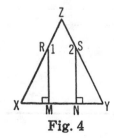

Fig. 4

a. Why is △ XMR ≅ △ YNS?   a. _____
b. Why is ∠ 1 = ∠ 2?   b. _____
c. RZ = SZ Why?   c. _____

40

9. Given: In Fig. 5 MO = NO, and ∠ 1 = ∠ 2.

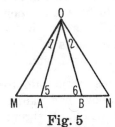

Fig. 5

a. Why is △ MAO ≅ △ NBO?   a. _____

b. Why is MA = NB?   b. _____

c. Why is ∠ 5 = ∠ 6?   c. _____

10. Given: In Fig. 6 RM = SN and MS = NR.

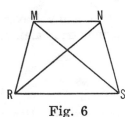

Fig. 6

a. Why is △ MSR ≅ △ NRS?   a. _____

b. Why is ∠ R = ∠ S?   b. _____

c. ∠ SRN = ∠ RSM Why?   c. _____

11. Given: In Fig. 7 AR = BS and AC = BC.

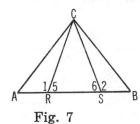

Fig. 7

a. Why is △ ARC ≅ △ BSC?   a. _____

b. Why is ∠ 1 = ∠ 2?   b. _____

c. ∠ 5 = ∠ 6 Why?   c. _____

12. Given: In Fig. 8 AC = BD, and $\overline{AD}$ and $\overline{BC}$ each ⊥ to $\overline{AB}$.

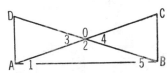

Fig. 8

a. Why is △ ABC ≅ △ BAD?   a. _____

b. Why is ∠ 1 = ∠ 5?   b. _____

c. AO = BO Why?   c. _____

13. Given: In Fig. 9 RX = SX and $\overline{XY}$ bisecting ∠ X.

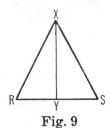

Fig. 9

a. Why is △ RXY ≅ △ SXY?   a. _____

b. Why is RY = SY?   b. _____

E. SYMMETRY

Geometric figures which have a balanced appearance with respect to one or more lines which they contain are said to be *symmetric*. The accompanying cross-section of a vase is symmetric with respect to line-segment MN. Lines or line-segments like MN, which divide a geometric figure into like halves that are in symmetric balance, are called *axes of symmetry*.

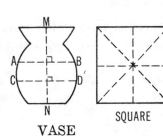

VASE

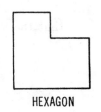

SQUARE   HEXAGON

41

We will observe that line-segment MN is the perpendicular bisector of dotted line-segments AB and CD. We will notice that an axes of symmetry of a polygon can be imagined to be a line upon which the polygon may be folded so that the two parts produced by folding will exactly fit together or *coincide*. From the accompanying figures, we see that a square has four axes of symmetry. The accompanying hexagon has no axes of symmetry and is, therefore, not symmetric.

A body (or a figure) may be balanced with respect to a plane, in which case it is said to have *planar symmetry*. An actual vase with a cross-section like the one shown above has planar symmetry with respect to an infinite number of planes passing through its axis MN. A figure or body has *point symmetry* when it is balanced with respect to a point. A sphere has all three of these types of symmetry, *axial, planar,* and *point* symmetry.

There is an abundance of symmetric patterns and designs in nature. A great many leaves, plants, and trees, and nearly all birds, fish, insects, animals, and people are in symmetric balance.

EXERCISES E.

A number of the following polygons and other figures are symmetric; a few are not. Draw all the lines of *axial symmetry* of each figure that has such. Then write the number of axes of symmetry which each figure has in the corresponding space below the figure. Place a zero (0) in the corresponding space of each figure that has no axis of symmetry.

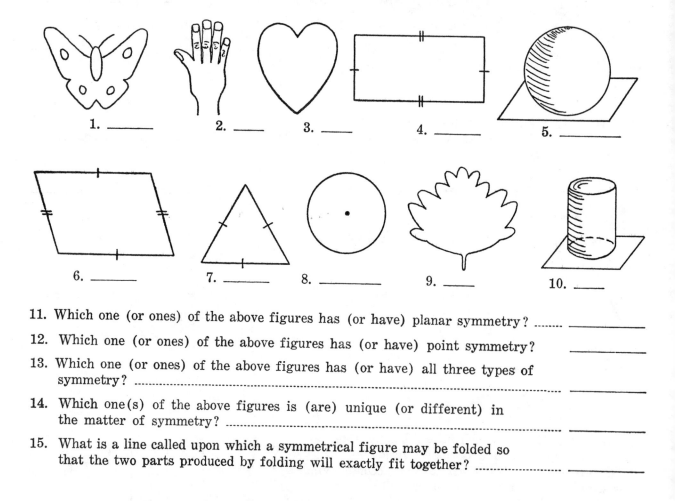

1. _____   2. ____   3. ___   4. ____   5. _____

6. _____   7. _____   8. _____   9. ____   10. ____

11. Which one (or ones) of the above figures has (or have) planar symmetry? .... _____

12. Which one (or ones) of the above figures has (or have) point symmetry?   _____

13. Which one (or ones) of the above figures has (or have) all three types of symmetry? .... _____

14. Which one(s) of the above figures is (are) unique (or different) in the matter of symmetry? .... _____

15. What is a line called upon which a symmetrical figure may be folded so that the two parts produced by folding will exactly fit together? .... _____

42

Unit III.

CONSTRUCTION PROBLEMS AND THEIR PROOFS

A. BISECTING LINE-SEGMENTS AND CONSTRUCTING PERPENDICULARS TO THEM

In Geometry a *construction* refers to a geometric construction to be made and then proved to be right. After a construction has been VERIFIED BY PROOF, its method of construction may be ACCEPTED for use henceforth in the work of Geometry.

Make each of the following constructions neatly and accurately with compass and straight-edge, leaving all construction lines.

One of the simplest constructions that one can make in plane geometry is that of drawing the *perpendicular bisector* of a line-segment. This consists in drawing a line, or line-segment, perpendicular to the given line-segment through its midpoint. In the accompanying figure $\overleftrightarrow{XY}$ is the perpendicular bisector of $\overline{AB}$. The construction is made in the following manner:

CONSTRUCTION 1

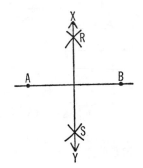

(1) With A as center and with the compass (also called "compasses") opened to a distance greater than half $\overline{AB}$ draw an arc above $\overline{AB}$ and one below $\overline{AB}$.

(2) Similarly, with B as the center and with the same radius of your compass, draw another set of arcs so as to interesect the first two arcs at R and S respectively.

(3) Draw $\overleftrightarrow{XY}$ through R and S with pencil and straightedge.

To construct the perpendicular bisector of a given line-segment.

GIVEN: Line-segment AB.

REQUIRED: To construct the perpendicular bisector of $\overline{AB}$.

CONSTRUCTION: Follow the procedure used in the accompanying figure above. Call the intersection of the pair of arcs that are to be made above $\overline{AB}$, "R", and that below $\overline{AB}$, "S". Draw $\overleftrightarrow{RS}$. Call the intersection of $\overline{AB}$ and $\overleftrightarrow{RS}$ "O".

$\overleftrightarrow{RS}$ is the perpendicular bisector of $\overline{AB}$.

PROOF. Draw auxiliary $\overline{AR}$, $\overline{BR}$, _____, and _____.

STATEMENTS	REASONS
1. AR = BR and AS = _____	1. Construction ....
2. RS = _____	2. .... Property of Equality
3. △ SAR ≅ △ _____	3. ....
4. Hence ∠ ARO = ∠ BRO	4. ....
5. Hence △ AOR ≅ △ BOR	5. ....
6. ∴ AO = BO	6. ....
7. Also ∠ AOR = ∠ BOR	7. ....
8. Hence $\overline{RS}$ is ⊥ to $\overline{AB}$	8. Def. of ? ....
9. ∴ $\overleftrightarrow{RS}$ is the ⊥ bisector of $\overline{AB}$	9. Def. of ? ....

CONSTRUCTION 2

To construct a perpendicular to a line (or line-segment) at a point on the line (or line-segment).

GIVEN: Line-segment MN with point C.

REQUIRED: To construct a perpendicular to $\overline{MN}$ at point C.

CONSTRUCTION: With point C as center and with the compass opened to any convenient, fixed radius, draw an arc cutting $\overline{MN}$ at the left of C, (calling the intersection "A") and an arc at the right of C, (calling the intersection "B"). Now with a fixed radius greater than half $\overline{AB}$, and with A and B as centers, draw a set of intersecting arcs above $\overline{MN}$ (calling their intersection "O"). Then draw a line-segment through points O and C.

$\overline{OC}$ is $\perp$ to $\overline{MN}$ at point C.

PROFF. Draw auxiliary $\overline{AO}$ and _____ .

STATEMENTS	REASONS
1. AC = _____	1. Construction ....
2. AO = _____	2. ....
3. CO = _____	3. ....
4. Hence $\triangle$ _____ $\cong$ $\triangle$ _____	4. ....
5. Hence $\angle$ MCO = $\angle$ _____	5. ....
6. $\therefore$ $\overline{OC}$ is $\perp$ to $\overline{MN}$ at point C.	6. ....

All geometric constructions are made with a pencil, compass, and straightedge only. NO MEASURING SCALE of any kind is ever permitted.

1. In the accompanying figure $\overleftrightarrow{PR}$ has been constructed perpendicular to $\overline{AB}$ from point P. The construction is made in the following manner:

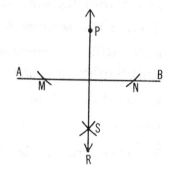

   (1) With point P as center and with compass opened to any convenient radius, draw arcs cutting $\overline{AB}$ at M and N.

   (2) With M and N as centers and with a fixed radius greater than half $\overline{MN}$, draw arcs intersecting at S.

   (3) Draw $\overline{PR}$ through P and S. A similar procedure would be used, if point P were *on* $\overline{AB}$.

CONSTRUCTION 3

To construct a perpendicular to a line (or line-segment) from a point without the line (or line-segment).

GIVEN: Line-segment AC and P, any point without $\overline{AC}$.

REQUIRED: To construct a perpendicular to $\overline{AC}$ from point P.

CONSTRUCTION: Follow the procedure used in the accompanying figure above. Call the intersection of the arc with AC at the left "R" and that at the right "S". Call the intersection of the pair of arcs below $\overline{AC}$ "W". Then draw a line-segment through points P and W, calling the intersection of $\overline{PW}$ with $\overline{AC}$ "O".

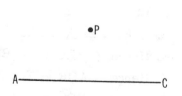

$\overline{PW}$ is $\perp$ to $\overline{AC}$.

PROOF: Draw auxiliary $\overline{RP}$, $\overline{SP}$, $\overline{RW}$, and $\overline{SW}$.

STATEMENTS	REASONS
1. △ _____ ≅ △ _____	1. ....
2. Hence △ _____ ≅ △ _____	2. ....
3. Hence ∠ AOP = ∠ COP	3. ....
4. ∴ $\overline{PW}$ is ⊥ to $\overline{AC}$	4. ....

CONSTRUCTION EXERCISES A.

Make the following constructions with compass and straightedge, leaving construction lines and arcs.

1. Bisect the following line-segments geometrically, using compass and straightedge only. Leave all construction lines.

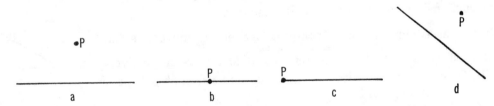

     a.   b.   c.

2. Construct geometrically a perpendicular to each of the following line-segments through the corresponding point P.

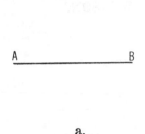 

     a   b   c   d

3. Place an X after each of the following items which is NOT AN ACCEPTABLE TOOL to use in making geometric constructions:

a. A compass _____   c. A straightedge _____   e. A pencil _____

b. A T-square _____   d. A ruler or scale _____   f. A protractor _____

B. BISECTING AN ANGLE AND CONSTRUCTING AN ANGLE EQUAL TO ANOTHER ANGLE

A line, or ray, that divides an angle into two equal parts is called its *bisector*. In the accompanying figure, $\overrightarrow{OC}$ is the bisector of angle AOB. The construction is made in the following manner:

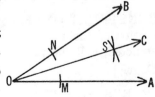

(1) With vertex O as center and with compass opened to any convenient radius, draw arcs cutting sides OA and OB at M and N respectively.

(2) With M and N as centers and with a fixed radius, great enough to strike a pair of arcs within the angle, draw arcs interesting at S.

(3) Draw $\overrightarrow{OC}$ through O and S with pencil and straightedge.

CONSTRUCTION 4

To bisect a given angle.

GIVEN: ∠ RST.

REQUIRED: To bisect ∠ RST.

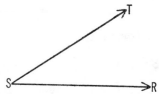

CONSTRUCTION: Follow the procedure used in the accompanying figure above, calling the intersection of the arc with $\overset{\bullet\longrightarrow}{SR}$ "C" and that of the arc with $\overset{\bullet\longrightarrow}{ST}$ "A". Call the point of intersection of the pair of arcs between $\overset{\bullet\longrightarrow}{SR}$ and $\overset{\bullet\longrightarrow}{ST}$ "O".

$\overset{\bullet\longrightarrow}{SO}$ is the bisector of ∠ RST.

PROOF. Draw auxiliary $\overline{AO}$ and _____

STATEMENTS		REASONS
1. SO = _____	1.	.... Property of Equality
2. SA = _____	2.	Construction ....
3. AO = _____	3.	....
4. Hence △ _____ ≅ △ _____	4.	....
5. ∴ ∠ TSO = ∠ _____	5.	....
6. ∴ $\overset{\bullet\longrightarrow}{SO}$ is the bisector of ∠ RST	6.	....

2. **In the accompanying figure** ∠ O′ **has been constructed equal to** ∠ O. **The construction is made in the following manner:**

   (1) With O as center and with compass opened to any convenient radius, draw arcs cutting $\overset{\bullet\longrightarrow}{OA}$ and $\overset{\bullet\longrightarrow}{OB}$ at M and N respectively.

   (2) With O′ as center and with the *same radius* used in step 1, draw any convenient arc M′N′.

   (3) By means of the compass measure the distance from M to N.

   (4) With M′ as center and with the same radius used in step 3, draw an arc intersecting the first arc at N′.

   (5) Draw $\overset{\bullet\longrightarrow}{O'B'}$ through points O′ and N′.

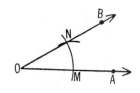

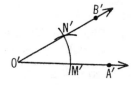

CONSTRUCTION 5

To construct at a point on a line (or line-segment) an angle equal to a given angle.

GIVEN: ∠ WOX **and point P on line-segment MN.**

REQUIRED: To construct an angle with its vertex at point P equal to ∠ WOX.

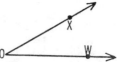

CONSTRUCTION: Follow the procedure used in the above accompanying figure, calling the intersection of the arc with OX "C" and that of the arc with OW "D". In the angle that is being constructed, call the intersection of the arc with MN "R" and the intersection of the two arcs "S". Draw $\overline{PS}$.

∠ RPS = ∠ WOX.

PROOF. Draw auxiliary $\overline{DC}$ and _____.

STATEMENTS	REASONS
1. OC = OD = PR = PS	1. ....
2. DC = _____	2. Construction ....
3. Hence △ _____ ≅ △ _____	3. ....
4. ∴ ∠ RPS = ∠ WOX	4. ....

CONSTRUCTION EXERCISES B

Make the following constructions accurately with compass and straightedge in the corresponding spaces provided for constructions.

1. Bisect the following angles geometrically with compass and straightedge. Leave all construction lines.

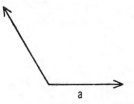 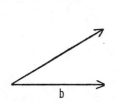 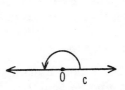 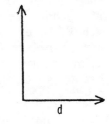

a   b   0   c   d

2. How many degrees does *each* angle at d contain? _____

3. Construct an angle geometrically equal to each of the following angles with its vertex at the point P on the corresponding segment below the angle.

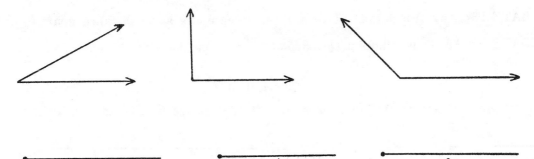

P   a   P   b   P   c

---

4. Construct a triangle that will have line-segments **x** and **y** as two of its sides and ∠ **z** as the angle between these two sides.

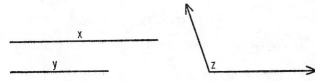

4.

---

5. Construct a triangle that will have ∠ **r** and ∠ **s**, and **m** as the side between these two angles.

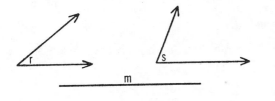

5.

47

Unit IV.

PERPENDICULAR AND PARALLEL LINE RELATIONSHIPS • CONVERSE THEOREMS

A. COMPREHENSIVE REVIEW OF THE PROPERTIES OF PARALLEL LINES

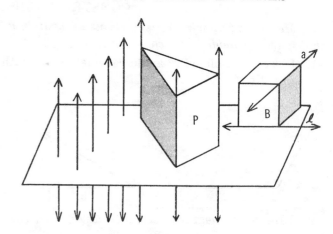

We have learned that any TWO parallel lines ALWAYS lie in the same plane. A study of the accompanying figure will show that three or more parallel lines MAY lie in the same plane, but that they NEED NOT necessarily lie in the same plane. We will observe that in prism P, each PAIR of vertical edges lies in the same plane. However, the three vertical edges of the prism are segments of THREE parallel lines that do not lie in the same plane.

Let us observe that TWO non-intersecting, non-coplanar lines (like lines a and l in the edges of the box B) are called *skew lines*.

POSTULATE 27: **If two lines are in the same plane, they are either parallel or intersecting.** (A dichotomy principle)

POSTULATE 28: **Any two parallel lines are everywhere the same distance apart.**

POSTULATE 29: **All straight lines perpendicular to the same plane are parallel.**

THEOREM 21

If two straight lines are parallel to a third line, then they are parallel to each other.

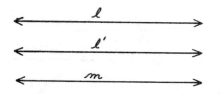

GIVEN: lines l and l', each parallel to line m.

TO PROVE: that line l is parallel to line l'.

PROOF	STATEMENTS	REASONS

PROOF   STATEMENTS

1. If l and l' are not parallel, then they will intersect at some point P.
2. But l and l' cannot possibly intersect.
3. ∴ l and l' are parallel.

REASONS

1. Definition of non-parallel lines in the same plane.
2. Theorem 9
3. Definition of parallel lines.

PRELIMINARY EXERCISES A

Underline correct words and fill answer-spaces correctly in the following statements.

1. The two kinds of straight lines which never meet are:

    (1) _____ lines, which, in PLANE geometry (but not in solid geometry) must lie in the same plane.

    (2) _____ lines, which never lie in the same plane.

2. Hence straight lines which never meet are (always, sometimes, never) parallel lines.

3. Two curved lines which never meet are (always, sometimes, never) parallel lines.

4. Through a given point WITHOUT a line (one, two, three, any number of) lines (s) can be drawn parallel to a given line.

5. Through a given point WITHOUT a line (one, two, three, any number of) line (s) can be drawn perpendicular to a given line.

6. Through a given point ON a line (one, two, three, any number of) line (s) can be drawn perpendicular to a given line.

7. Two straight lines in the same plane must be either _____ or they must _____.

8. Any two _____ lines are everywhere the same distance apart.

9. Straight lines parallel to the same line are _____ to each other.

10. Straight lines perpendicular to the same plane are _____.

B. ANGLES FORMED BY LINES AND TRANSVERSALS • CONVERSE THEOREMS

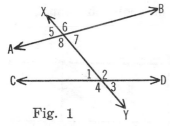

Fig. 1

A straight line intersecting two or more straight lines at different points is called a *transversal*. See XY in Fig. 1. The four angles formed by two lines with their transversal lying inside the two lines are called *interior angles*. Those lying outside the two lines are called *exterior angles*. In Fig. 1 ∡ 1, 2, 7, and 8 are interior angles, and ∡ 3, 4, 5, and 6 are exterior angles. A pair of now-adjacent interior angles lying on opposite sides of a transversal are known as *alternate-interior angles*, whereas a pair of now-adjacent exterior angles lying on opposite sides of a transversal are known as *alternate exterior angles*. The alternate-interior angles in Fig. 1 are ∡ 1 and 7, and ∡ 2 and 8, and the alternate-exterior angles are ∡ 3 and 5 and ∡ 4 and 6. A pair of exterior-interior angles which lie on the same side of a transversal are called *corresponding angles*. The corresponding angles in Fig. 1 are ∡1 and 5, ∡ 4 and 8, ∡ 2 and 6, and ∡ 3 and 7. In Fig. 1 ∡ 1 and 8 and ∡ 2 and 7 are pairs of interior angles lying on the same side of the transversal.

PRELIMINARY EXERCISES B.

1. Fill each answer-space below with the correct answer.

_____a. A straight line which intersects two or more straight lines at different points.

_____b. Those angles formed by two lines and their transversal which lie outside the two lines.

_____c. Those angles formed by two lines and their transversal which lie inside the two lines.

_____d. Pairs of interior angles on the same side of a transversal.

_____e. Pairs of exterior angles lying on opposite sides of a transversal.

_____f. Pairs of exterior-interior angles which lie on the same side of a transversal and on the same side of the lines cut by the transversal.

_____g. Pairs of interior angles lying on opposite sides of a transversal.

49

2. Refer to the accompanying figure in filling the following answer-spaces. In cases that require a series of SINGLE angles as answers, write the answers in this manner: 2, 4, 7. In cases that require PAIRS of angles as single answers, write the answers in this manner: 7-5, 3-2, 1-8.

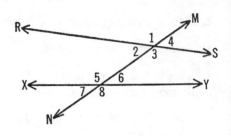

a. The transversal is _____.

b. The interior angles are _____.

c. The exterior angles are _____.

d. The pairs of alternate-interior angles are _____.

e. The pairs of alternate-exterior angles are _____.

f. The pairs of corresponding angles are _____.

g. The pairs of interior angles lying on the same side of the transversal are _____.

THEOREM 22

If two parallel lines are cut by a transversal, then the alternate-interior angles are equal.

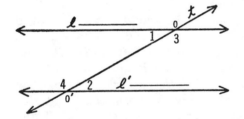   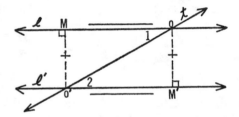

GIVEN: Two parallel lines, l and l′, cut by transversal t, making the pair of alternate-interior angles 1 and 2 and the pair of alternate-interior angles 3 and 4.*

TO PROVE: $\angle 1 = \angle 2$ and $\angle 3 = \angle 4$

PROOF   STATEMENTS   REASONS

1. From point O′ the intersection of transversal t and l′, draw perpendicular O′M to line l and from point O, the intersection of the transversal with line l, draw perpendicular OM′ to line l′.

    1. Theorem 13 ....

2. O′M = OM′

    2. Post. 28 ....

3. OO' = OO'

    3. Why? ....

4. Hence $\triangle OMO' \cong \triangle O'M'O$

    4. H.S. ....

5. $\angle 1 = \angle 2$

    5. Why? ....

6. $\angle 1$ and $\angle 3$ are supplementary. Also $\angle 2$ and $\angle 4$ are supplementary.

    6. Definition of supplementary adjacent angles.

7. $\therefore \angle 3 = \angle 4$

    7. Why? ....

*We will note that short line-segments near lines l and l′ are used to indicate that these lines are parallel.

COR. 1. If two parallel lines are cut by a transversal, the corresponding angles are equal.

GIVEN: Two ∥ lines AB and CD cut by transversal MN.

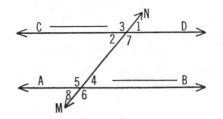

TO PROVE: that ∠ 1 = ∠ _____ (or ∠ 6 = ∠ _____).

PROOF. STATEMENTS

1. ∠ 2 = ∠ 4
2. ∠ 2 = ∠ 1
3. ∴ ∠ 1 = ∠ 4

REASONS

1. Th.? ....
2. Unit 1, Th.? ....
3. .... Principle

COR. 2. If two parallel lines are cut by a transversal, the alternate-exterior angles are equal.

GIVEN: Two ∥ lines AB and CD cut by transversel MN.

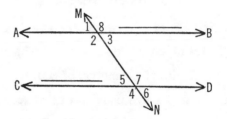

TO PROVE: that ∠ 4 = ∠ _____ (or ∠ 1 = ∠ 6).

PROOF. STATEMENTS

1. ∠ 7 = ∠ 2
2. ∠ 7 = ∠ _____ and ∠ 2 = ∠ _____
3. ∴ ∠ 4 = ∠ _____

REASONS

1. ....
2. ....
3. .... Principle

COR. 3. If two parallel lines are cut by a transersal, each pair of interior angles on the same side of the transversal are supplementary.

GIVEN: Two ∥ lines AB and CD cut by transversal MN.

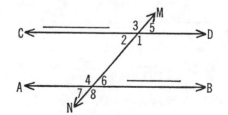

TO PROVE: that ∠ 2 + ∠ _____ = 180° (or that ∠ 1 + ∠ 6 = 180°)

PROOF. STATEMENTS

1. ∠ 2 + ∠ 1 = 180°
2. ∠ 1 = ∠ _____
3. ∴ ∠ 2 + ∠ 4 = 180°

REASONS

1. Def. of a pair of? ....
2. Unit 4, Th? ....
3. ....

COR. 4. If a straight line is perpendicular to one of two parallel lines, it is perpendicular to the other also.

GIVEN: $\overleftrightarrow{AB} \perp$ to $\overleftrightarrow{CD}$ and line t $\perp$ to $\overleftrightarrow{AB}$.

TO PROVE: that line t is $\perp$ to $\overleftrightarrow{CD}$ also.

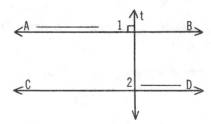

PROOF   STATEMENTS

	REASONS
1. $\angle 2 = \angle 1$	1. Th. 22, Cor. 1
2. $\angle 1 =$ a right $\angle$	2. Def. of $\perp$ lines.
3. $\angle 2 =$ a right $\angle$	3. Substitution Principle
4. $\therefore$ line t is $\perp$ to $\overleftrightarrow{CD}$.	4. Rt. $\angle$ have $\perp$ sides

In some theorems and corollaries the hypotheses and the conclusions may be INTERCHANG-ED. Such theorems and corollaries are called *converse theorems* and *converse corollaries*. For example:

HYPOTHESIS   CONCLUSION

If the ANGLES of a triangle are equal, the SIDES opposite those angles are equal.

If the SIDES of a triangle are equal, the ANGLES opposite those sides are equal.

All principles of geometry, of course, are not reversible. For example:

All straight angles are equal. But all equal angles are not straight angles.

Theorem 23 which follows is the converse of Theorem 22 above. Likewise, the corollaries that go with Theorem 23 are converses of the corollaries that go with Theorem 22.

THEOREM 23

Two straight lines (in the same plane) cut by a transversal are parallel, if the alternate-interior angles formed are equal.

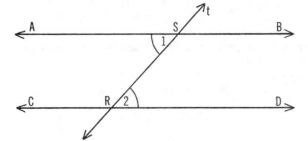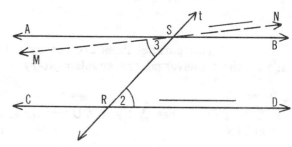

GIVEN: $\overleftrightarrow{AB}$ and $\overleftrightarrow{CD}$ cut by transversal t, making $\angle 1 = \angle 2$.

TO PROVE: $\overleftrightarrow{AB}$ is $\parallel$ to $\overleftrightarrow{CD}$.

PROOF   STATEMENTS

	REASONS
1. Let us draw $\overleftrightarrow{MN}$ through point S $\parallel$ to $\overleftrightarrow{CD}$.	1. Th. 9 ....
2. $\angle 3 = \angle 2$	2. Th. ? ....
3. But $\angle 1 = \angle 2$	3. Given ....
4. $\angle 1 = \angle 3$	4. Substitution Principle ....
5. $\therefore \overleftrightarrow{AB}$ must coincide with $\overleftrightarrow{MN}$, making $\overleftrightarrow{AB}$ $\parallel$ to $\overleftrightarrow{CD}$.	5. Post. ? ....

52

COR. 1. Two straight lines (in the same plane) cut by a transversal are parallel, if the corresponding angles made are equal.

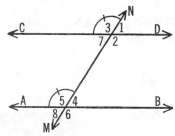

GIVEN: $\overleftrightarrow{AB}$ and $\overleftrightarrow{CD}$ cut by transversal $\overleftrightarrow{MN}$ making $\angle 3 = \angle 5$.

TO PROVE: that $\overleftrightarrow{AB}$ is ‖ to $\overleftrightarrow{CD}$.

PROOF.　　STATEMENTS

1. $\angle 3 = \angle 2$
2. $\angle 3 = \angle 5$
3. Hence $\angle 2 = \angle 5$
4. ∴ $\overleftrightarrow{AB}$ is ‖ to $\overleftrightarrow{CD}$

REASONS

1. ....
2. ....
3. ....
4. Th. 23 ....

COR. 2. Two straight lines (in the same plane) cut by a transversal are parallel, if the alternate-exterior angles made are equal.

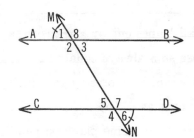

GIVEN: $\overleftrightarrow{AB}$ and $\overleftrightarrow{CD}$ cut by transversal $\overleftrightarrow{MN}$ making $\angle 1 = \angle 6$.

TO PROVE: that $\overleftrightarrow{AB}$ is ‖ to $\overleftrightarrow{CD}$.

PROOF.　　STATEMENTS

1. $\angle 1 = \angle 3$ and $\angle 6 = \angle 5$
2. $\angle 1 = \angle 6$
3. Hence $\angle 3 = \angle 5$
4. ∴ $\overleftrightarrow{AB}$ is ‖ to $\overleftrightarrow{CD}$

REASONS

1. _____
2. _____
3. _____
4. _____

COR. 3. Two straight lines (in the same plane) cut by a transversal are parallel, if a pair of interior angles formed on the same side of the transversal are supplementary.

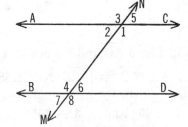

GIVEN: $\overleftrightarrow{AC}$ and $\overleftrightarrow{BD}$ cut by transversal $\overleftrightarrow{MN}$ making $\angle 2 + \angle 4 = 180°$.

TO PROVE: that $\overleftrightarrow{AC}$ is ‖ to $\overleftrightarrow{BD}$.

PROOF.　　STATEMENTS

1. $\angle 2 + \angle 1 = 180°$
2. $\angle 2 + \angle 4 = 180°$
3. Hence $\angle 2 + \angle 4 = \angle 2 + \angle 1$
4. Hence $\angle 4 = \angle 1$
5. ∴ $\overleftrightarrow{AC}$ is ‖ to $\overleftrightarrow{BD}$

REASONS

1. _____
2. _____
3. _____
4. _____
5. _____

COR. 4. **If two straight lines (in the same plane) are perpendicular to the same line, then they are parallel.**

GIVEN: $\overleftrightarrow{AB}$ AND $\overleftrightarrow{CD}$ each perpendicular to line t, and all lying in the same plane.

TO PROVE: $\overleftrightarrow{AB}$ is $\parallel$ $\overleftrightarrow{CD}$.

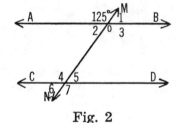

PROOF	STATEMENTS	REASONS
1. $\angle 1 = \angle 2$		1. All right $\angle$ are = ...
2. $\therefore$ $\overleftrightarrow{AB}$ is $\parallel$ to $\overleftrightarrow{CD}$.		2. Th.? ....

EXERCISES B

1. Fill each answer-space below with the correct term:

   a. Parallel lines cut by a transversal form with the transversal equal _____ $\angle$, equal _____ $\angle$, and equal _____ $\angle$.

   b. Parallel lines cut by a transversal form with the transversal _____ $\angle$ whose sum always equals _____ degrees.

   c. A theorem in geometry in which the hypothesis and the conclusion may be interchanged is known as a (n) _____ theorem.

   d. Lines in the same plane perpendicular to the same line are _____.

   e. Two lines parallel to a third line are _____.

   f. Lines perpendicular to the same plane are _____.

2. Given: In Fig. 2 two $\parallel$ lines, AB and CD, cut by transversal MN, making $\angle$ AOM = 125°. How many degrees are there,

   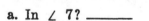

   a. In $\angle$ 7? _____   d. In $\angle$ 3? _____

   b. In $\angle$ 2? _____   e. In $\angle$ 4? _____

   c. In $\angle$ 5? _____   f. In $\angle$ 4 + $\angle$ 2? _____

   Fig. 2

3. Given: In Fig. 3 $\overleftrightarrow{AC}$ and $\overleftrightarrow{RS}$ cut by transversal XY. Are $\overleftrightarrow{AC}$ and $\overleftrightarrow{RS}$ NECESSARILY parallel,

   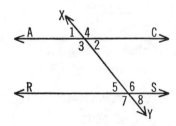

   a. If $\angle$ 1 = 40° and $\angle$ 5 = 40°? _____

   b. If $\angle$ 1 = 60° and $\angle$ 6 = 120°? _____

   c. If $\angle$ 3 + $\angle$ 7 = 180°? _____

   d. If $\angle$ 2 = 20° and $\angle$ 5 = 20°? _____

   e. If $\angle$ 1 = 25° and $\angle$ 8 = 25°? _____

   f. If $\angle$ 1 + $\angle$ 3 = 180°? _____

   g. If $\angle$ 2 = 90° and $\angle$ 6 = 90°? _____

   Fig. 3

   h. If $\angle$ 5 = 90° and $\angle$ 7 = 90°? _____

   i. If $\angle$ 4 + $\angle$ 8 = 180°? _____

   j. If $\angle$ 4 = 100° and $\angle$ 5 = 50°? _____

4. In Fig. 4 show whether $\overleftrightarrow{RS}$ is $\parallel$ to $\overleftrightarrow{TW}$, if $\dfrac{x + 15°}{5} + 2x = 69°$

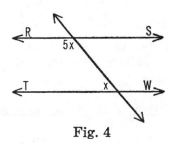

Solution: _____

_____

_____

Fig. 4

*5. Through point P construct a line parallel to $\overline{RS}$ on the basis of the principle of THEOREM 23.

• P

R _____ S

C. RELATIONSHIPS BETWEEN PLANES AND LINES THAT INTERSECT
THEOREM 24

Two planes perpendicular to the same line are parallel.

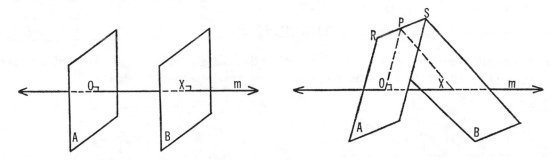

REMARKS: Suppose we are given planes A and B each $\perp$ to line m at points O and X respectively.
1. If planes A and B are not parallel, then they will intersect in some straight line RS. (Post. 7).
2. Then from any point P in RS we would have PO $\perp$ to line m and PX $\perp$ to line m. (Because line m is $\perp$ to planes A and B) 3. Then there would be TWO perpendiculars to line m from point P, which is impossible. (Theorem 13). Therefore, planes A and B are $\parallel$.

THEOREM 25

If two parallel planes are cut by a third plane, then the lines of intersection are parallel.

REMARKS: Suppose we are given planes A and B cut by plane T.

1. Then intersections MN and RS become straight lines. (Post. 7)

2. $\overleftrightarrow{MN}$ and $\overleftrightarrow{RS}$ lie in the same plane. (Given)

3. But $\overleftrightarrow{MN}$ and $\overleftrightarrow{RS}$ cannot intersect. (Because they also lie in parallel planes A and B.)

4. Therefore, $\overleftrightarrow{MN}$ and $\overleftrightarrow{RS}$ are parallel. (Definition of two parallel lines.)

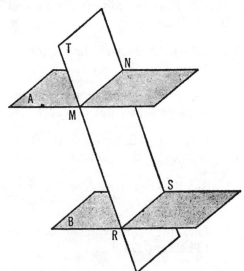

If two parallel planes are cut by a third plane, then the alternate-interior dihedral angles formed are equal.

REMARKS: 1. In the accompanying figure, plane

∠ 1 = plane ∠ 2 (Theorem 22).

2. But dihedral ∠ A — MN — X = plane ∠ 1 and dihedral ∠ B — RS — Y = plane ∠ 2 (A dihedral ∠ is measured by its plane ∠)

3. Therefore, dihedral ∠ A — MN — X = dihedral ∠ B — RS — Y. (Substitution Principle)

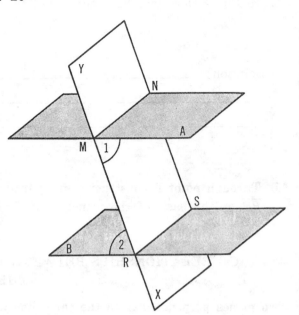

THEOREM 27

If a line is perpendicular to each of two intersecting lines of a plane at their point of intersection, then that line is perpendicular to the plane of those two intersecting lines.

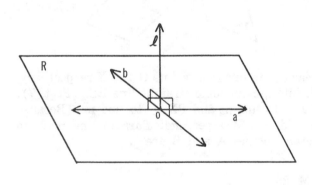

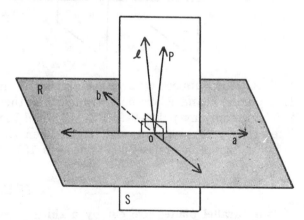

GIVEN: Line l ⊥ to both lines *a* and *b* in plane R at their point of intersection O.
TO PROVE: that line l is ⊥ to plane R.

PROOF: 1. Line l with line a forms a plane S, which intersects plane R along line a. (Theorem 2 and Post. 7).

2. Let us suppose that line l is not ⊥ to plane R. Then there is some other line P that is ⊥ to plane R at point O. (Post. 2).

3 Line l is ⊥ to line *b* at O (Given) and line P is ⊥ to line b at point O (Definition of a perpendicular to a plane.)   4. Hence lines P and l both lie in plane S (Post. 22).

5. But line l is ⊥ to line *a* (Given) and line P is ⊥ to line *a* (Definition of a perpendicular to a plane).

6. Therefore, line l must coincide with line P, which makes it perpendicular to plane R. (Theorem 11)

THEOREM 28

A line perpendicular to one of two parallel planes is perpendicular to the other.

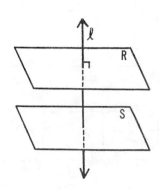 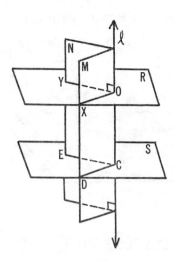

GIVEN: Plane R ∥ to plane S and line l ⊥ to plane R

TO PROVE: Line l is ⊥ to plane S

PROOF   STATEMENTS

REASONS

1. Pass a plane M through line l intersecting plane R in $\overleftrightarrow{OX}$ and plane S in $\overleftrightarrow{CD}$. Also pass a plane N through line l intersecting plane R in $\overleftrightarrow{OY}$ and plane S in $\overleftrightarrow{CE}$.

1. Post.? ....

2. $\overleftrightarrow{OX}$ is ∥ to $\overleftrightarrow{CD}$ and $\overleftrightarrow{OY}$ is ∥ to $\overleftrightarrow{CE}$.

2. Th.? ....

3. Line l is ⊥ to $\overleftrightarrow{OX}$ and to $\overleftrightarrow{OY}$.

3. Definition of a line ⊥ to a plane ....

4. Hence l is ⊥ to $\overleftrightarrow{CD}$ and l is ⊥ to $\overleftrightarrow{CE}$

4. Th. 22, Cor.? ....

5. Therefore, l is ⊥ to plane S

5. Th.? ....

THEOREM 29

If two planes intersect, the vertical dihedral angles formed are equal.

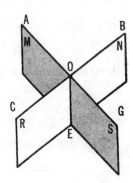

1. Why is ∠AOB = ∠COG? _____

PROOF:

2. Why is dihedral ∠M-OE-N = ∠AOB and why is dihedral R-OE-S = ∠COG? _____

_____

3. Then why does dihedral ∠ M-OE-N = dihedral ∠ R-OE-S?

_____

4. Similarly, dihedral ∠ M-OE-R = dihedral ∠ N-OE-S

57

THEOREM 30

If one of two parallel lines is perpendicular to a plane, then the other is also perpendicular to the plane.

GIVEN: Parallel lines P and l with line P ⊥ to plane R.

TO PROVE: Line l is also ⊥ to plane R.

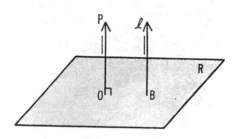 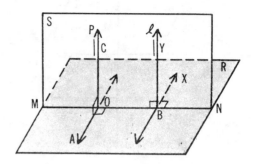

PROOF   STATEMENTS

REASONS

1. Lines P and l form a plane S.

1. Th.? ....

2. Through point O, the foot of line P in plane R, construct $\overleftrightarrow{AO}$ ⊥ to $\overleftrightarrow{MN}$, the line of intersection of planes R and S.

2. Th.? ....

3. AO is also ⊥ to PO.

3. Def. of a ⊥ to a plane.

4. So ∠AOC is a rt. ∠ as well as a plane ∠ of dihedral ∠ R — MN — S

4. Def. of a rt. ∠ and def. of a plane ∠ of a dihedral ∠

5. Hence dihedral ∠ R-MN-S is a rt. dihedral ∠

5. A dihedral ∠ is measured by its plane ∠

6. Line l is ⊥ to line MN

6. Th. 22, Cor.? ....

7. In plane R construct $\overleftrightarrow{XB}$ ⊥ to $\overleftrightarrow{MN}$.

7. Th.? ....

8. ∠XBY is a plane ∠ of dihedral ∠ R-MN-S

8. Why? ....

9. Hence ∠XBY is a rt. ∠.

9. A plane ∠ is measured by its dihedral ∠

10. So $\overleftrightarrow{YB}$ (or line l) is ⊥ to $\overleftrightarrow{XB}$ also.

10. Definition of ⊥ lines.

11. ∴ line l is ⊥ to plane R

11. Th.? ....

EXERCISES C

Fill each answer-space below with the correct missing word.

1. Planes _____ to the same line are parallel.

2. The lines of intersection formed by a plane cutting across parallel planes are _____ .

3. The alternate-interior dihedral angles formed by a plane cutting across two parallel planes are _____ .

4. A line perpendicular to one of two _____ planes is perpendicular to the other.

5. In order to be perpendicular to a plane, a line needs to be made perpendicular to only _____ of the lines of the plane passing through its foot.

6. A line perpendicular to one of two _____ planes is perpendicular to the other.

7. If two planes intersect, the vertical dihedral angles formed are _____.

8. Two planes perpendicular to the same plane are _____.

9. Two planes parallel to the same plane are _____.

10. The common intersection of three planes is always a(n) _____.

D.   ANGLES WITH PARALLEL SIDES
THEOREM 31

If two angles have their sides parallel, right (initial) side to right (initial) side and left (terminal) side to left (terminal) side, the angles are equal.

GIVEN: $\angle$ S and S′ with i ∥ to i′ and t ∥ to t′.

TO PROVE: that $\angle$ S = $\angle$ S′.

PROOF: Extend sides i and t′ until they meet. *

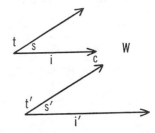

STATEMENTS	REASONS
1. $\angle$ S = $\angle$ _____	1. _____
2. $\angle$ S′ = $\angle$ _____	2. _____
3. ∴ $\angle$ S = $\angle$ S′	3. _____
Therefore _____	

THEOREM 32

If two angles have their sides parallel, right (initial) side to left (terminal) side and left (terminal) side to right (initial) side, the angles are supplementary.

GIVEN: $\angle$ r and r′ with i ∥ to t′ and to ∥ to i′.

TO PROVE: that $\angle$ r + $\angle$ r′ = 180°.

PROOF: Extend side i until it meets side i′. *

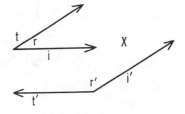

STATEMENTS	REASONS
1. $\angle$ r′ + $\angle$ x = _____°	1. _____
2. $\angle$ x = $\angle$ _____	2. _____
3. ∴ $\angle$ r′ + $\angle$ r = 180°	3. _____
Therefore _____	

* The definition of a ray gives us authority to extend these sides, while Theorem 9 tells us why these extensions will meet.

Do not make any additional constructions in proving the following exercises.

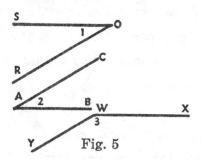

1. Given: In Fig. 5 $\overline{OS}$ ∥ to $\overline{AB}$, $\overline{OR}$ ∥ to $\overline{AC}$, $\overline{WX}$ ∥ to $\overline{AB}$ and $\overline{WY}$ ∥ to $\overline{AC}$.

   To prove: that ∠ 1 + ∠ 3 = 180°.

Fig. 5

Proof.   Statements   **Reasons**

1. ∠ 2 + ∠ ——— = 180°   1. _____

2. ∠ ——— = ∠ ———   2. _____

3. ∴ ∠ 1 + ∠ ——— = 180°   3. _____

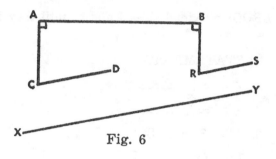

2. Given: In Fig. 6 $\overline{CA}$ and $\overline{RB}$ each ⊥ to $\overline{AB}$, and $\overline{CD}$ and $\overline{RS}$ each ∥ to $\overline{XY}$.

   To prove: that ∠ C = ∠ R.

Fig. 6

Proof.   Statements   **Reasons**

1. $\overline{CD}$ is ∥ to $\overline{RS}$ 1. _____

2. $\overline{CA}$ is ∥ to $\overline{RB}$ 2. _____

3. ∴ ∠ C = ∠ R   3. _____

3. Fill each answer-space below with the correct term:

   a. Two angles which have their sides parallel, right side to left side and left side to right side, are always _____

   b. Two angles which have their sides parallel, right side to right side and left side to left side, are always _____

Unit V.

ANGLES OF A TRIANGLE. ANGLES WITH PERPENDICULAR SIDES

A. ANGLES OF A TRIANGLE

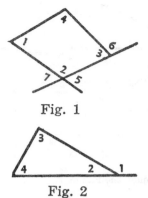

Fig. 1

Fig. 2

An *interior angle* of a polygon is any one of the angles within the polygon that is formed by a pair of its sides meeting at a vertex of the polygon. In Fig. 1, ∡ 1, 2, 3, and 4 are interior angles. An *exterior angle* of a polygon is an angle formed at any vertex of the polygon by one of its sides and the extension of the other side. In Fig 1 ∡ 5, 6, and 7 are exterior angles. Since adjacent angles are angles having a common vertex and a common side between them, it follows that any two angles that do not have a common vertex must be classified as *non-adjacent* (or *remote*) *angles*. In Fig. 2 ∠ 1 is an exterior angle of the triangle with ∠ 2 as its adjacent interior angle and with ∡ 3 and 4 as its two non-adjacent interior angles.

THEOREM 33

The sum of the (interior) angles of a triangle is equal to a straight angle (or 180°).

GIVEN: △ ABC with interior ∡ 1, 2, and 3.

TO PROVE: that ∠ 1 + ∠ 2 + ∠ 3 = a st. ∠ or 180°.

PROOF. Draw $\overleftrightarrow{MN}$ through C parallel to _____. *

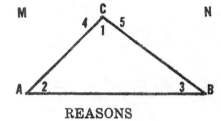

STATEMENTS	REASONS
1. ∠ ____ + ∠ ____ + ∠ ____ or ∠ MCN = a st. ∠ or 180°	1. The _____ Postulate ____
2. But ∠ 4 = ∠ ____ and ∠ 5 = ∠ ____	2. Unit 4, Th.? _____
3. ∴ ∠ 1 + ∠ 2 + ∠ 3 = a st. ∠ or 180°.	3. _____
Therefore _____	

COR. 1.   An exterior angle of a triangle is equal to the sum of the two non-adjacent (or remote) interior angles and is greater than either of them.

GIVEN: △ ABC with interior ∡ 1, 2, and 3, and exterior ∠ 4.

TO PROVE: (1) that ∠ 4 = ∠ 1 + ∠ 2 and (2) that ∠ 4 > either ∠ 1 or ∠ 2.

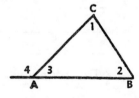

PROOF. STATEMENTS	REASONS
1. ∠ 4 + ∠ 3 = _____°	1. Def. of ? _____
2. ∠ 1 + ∠ 2 + ∠ 3 = _____	2. Th.? _____
3. Hence ∠ 4 + ∠ 3 = _____	3. _____ Principle
4. ∴ ∠ 4 = ∠ 1 + ∠ 2	4. _____ Property of Equality
5. Also ∠ 4 > either ∠ 1 or ∠ 2.	5. The sum of two ∡ is greater than either of them
Therefore _____	

* Theorem 9 gives us the authority to make this construction.

COR. 2. A triangle can have only one obtuse angle.

GIVEN: △ RST with ∠ S obtuse.

TO PROVE: that ∡ R and T are acute angles.

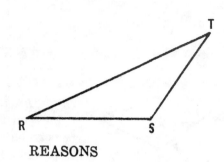

PROOF.   STATEMENTS

1. ∠ R + ∠ S + ∠ T = ———°

2. ∠ S > 90°

3. Hence ∠ R + ∠ T < 90°

 4. Hence ∠ R and ∠ T are each < 90°*

5. ∴ ∠ R and ∠ T are acute angles

   Therefore ————————————————

REASONS

1. ....

2. Def. of ? ....

3. Prop. of Equality No. ....

4. Neither of two ∡ can equal their sum ....

5. ....

COR. 3. If two triangles have two angles of the one equal to the two angles of the other, the third angles are equal.

GIVEN: ∡ ABC and A′B′C′ with ∠ A = ∠ A′
and ∠ B = ∠ B′

TO PROVE: that ∠ ——— = ∠ ———

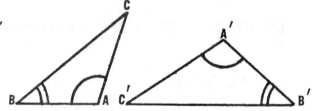

PROOF.   STATEMENTS

1. ∠ A + ∠ —— + ∠ —— = ——°

2. ∠ A′ + ∠ —— + ∠ —— = ——°

3. Hence ∠ A + ∠ —— + ∠ —— = ∠ ——
    + ∠ —— + ∠ ——

4. ∠ A = ∠ —— and ∠ B = ∠ ——

5. ∴ ∠ —— = ∠ ——

   Therefore ————————————————

REASONS

1. Th. ? ....

2. ....

3. .... Property of Equality

4. ....

5. .... Property of Equality

COR. 4. The acute angles of a right triangle are complementary.

GIVEN: Rt. △ ABC with ∠ B = a rt. ∠.

TO PROVE: that ∠ ——— + ∠ ——— = 90°.

PROOF.   STATEMENTS

1. ∠ —— + ∠ —— + ∠ —— = 180°

2. But ∠ B = ———°

3. ∴ ∠ —— + ∠ —— = ———°

   Therefore ————————————————

REASONS

1. Th. ? ....

2. Def. of ? ....

3. .... Principle

* Do we see that if ∠ R = 90°, then we could write step 3 as: 90 + ∠ T < 90°? This would give us: ∠ T < 0, an impossibility.

COR. 5. The bisectors of any two angles of a triangle intersect.

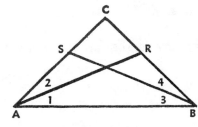

GIVEN: △ ABC with $\overline{AR}$ bisecting ∠ A and $\overline{BS}$ bisecting ∠ B, making ∠ 1 = ∠ 2 and ∠ 3 = ∠ 4.

TO PROVE: that $\overline{AR}$ and $\overline{BS}$ will intersect.

PROOF.   STATEMENTS

	REASONS

1. If $\overline{AR}$ and $\overline{BS}$ do not meet, they are ∥.   1. Unit 4, Post.? ....

2. Then (if $\overline{AR}$ and $\overline{BS}$ are ∥) ∠ 1 + ∠ 3 = _____°   2. Th. 22, Cor.? ....

3. But ∠ A + ∠ B + ∠ C = _____°   3. Th.? ....

4. Hence ∠ 1 + ∠ 3 ≠ 180°.   4. A part of a sum does not equal the entire sum.

5. ∴ $\overline{AR}$ and $\overline{BS}$ cannot possibly be ∥, and will intersect.   5. Post? ....

Therefore _____

COR. 6. Two lines that are perpendicular respectively to two non-parallel lines will meet at a point.

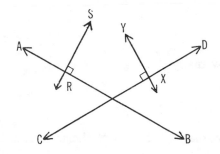

GIVEN: $\overleftrightarrow{RS}$ and $\overleftrightarrow{XY}$ ⊥ to the two intersecting lines AB and CD respectively.

TO PROVE: that $\overleftrightarrow{RS}$ and $\overleftrightarrow{XY}$ will intersect.

PROOF.   STATEMENTS

1. If $\overleftrightarrow{RS}$ and $\overleftrightarrow{XY}$ do not meet, they are ∥.   1. ....

2. $\overleftrightarrow{AB}$ is ⊥ $\overleftrightarrow{RS}$.   2. ....

3. If $\overleftrightarrow{RS}$ and $\overleftrightarrow{XY}$ are ∥, $\overleftrightarrow{AB}$ will be ⊥ to $\overleftrightarrow{XY}$ too.   3. Th. 22 Cor.? ....

4. But $\overleftrightarrow{CD}$ is ⊥ to $\overleftrightarrow{XY}$.   4. ....

5. Hence $\overleftrightarrow{AB}$ and $\overleftrightarrow{CD}$ would be ∥.   5. Th. 23 Cor.? ....

6. But $\overleftrightarrow{AB}$ and $\overleftrightarrow{CD}$ cannot be ∥.   6. Contradiction of? ....

7. ∴ $\overleftrightarrow{RS}$ and $\overleftrightarrow{XY}$ cannot be ∥, and must intersect.   7. Post? ....

Therefore _____

_____

EXERCISES   A

1. Fill each answer-space below with the correct answer:

   a. A triangle may have _____ acute angle (s), _____ obtuse angle (s), and _____ right angle (s)

   b. The sum of the three interior angles of a triangle is _____°

c. Each angle of an equilateral triangle contains _____°

d. The sum of the acute angles of any right triangle contains _____°

2. How many degrees are there in ∠ x of Fig. 3?

Ans. _____

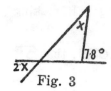

Fig. 3

3. How many degrees are there in each angle in the triangle of Fig. 4?

Ans. _____

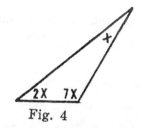

Fig. 4

4. In Fig. 5, MN is ∥ to XY. Find the number of degrees in ∠ R.

Ans. _____

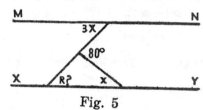

Fig. 5

5. How many degrees are there in ∠ C in △ ABC of Fig. 6?

Ans. _____

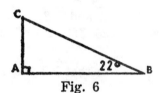

Fig. 6

6. How many degrees are there in each base angle in △ ABC of Fig. 7?

Ans. _____

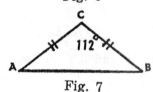

Fig. 7

CONSTRUCTION EXERCISES A

Make the following constructions accurately with compass and straightedge in the corresponding space provided for constructions. Leave all construction lines.

STATEMENTS	CONSTRUCTIONS
1. Construct an angle of 60°.	

STATEMENTS	CONSTRUCTIONS
2. Construct △ RST having given ∠ R, ∠ T, and side RS. 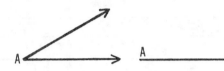	
3. Construct rt. △ ABC having given ∠ A and side AB. 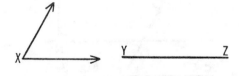	
4. Construct rt. △ XYZ having given ∠ X and leg YZ.	

B. ANGLES WITH PERPENDICULAR SIDES
THEOREM 34

If two angles have their sides perpendicular, right (initial) side to right (initial) side and left (terminal) side to left (terminal) side, the angles are equal.

GIVEN: ∠ 1 and ∠ 2 with i ⊥ to i′ and t ⊥ to t′.

TO PROVE: that ∠ 1 = ∠ 2.

PROOF. Extend the sides until they meet.*

STATEMENTS	REASONS
1. ∠ R = ∠ _____	1. Unit 1, Th.? ....
2. ∠ _____ = ∠ _____	2. ....
3. ∴ ∠ 1 = ∠ _____	3. Th. 33, Cor.? ....

*The definition of a ray gives us authority to extend the sides.

Therefore _____

_____

COR. 1. If two angles have their sides perpendicular, right (initial) side to left (terminal) side and left (terminal) side to right (initial) side, the angles are supplementary.

GIVEN: ∠ r and ∠ s with i ⊥ to t′ and with t ⊥ to i′.

TO PROVE: that ∠ s + ∠ r = _____°

PROOF. Extend the sides of the ∡ until they meet.*

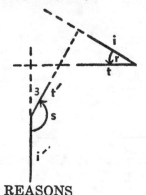

STATEMENTS	REASONS
1. ∠ r = ∠ 3	1. Th.? ....
2. ∠ s + ∠ 3 = _____°	2. ....
3. ∴ ∠ s + ∠ r = _____°	3. .... Principle

Therefore _____

_____

EXERCISES B

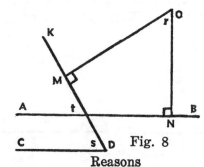

1. Given: In Fig. 8 $\overline{OM}$ ⊥ to $\overline{KD}$, $\overline{ON}$ ⊥ to $\overline{AB}$, and $\overline{AB}$ ∥ to $\overline{CD}$.

To prove: that ∠ r = ∠ s.

Fig. 8

Proof. Statements	Reasons
1. ∠ r = ∠ _____	1. _____
2. ∠ s = ∠ _____	2. _____
3. ∴ ∠ r = ∠ s	3. _____

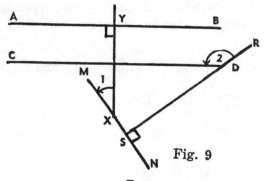

2. Given: In Fig. 9 $\overline{CD}$ ∥ to $\overline{AB}$, $\overline{XY}$ ⊥ to $\overline{AB}$, and $\overline{RS}$ ⊥ to $\overline{MN}$.

To prove: that ∠ 1 + ∠ 2 = 180°

Fig. 9

Proof. Statements	Reasons
1. $\overline{MX}$ is ⊥ to $\overline{DR}$	1. _____
2. $\overline{XY}$ is ⊥ to $\overline{DC}$	2. _____
3. ∴ ∠ 1 + ∠ 2 = 180°	3. _____

* The definitions of a ray and a line give us authority to extend the sides.

Unit VI.

PARALLELOGRAMS ● INVERSES ● CONTRAPOSITIVES ● SYLLOGYSMS
A. QUADRILATERALS: PARALLELOGRAMS AND TRAPEZOIDS ● DISTANCE

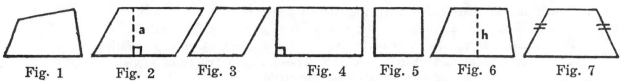

Fig. 1   Fig. 2   Fig. 3   Fig. 4   Fig. 5   Fig. 6   Fig. 7

All polygons that have four sides are called *quadrilaterals*. Quadrilaterals are classified according to the comparative size of their sides as well as to the kinds of angles which they have. A *parallelogram* is defined as any quadrilateral whose opposite sides are parallel. All the polygons above are quadrilaterals, but only those in figures 2, 3, 4, and 5 are parallelograms. A parallelogram whose angles are oblique is sometimes called a *rhomboid*. See Fig 2. An equilateral rhomboid is called a *rhombus*. See Fig. 3. A parallelogram whose angles are right angles is called a *rectangle*. See Fig. 4. An equilateral rectangle is a *square*. See Fig. 5.* The *base* of a polygon is generally considered to mean the horizontal side upon which it rests. A quadrilateral having one and only one pair of parallel sides is called a *trapezoid*. The parallel sides of a trapezoid are its *bases*. See Fig. 6. If the non-parallel sides of a trapezoid are equal, it is an *isosceles trapezoid*. See Fig. 7. The perpendicular distance between any two parallel sides of a parallelogram is an *altitude*. See *a* in Fig. 2. Similarly the perpendicular distance between the parallel sides of a trapezoid is its *altitude*. See *h* in Fig. 6. A quadrilateral with no two sides parallel is called a *trapezium*. See Fig. 1 above.

The various relationships involved in the classification of quadrilaterals are represented in the following diagram:

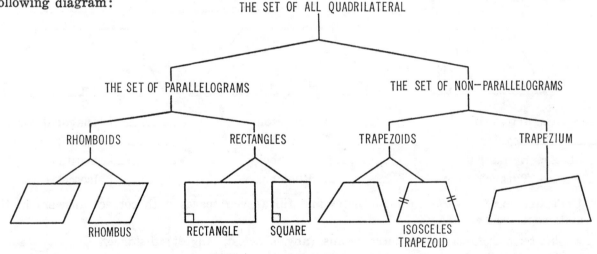

In plane geometry the term *distance* means straight-line (or linear) distance or shortest distance. Hence the following facts are obvious: The distance between two points is measured by the length of the straight line-segment joining them. See Fig. 8. The distance from a point to a line is measured by the length of the perpendicular from the point to the line. See Fig. 9. The distance between two parallel lines is measured by the length of the perpendicular between them. See Fig. 10. The shortest distance between two points upon a SPHERICAL SURFACE is the length of the *minor arc* of a *great circle* passing through them. A great circle is one which has the center

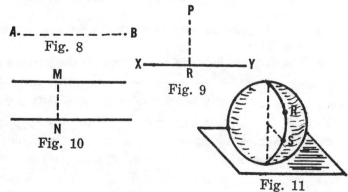

Fig. 11

* A rhombus is often regarded as any equilateral parallelogram. In that case, a square becomes a special type of rhombus as well as a special type of rectangle.

of a sphere as its own center and its circumference falling upon the surface of the sphere. In Fig. 11 the shortest distance between points R and S, measured upon the surface of the sphere, is minor arc RS.

EXERCISES A

1. Fill each answer-space below with the correct answer.
   _____a. A polygon having four and only four sides.
   _____b. A quadrilateral whose opposite sides are parallel.
   _____c. A parallelogram whose angles are right angles.
   _____d. An equilateral rhomboid.
   _____e. A parallelogram whose angles are oblique.
   _____f. An equilateral rectangle.
   _____g. A quadrilateral having one and only one pair of parallel sides.
   _____h. A trapezoid whose non-parallel sides are equal.
   _____i. The side on which a parallelogram rests.
   _____j. The perpendicular distance between a pair of parallel sides of a parallelogram.
   _____k. The parallel sides of a trapezoid.
   _____l. The perpendicular distance between the parallel sides of a trapezoid.

2. Fill the following answer-spaces with letters which correspond to those given in the figures or parts of figures below.

   _____a. Irregular   _____e. Trapezoid   _____i. Diagonal
   _____b. Regular   _____f. Square   _____j. Base
   _____c. Rectangle   _____g. Rhomboid   _____k. Altitude
   _____d. Parallelogram   _____h. Rhombus   _____l. Isosceles

3. Underline correct words in parentheses and fill answer-spaces with correct answers in the statements below.

   a. The term *distance* in geometry means (any, shortest, longest) distance.
   b. Hence the distance between two points is measured by the _____ line joining the two points.
   c. The distance from a point to a line is measured by the _____ from the point to the line.
   d. The distance between two parallel lines is measured by the _____ between the two lines.
   e. The distance between two points on the surface of a sphere is measured along the _____

_____

Answer each of the following true statements with a T and each false statement with an X.
GIVEN: Q = {All Quadrilaterals}   P = {All Parallelograms}   S = {All Squares}
N = {All Non-parallelograms}   T = {All Trapezoids}   R = {All Rectangles}
B = {All Rhomboids}   M = {All Rhombuses}

4. P ⊂ Q ____   6. S ⊂ R ____   8. R ⊂ N ____   10. R ∩ M = S ____
5. S ⊂ B ____   7. T ⊂ P ____   9. B ⊂ P ____

68

B. SOME PROPERTIES OF PARALLELOGRAMS AND PARALLEL LINES

THEOREM 35

The opposite sides and the opposite angles of a parallelogram are equal.

GIVEN: □ WXYZ.

TO PROVE: (1) that WX = _____ and WZ = _____ (2) that ∠ W = ∠ _____ and ∠ X = ∠ _____.

PROOF. STATEMENTS	REASONS
1. Draw $\overline{WY}$	1. Post.? ....
2. $\overline{WX}$ is ‖ to _____	2. ....
3. Hence ∠ 1 = ∠ 4	3. Th.? ....
4. $\overline{WZ}$ is ‖ to _____	4. ....
5. Hence ∠ 2 = ∠ _____	5. ....
6. WY = _____	6. ....
7. Hence △ WXY ≅ △ _____	7. ....
8. ∴ WX = _____, WZ = _____, and ∠ X = ∠ _____	8. ....
9. ∴ (since ∠ 1 = ∠ _____ and ∠ 2 = ∠ ___) ∠ W = ∠ _____	9. .... Property of Equality

Therefore _____

COR. 1. Segments of parallels included between parallels are equal.

GIVEN: Two ‖ lines MN and XY with $\overline{AD}$ and $\overline{BC}$, two ‖ segments included between $\overleftrightarrow{MN}$ and $\overleftrightarrow{XY}$.

TO PROVE: that AD = _____.

PROOF. STATEMENTS	REASONS
1. ABCD is a parallelogram	1. Def. of? ....
2. ∴ AD =_____	2. Th.? ....

Therefore _____

THEOREM 36

The diagonals of a parallelogram bisect each other.

GIVEN: □ WXYZ with diagonals $\overline{WY}$ and $\overline{XZ}$ intersecting at O.

TO PROVE: that WO = _____ and XO = _____.

PROOF. STATEMENTS	REASONS
1. WX is ‖ to ZY	1. ....
2. Hence ∠ 1 = ∠ _____ and ∠ 4 = ∠ _____	2. Th.? ....
3. WX = ZY	3. Th.? ....

4. Hence △ _____ ≅ △ _____   4. ....

5. ∴ WO = _____ and XO = _____   5. ....

   Therefore _____

COR. 1. If the diagonals of a quadrilateral bisect each other, the quadrilateral is a parallelogram.

GIVEN: Quadrilateral RSWX with diagonals RW
and SX bisecting each other at their intersection O.

TO PROVE: that quadrilateral RSWX is a ▱.

PROOF.   STATEMENTS   REASONS

1. RO = _____ and XO = _____   1. ....

2. ∠ O = ∠ _____ and ∠ 3 = ∠ _____   2. ....

3. Hence △ XOW ≅ △ _____   3. ....

4. Hence ∠ 4 = ∠ _____   4. ....

5. ∴ $\overline{WX}$ is ∥ to $\overline{RS}$.   5. Th.? ....

6. △ ROX ≅ △ _____   6. ....

7. Hence ∠ 6 = ∠ _____   7. ....

8. ∴ $\overline{RX}$ is ∥ to $\overline{SW}$.   8. ....

9. ∴ quadrilateral RSWX is a ▱   9. ....

   Therefore _____

COR. 2. If the diagonals of a parallelogram are equal, the parallelogram is a rectangle.

GIVEN: ▱ ABCD in which AC = BD.

TO PROVE: that ▱ ABCD is a rectangle.

PROOF.   STATEMENTS   REASONS

1. AC = BD.   1. ....

2. AO = CO and BO = DO.   2. Th.? ....

3. AO = BO and CO = BO.   3. .... Property of Equality

4. Hence △ AOB and BOC are isosceles 4. ....

5. ∠ 1 + ∠ 2 + ∠ 3 + ∠ 4 = _____°   5. Unit 5, Th.? ....

6. But ∠ 1 = ∠ _____ and ∠ 3 = ∠ _____   6. Unit 2, Th.? ....

7. ____ ∠ 2 + ____ ∠ 3 = ____°   7. .... Principle

8. ∠ 2 + ∠ 3 (or ∠ B) = a rt. ∠   8. .... Property of Equality

9. ∠ D = ∠ B or a rt. ∠   9. Unit 6, Th.? ....

10. Similarly, we can prove that ∠ A and ∠ C
    are both rt. ∡.   10. ....

11. ∴ ▱ ABCD is a rectangle.

   Therefore _____

COR. 3. **Any two consecutie angles of a parallelogram are supplementary.**

GIVEN: ▱ ABCD

TO PROVE: that ∠ A + ∠ D = 180°.

PROOF   STATEMENTS

1. $\overline{AB}$ is ∥ to $\overline{DC}$ 1. ....

2. ∴ ∠ A + ∠ D = 180°   2. ....

   Therefore _____

THEOREM 37

If the opposite sides of a quadrilateral are equal, the figure is a parallelogram.

GIVEN: Quadrilateral WXYZ with WX = _____
and WZ = _____.

TO PROVE: that quadrilateral WXYZ is a ▱.

PROOF. Draw diagonal WY. (Post. 3)

    STATEMENTS   REASONS

1. △ WYZ ≅ △ _____   1. ....

2. Hence ∠ t = ∠ ____ and ∠ r = ∠ ____   2. ....

3. ∴ $\overline{ZY}$ is ∥ to $\overline{WX}$ and $\overline{WZ}$ is ∥ to $\overline{XY}$ 3. Th.? ....

4. ∴ quadrilateral WXYZ is a ▱   4. ....

   Therefore _____

THEOREM 38

If two sides of a quadrilateral are equal and parallel, the figure is a parallelogram.

GIVEN: Quadrilateral WRST with RS = WT,
and $\overline{RS}$ ∥ to $\overline{WT}$.

TO PROVE: that quadrilateral WRST is a ▱.

PROOF. Draw diagonal RT. Post. _____

    STATEMENTS   REASONS

1. RT = _____   1. ....

2. ∠ 2 = ∠ _____   2. ....

3. RS = _____   3. ....

4. △ RST ≅ △ _____   4. ....

5. Hence RW = _____   5. ....

6. ∴ quadrilateral WRST is a ▱   6. Unit 6, Th.? ....

   Therefore _____

EXERCISES B.

As you work the following exercises, remember to indicate linear parts of a figure given equal with the same number of short dashes and angles given equal with the same number of arcs. *Do NOT draw any additional lines.*

Answers.

1. Given: In Fig. 12 MN = XY and XM = YN.

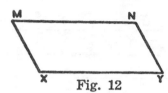
Fig. 12

a. Why is quadrilateral XYNM a □?   a. —————————

b. Why does ∠ X + ∠ Y = 180°?   b. —————————

2. Given: In Fig. 13 $\overline{WX}$ ∥ to $\overline{ZY}$ and ∠ 1 = ∠ 2.

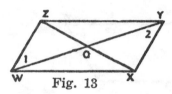
Fig. 13

a. Why is quadrilateral WXYZ a □?   a. —————————

b. Why does ZO = XO?   b. —————————

3. Given: In Fig. 14 AB = DC and ∠ A + ∠ D = 180°

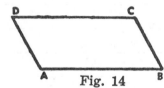
Fig. 14

a. Why is quadrilateral ABCD a □?   a. —————————

b. Why does ∠ A = ∠ C?   b. —————————

4. Given: In Fig. 15 $\overline{RT}$ and $\overline{WS}$ with RO = TO and WO = SO.

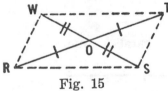
Fig. 15

a. Why is quadrilateral RSTW a □?   a. —————————

b. Why does WR = ST?   b. —————————

5. Given: In Fig. 16 rhombus ABCD.

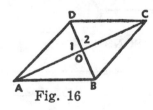
Fig. 16

a. Why is △ ADO ≅ △ CDO?   a. —————————

b. Why does ∠ 1 = ∠ 2?   b. —————————

c. Why is $\overline{DB}$ ⊥ to $\overline{AC}$?   c. —————————

6. Given: In Fig. 17 ∠ 1 = ∠ 2 and ∠ 3 = ∠ 4.

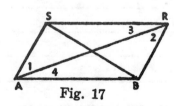
Fig. 17

a. Why is quadrilateral ABRS a □?   a. —————————

b. Why does AB = RS?   b. —————————

72

7. Given: In Fig. 18 isosceles trapezoid ABCD.
   To prove: that ∠ A = ∠ B.

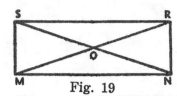

Fig. 18

   a. Why is $\overline{DM}$ ∥ to $\overline{CN}$?   a. _____

   b. Why does DM = CN?   b. _____

   c. Why is △ AMD ≅ △ BNC?   c. _____

   d. ∴ Why does ∠ A = ∠ B?   d. _____

8. Given: In Fig.19 MR = NS, SO = NO, and MO = RO.

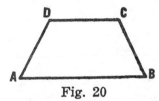

Fig. 19

   a. Why is quadrilateral MNRS a ▱?   a. _____

   b. Why is quadrilateral MNRS a
        rectangle?   b. _____

9. Given: In Fig. 20 isosceles trapezoid ABCD having AD = BC.

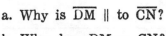

Fig. 20

   To prove: ∠ A = ∠ B.

PROOF   STATEMENTS   REASONS

Suggestion: Draw $\overline{DM}$ and $\overline{CN}$ ⊥ to base $\overline{AB}$.

_____   _____

_____   _____

_____   _____

_____   _____

_____   _____

10. A quadrilateral is always a parallelogram —

   a. If each pair of opposite sides meet the definition of being _____

   b. If each pair of opposite sides are _____

   c. If its diagonals _____

   d. If it has a pair of sides that are both _____ and _____

Make the following constructions accurately with compass and straightedge in the corresponding spaces provided for constructions.

STATEMENTS	CONSTRUCTIONS
1. Construct a parallelogram having given its two adjacent sides RS and RT, and ∠ R between them. R———————S R———T R (angle figure)	
2. Construct a parallelogram having given its two adjacent sides AB and BC, and diagonal AC. A———————B B————C A———————————C	
3. Construct a parallelogram having given its two adjacent sides M and N and altitude a. ——M—— ——N—— ——a——	

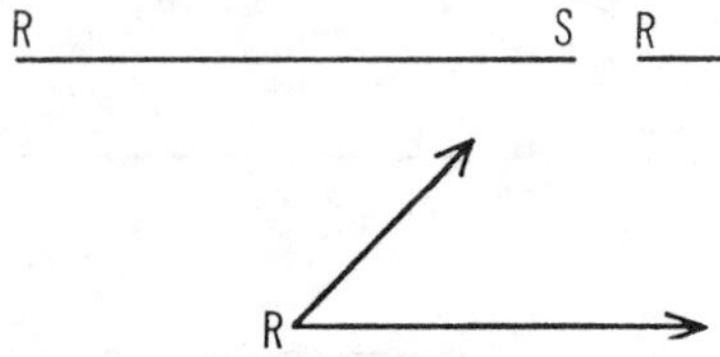

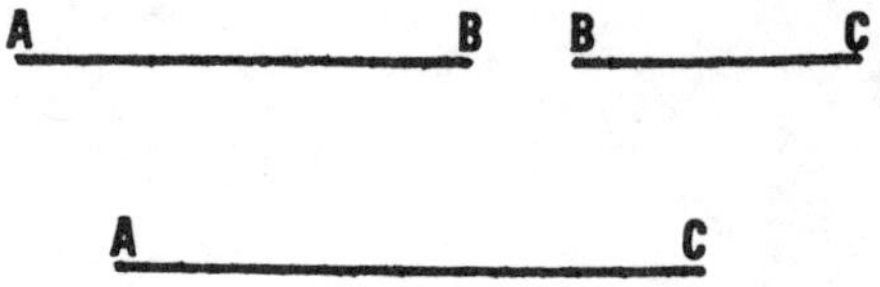

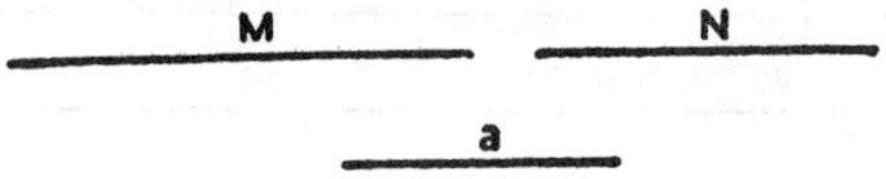

C. PARALLELS CUT BY TWO OR MORE TRANSVERSALS
THEOREM 39

If a number of parallels intercept equal distances on one transversal, they intercept equal distances on every transversal.

GIVEN: $\overleftrightarrow{aa'}$, $\overleftrightarrow{bb'}$, and $\overleftrightarrow{cc'}$, ‖ lines cut by transversals $\overleftrightarrow{WX}$ and $\overleftrightarrow{YZ}$, and KM = MN.

TO PROVE: that OP = _____.

PROOF. Draw $\overline{OV}$ and $\overline{PH}$ each ‖ to transversal WX. Post. _____

STATEMENTS	REASONS
1. $\overline{OV}$ and $\overline{PH}$ are ‖ to $\overline{WX}$.	1. ....
2. Hence $\overline{OV}$ is ‖ to $\overline{PH}$.	2. Unit 4, Th.? ....
3. KM = MN.	3. ....
4. OV = KM and PH = MN.	4. Th. 35, Cor.? ....
5. Hence OV = _____	5. .... Principle
6. ∠ 1 = ∠ _____ and ∠ s = ∠ _____	6. Th. 22, Cor.? ....
7. Hence ∠ 3 = ∠ _____	7. Th. 33, Cor.? ....
8. Hence △ OVP ≅ △ PHR.	8. ....
9. ∴ OP = _____	9. ....
Therefore _____	

COR. 1. The line-segment joining the midpoints of two sides of a triangle is parallel to the third side and equal to one-half the third side.

GIVEN: △ ABC with AR = CR and BS = CS.

TO PROVE: (1) that $\overline{RS}$ ‖ to $\overline{AB}$ and (2) that RS = ½ AB.

PROOF. Extend $\overline{RS}$ from S to M making SM = RS. Connect B and M. (Posts. 23 and 3)

STATEMENTS	REASONS
1. CS = BS.	1. ....
2. RS = SM.	2. Construction ....
3. ∠ 1 = ∠2.	3. ....
4. Hence △ _____ ≅ △ _____	4. ....
5. Hence ∠ 3 = ∠ _____	5. ....
6. $\overline{AR}$ is ‖ to $\overline{BM}$.	6. Unit 4, Th.? ....
7. BM = CR.	7. ....
8. AR = CR.	8. ....
9. Hence AR = _____	9. Substitution or .... Property of Equality

10. Hence ABMR is a ▱
11. ∴ RS is ‖ to AB.
12. RM = AB.
13. ∴ RS (or ½ RM) = ½ AB.
   Therefore _____

10. Unit 6, Th.? _____
11. _____
12. Th.? _____
13. _____ Property of Equality

COR. 2. If the bisector of one side of a triangle is parallel to another side, it bisects the third side, and is equal to one-half the side to which it is parallel.

GIVEN: △ ABC with $\overline{MN}$ drawn through M, the midpoint of $\overline{AC}$, and ‖ to $\overline{AB}$.

TO PROVE: (1) that _____ = _____ and (2) that MN = ½ AB.

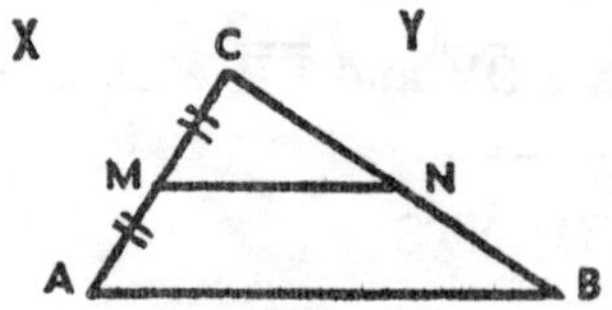

PROOF. Draw $\overleftrightarrow{XY}$ through C ‖ to $\overline{AB}$.   Th. _____

STATEMENTS	REASONS
1. $\overline{MN}$ is ‖ to $\overline{AB}$.	1. _____
2. $\overleftrightarrow{XY}$ is ‖ to $\overline{AB}$.	2. _____
3. Hence $\overleftrightarrow{XY}$ is ‖ to $\overline{MN}$.	3. Unit 4, Th.? _____
4. But AM = _____	4. _____
5. ∴ _____ = _____	5. Th.? _____
6. ∴ MN = _____	6. Th.?, Cor.? _____
Therefore _____	

THEOREM 40

The midpoint of the hypotenuse of a right triangle is equidistant from the three vertices.

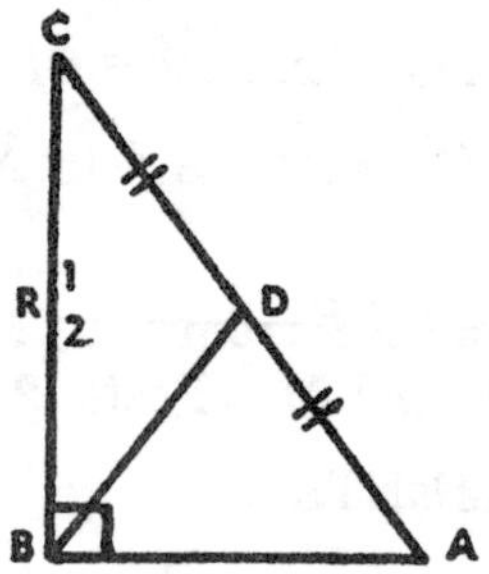

GIVEN: Rt. △ ABC with D the midpoint of its hypotenuse.

TO PROVE: that DA = _____ = _____.

PROOF. Through Point D draw $\overline{DR}$ ‖ to $\overline{AB}$.
   Th. _____

STATEMENTS	REASONS
1. CR = _____	1. Th.?, Cor.? _____
2. $\overline{CB}$ is ⊥ to $\overline{DR}$.	2. Th. 22, Cor.? _____
3. Hence ∠ 1 = ∠ 2.	3. _____
4. DR = _____	4. _____ Property of Equality
5. △ _____ ≅ △ _____	5. _____
6. Hence CD = BD.	6. _____
7. ∴ DA = _____ = _____	7. _____ Property of Equality
Therefore _____	

76

THEOREM 41

In a 30-60 degree right triangle, the shorter side (or leg) is one-half the **hypotenuse.**

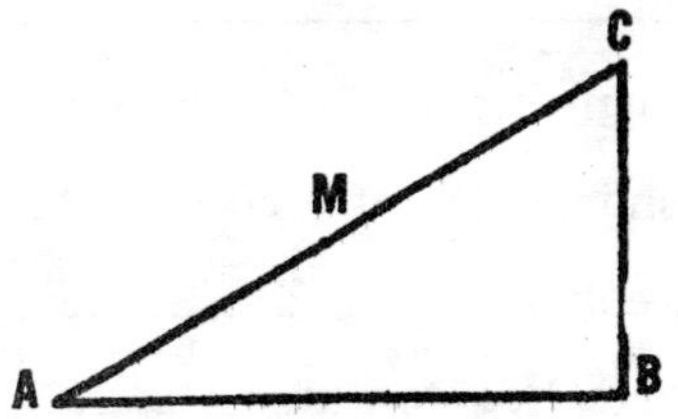

GIVEN: Rt. △ ABC with ∠ B = 30° and ∠ C = 60°.

TO PROVE: that AC = ½ BC.

PROOF. From M, the midpoint of $\overline{CB}$, draw $\overline{MA}$. (Post. 3)

STATEMENTS	REASONS
1. MC = MA = MB.	1. Unit 6, Th.? ....
2. ∠ 1 = 60°.	2. Unit 2, Th.? ....
3. Hence ∠ 3 = _____°	3. Unit 5, Th.? ....
4. ∴ AC = CM or ½ BC.	4. Unit 2, Th.? ....

Therefore _____

THEOREM 42

If the shorter leg of a right triangle is one-half its **hypotenuse, then the angle opposite the shorter leg contains 30 degrees.**

GIVEN: Right △ ABC with BC = ½ AC.

TO PROVE: ∠ A = 30°

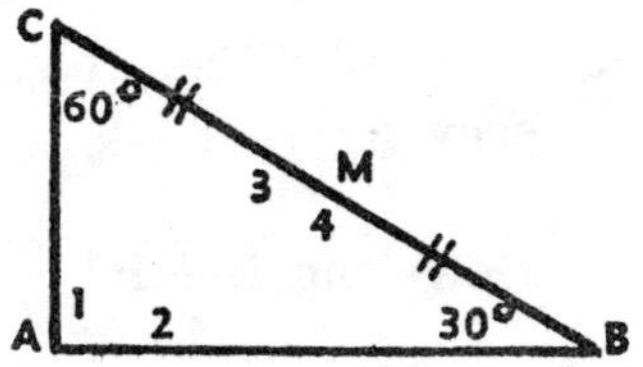

PROOF

Suggestion: From M, the midpoint of the hypotenuse, AC, draw auxiliary line-segment MB. Post. _____

STATEMENTS	REASONS
1. MB = MC	1. Th.? ....
2. BC = ½ AC (or MC)	2. ....
3. Hence BC = MC = MB	3. .... Property of Equality
4. ∴ △ BMC is equilateral.	4. ....
5. Hence ∠ C = 60°	5. Unit 2, Th.? Cor.? ....
6. ∴ ∠ A = 30°	6. Th. 33, Cor.? ....

Therefore _____

EXERCISES C

1. Fill each answer-space below with the correct term:

   a. Equally spaced parallel lines will cut off _____ distances on any one transversal.

   b. A line-segment drawn from the midpoint of one side of a triangle parallel to a second side will _____ the third side.

77

c. The shorter leg of any 30-60 degree right triangle equals _____

d. The midpoint of the hypotenuse of any right triangle is _____ from
the _____

e. A line-segment connecting the midpoints of two sides of a triangle is _____

f. If the shorter leg of a right triangle equals one-half the hypotenuse, then the angle opposite
to and equal to _____

the shorter leg contains _____ degrees.

g. A line-segment drawn through the midpoint of one side of a triangle and parallel to another side is equal to _____ the side to which it is _____

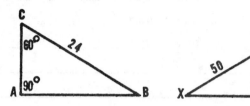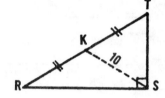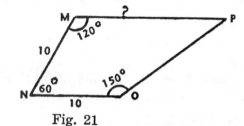

2. How long is side AC of △ ABC? _____

3. How many degrees are there in ∠ Z of △ XYZ? _____

4. How long is side RT of △ RST? _____

5. Given: In Fig. 21 quadrilateral MNOP as
shown.

How long is $\overline{MP}$?

Hint: First draw a certain auxiliary line.

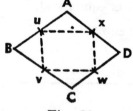

Fig. 21

Answer. _____

6. Given: In Fig. 22 quadrilateral ABCD the midpoints (u, v, w, x) of whose sides are connected
as shown, forming quadrilateral uvwx.

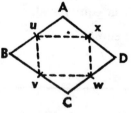

Fig. 22

To prove: that uvwx is a ▱.

Proof. Draw diagonal BD as an auxiliary line.

Statements	Reasons
1. $\overline{ux}$ is ‖ to _____ and = ½ _____	1. _____
2. $\overline{vw}$ is ‖ to _____ and = ½ _____	2. _____
3. Hence $\overline{ux}$ is ‖ to _____	3. _____
4. Also ux = _____	4. _____
5. ∴ uvwx is a ▱	5. _____

78

7. Divide a line-segment which is equal in length to MN into three equal parts, making use of the four equally spaced parallel line-segments below. Use your compass and straightedge.

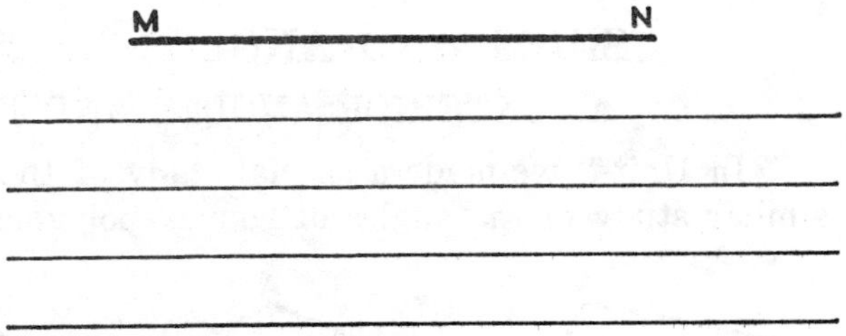

M _____ N

_____

_____

_____

_____

8. State the theorem upon which the authority for this construction is based.

_____

_____

D. INVERSE STATEMENTS AND CONTRAPOSITIVE STATEMENTS ● SYLLOGYSMS

The *inverse* of a theorem negates (falsifies) both the hypothesis and the conclusion of that theorem.

The *contrapositive* of a theorem is the converse of its inverse.

EXAMPLES:

1. THEOREM: **If two angles are right angles,** the angles are equal.

1i. CORRESPONDING INVERSE: **If two angles are NOT right angles, the angles are unequal.** (FALSE)

1c. CORRESPONDING CONTRAPOSITIVE: **If two angles are unequal,** they are not right angles. (TRUE)

2. THEOREM: **If a triangle is equilateral, it is equiangular.**

2i. CORRESPONDING INVERSE: **If a triangle is NOT equilateral,** it is NOT equiangular. (TRUE)

2c. CORRESPONDING CONTRAPOSITIVE: **If a triangle is NOT equiangular, it is NOT equi-**lateral. (TRUE)

A **syllogism** is a deductive proof consisting of **three statements which appear in this order:**

1. The *major premise* (an assumed general statement)

2. The *minor premise* (an assumed specific statement)

3. The *conclusion* (which follows logically from the other two statements)

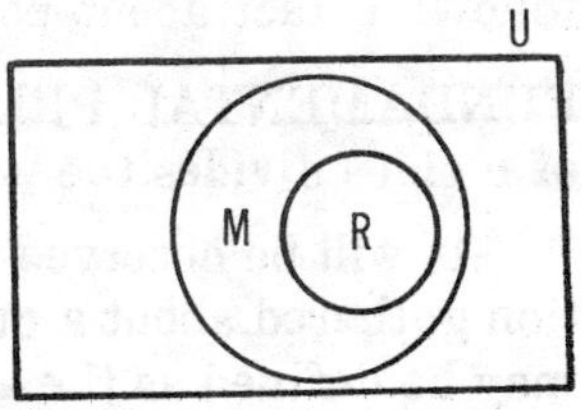

EXAMPLE:

GIVEN: U = {all mortal things}   M = {all men}   R = {all Romans}

1. Major premise: All men are mortal.   M ⊂ U
2. Minor premise: All Romans are men   R ⊂ M
3. ∴ all Romans are mortal.   ∴ R ⊂ U

EXERCISES D

1. State the *inverse* and the *contrapositive* of THEOREM 6 and determine whether each is true or false.

   a. The inverse: _____

   b. The contrapositive: _____

Unit VII.

SIDES AND ANGLES OF POLYGONS. INDIRECT PROOF

A. INTERIOR ANGLES AND EXTERIOR ANGLES OF POLYGONS

In Unit 2 we made a special study of the angles of triangles. Now we are going to make a similar study of the angles of convex polygons of more than three sides.

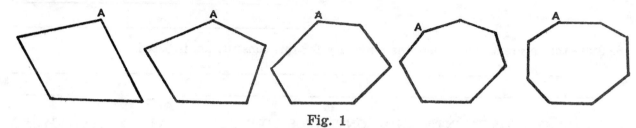

Fig. 1

PRELIMINARY EXERCISES A.

1. Draw all possible diagonals from a single vertex (A) of each of the polygons of Fig. 1. (Post. 3)

   Then refer to these polygons in filling the following blanks with correct answers.

   a. The quadrilateral has _____ sides, _____ angles, and is divided into _____ △.

   b. The pentagon has _____ sides, _____ angles, and is divided into _____ △.

   c. The hexagon has _____ sides, _____ angles, and is divided into _____ △.

   d. The heptagon has _____ sides, _____ angles, and is divided into _____ △.

   e. The octagon has _____ sides, _____ angles, and is divided into _____ △.

   Determine the correct answers of the following questions from the above relationships.

2. Into how many △ can a polygon be divided by drawing all possible diagonals from a single vertex,

   a. If the polygon has 15 sides? _____   c. If the polygon has 9 angles? _____

   b. If the polygon has 100 sides? _____   d. If the polygon has n sides? _____

   A study of the information gathered in PRELIMINARY EXERCISES A above reveals the following fact about polygons, which we shall call *Fundamental Principle I*:

FUNDAMENTAL PRINCIPLE I: All possible diagonals drawn from one vertex of any polygon of n sides divides the polygon into (n—2) triangles.

It will be observed that **Fundamental Principle** I was determined from a study of the information gathered about a number of specific polygons. This is an example of *inductive reasoning*, which may be defined as the arrival at a GENERAL CONCLUSION from a study of a number of specific cases. Scientists use inductive reasoning when they establish a law from data gathered in laboratories. Inductive reasoning is the opposite of deductive reasoning, which was defined on page 15.

3. How many sides does a polygon have,

   a. If it can be divided into 30 △ by diagonals drawn from one vertex? _____

   b. If it can be divided into 100 △ by diagonals drawn from one vertex? _____

4. Fill the following answer-spaces with correct answers.

   What is the sum of the ∡ of a polygon, if it is composed of —

   a. one △? _____°   c. 15 △ formed by diagonals drawn from one vertex? _____°

   b. 15 sides? _____°   d. n sides? _____°   e. 22 angles _____°

5. What is that kind of thinking called in which one forms *general conclusions* from a study of specific cases? _____

80

By this time we should realize that it is IMPOSSIBLE for us to draw a *perfectly generalized polygon*. However, our use of a *special figure* (a hexagon or an octagon, for example) in the establishment of a general proof is *perfectly sound* as long as the special features of the polygon, such as the number of its sides or the size of its angles, do not enter into the establishment of the proof.

THEOREM 43

The sum of the interior angles of a polygon of n sides is (n—2) straight angles (or (n—2) 180°)

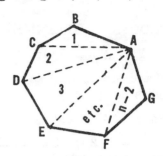

GIVEN: Polygon ABCDE .... with n sides.

TO PROVE: that $\angle A + \angle B + \angle C + \angle D + \angle E = (n-2)$ st. $\angle$.

PROOF. Draw all possible diagonals from any one vertex, such as vertex A. Post. _____

STATEMENTS	REASONS
1. There are (n-2) △ in the polygon.	1. Fundamental Principle? ....
2. The sum of the ∠ of each △ = _____ st. ∠	2. Th.? ....
3. Hence the sum of the ∠ of all the (n-2) △ = (n-2) 180°	3. .... Property of Equality
4. But ∠A + ∠B + ∠C, etc. = the sum of all the ∠ composing the (n - 2) △ of the polygon.	4. .... Principle
5. ∴ ∠A + ∠B + ∠C, etc. = (n - 22) 180°.	5. .... Principle
Therefore _____	

COR. 1.   Each interior angle of an equiangular polygon of n sides contains $\dfrac{(n-2) \text{ st. } \angle}{n}$, or $\dfrac{(n-2)\ 180°}{n}$.

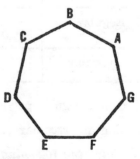

GIVEN: Equiangular polygon ABCDE ... with n sides and, therefore, with n ∠.

TO PROVE: that each interior ∠ of the polygon = $\dfrac{(n-2)\ 180°}{n}$.

PROOF.   STATEMENTS | REASONS
STATEMENTS	REASONS
1. The n ∠ of the polygon = (n—2) 180°	1. Th.? ....
2. ∴ each interior ∠ = $\dfrac{(n-2)\ 180°}{n}$	2. .... Property of Equality
Therefore _____	

81

COR. 2. The sum of the exterior angles of any polygon, formed by producing each side in succession, is equal to two straight angles (or 360°).

GIVEN: Polygon ABC . . . with n sides and n angles and ext. $\angle$ a, b. c . . .

TO PROVE: that $\angle$ a $+$ $\angle$ b $+$ $\angle$ c . . . $= 2$ st. $\angle$ (or 360°).

PROOF. STATEMENTS	REASONS
1. $\angle$ 1 $+$ $\angle$ a $= 180°$	1. Def. of? ....
2. There are _____ adjacent exterior-interior pairs of $\angle$.	2. Given ....
3. So $\angle$ 1 $+$ $\angle$ a $+$ $\angle$ 2 $+$ $\angle$ b. . . $= 180$ n°	3. .... Property of equality
4. $\angle$ 1 $+$ $\angle$ 2 $+$ $\angle$ 3 . . . $= (n-2)$ 180°, or 180 n° $-$ 360°	4. Th.? ....
5. $\therefore$ $\angle$ a $+$ $\angle$ b $+$ $\angle$ c . . . $= 360°$	5. .... Property of equality
Therefore _____	

EXERCISES A

Fill the answer-spaces in the table below with correct answers.

Kind of Polygon	No. of sides n	Sum of int $\angle$	Value of each int. $\angle$	Sum of ext. $\angle$	Value of Each ext. $\angle$
1. Regular	12				
2. Regular	8				
3. Equiangular			120°		
4. Regular					36°
5. Irregular		5400°	$\times$		$\times$

6. Can a regular polygon have an exterior $\angle$ of 35°? _____; of 45°? _____

7. Can an irregular polygon have an exterior $\angle$ of 35° _____

Solve the following exercises.

8. Seven $\angle$ of an octagon have the following values: 100°, 135°, 150°, 130°, 140°, 160°, and 165°. How many degrees are there in the remaining $\angle$?

Solution: Answer _____

9. How many sides has a polygon, if the sum of the interior $\angle$ is equal to the sum of the exterior $\angle$?

Solution: Answer _____

82

B. TRIANGLES WITH UNEQUAL SIDES AND UNEQUAL ANGLES • INDIRECT PROOF

THEOREM 44

If two sides of a triangle are unequal, the angle opposite the greater side is greater than the angle opposite the smaller side. (proof often optional)

GIVEN: △ RST with ST > RT.

TO PROVE: that ∠ R > ∠ S.

PROOF: On $\overline{TS}$ lay off $\overline{TD}$ equal to $\overline{TR}$, and draw $\overline{RD}$. Posts. _____

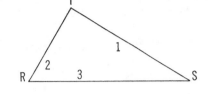

STATEMENTS	REASONS
1. ∠R = ∠3 + ∠2	1. Angle-Addition Postulate ....
2. 0° < ∠3	2. Post.? ....
3. ∠ R > ∠ 2	3. Post. 11 ....
4. ∠ 1 > ∠ S	4. Th. 33, Cor.? ....
5. But ∠ 1 = ∠ 2	5. Unit 2, Th.? ....
6. Hence ∠ 2 > ∠ S	6. ....
7. ∴ ∠ R > ∠ S	7. .... Property of Inequality

Therefore _____

INDIRECT PROOF BY EXCLUSION

The methods we have been using to prove principles in geometry are known as direct methods of proof. We shall find it convenient at times to prove geometric principles by a method called indirect proof by *exclusion,* which is composed of the following essential steps:

1. An enumeration of all the PLAUSIBLE conclusions that may have a bearing on the principle that is being investigated. (Use of the trichotomy principle*)

2. The systematic elimination of all these conclusions, one by one, except the one to be proved. This is done by showing that all the other plausible conclusions are *impossible* because they lead to CONTRADICTIONS of the hypothesis.

The following example may serve as a simple illustration of an indirect proof by exclusion. Suppose that Miss Roberts has found a green pencil on the floor of her classroom, which was lost there during the recitation. On inquiry, Miss Roberts is informed that each of three pupils has lost a pencil. Charles has lost a red pencil, Harry a black one, and Mary a yellow one. Mary is color-blind, and is therefore unable to give the color of the pencil which she has lost. Miss Robert's determination of the ownership of the pencil found may be expressed in the following manner:

STATEMENTS	REASONS
1. The pencil belongs either to Charles, Harry, Mary, or John.	1. Enumeration of all possibilities. (Trichotomy)
2. It does not belong to Charles.	2. Charles has lost a red pencil.
3. It does not belong to Harry.	3. Harry has lost a black pencil.
4. ∴ it must belong to Mary.	4. Elimination of all other possibilities. (Trichotomy)

The above form of proof is also known as *proof by elimination.* Proposition 3 below is proved by both the DIRECT METHOD of proof and the INDIRECT METHOD of proof. Some students prefer the direct method of proof; others prefer the indirect method.

* According to the Principle of Trichotomy a quantity is either equal to, greater than, or less than another quantity of the same kind.

THEOREM 45

If two angles of a triangle are unequal, the side opposite the greater angle is greater than the side opposite the smaller angle. (proof often optional)

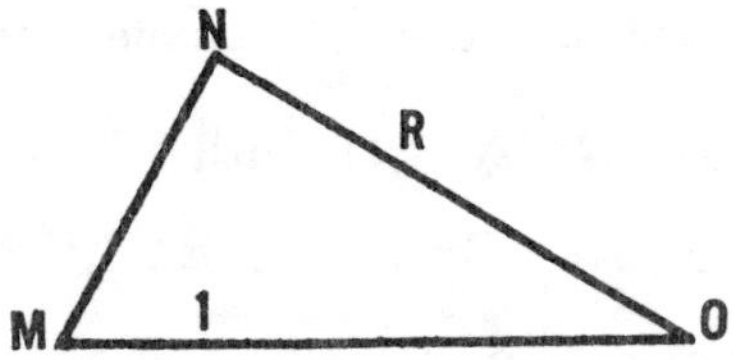

GIVEN: $\triangle$ MNO with $\angle$ M $>$ $\angle$ O.

TO PROVE: that ON $>$ MN.

PROOF. (Direct Method) Draw $\overline{MR}$, making $\angle 1 = \angle$ O.

STATEMENTS	REASONS
1. MR + NR $>$ MN	1. Post.? ....
2. But MR = OR	2. Th.? ....
3. So OR + NR $>$ MN	3. .... Property of Equality
4. But OR + NR = ON	4. .... Principle
5. $\therefore$ ON $>$ _____	5. .... Principle

Therefore _____

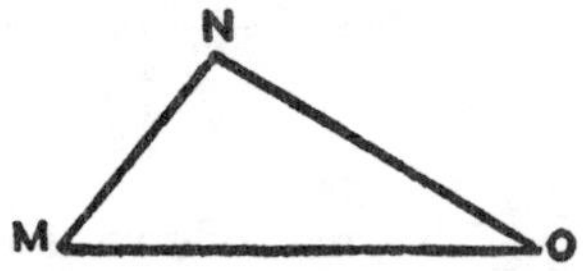

PROOF. (Indirect Method)   STATEMENTS

REASONS

1. Either ON = MN, or ON $<$ MN, or ON $>$ MN
1. .... Principle

2. If ON = MN, then $\angle$ ____ must = $\angle$ ____
2. ....

3. But this is impossible, and therefore ON $\neq$ MN
3. Contradiction of? ....

4. If ON $<$ MN, then $\angle$ M must be $<$ $\angle$ ____
4. Th.? ....

5. But this is impossible, and therefore ON $\not<$ MN
5. ....

6. $\therefore$ ON $>$ MN
6. ....

Therefore _____

THEOREM 46

If two triangles have two sides of one equal respectively to two sides of the other, but the included angle of the first greater than the included angle of the second, then the third side of the first is greater than the third side of the second. (proof often optional)

GIVEN: ⚠ MNO and M′N′O′ with MO = M′O′, MN = M′N′, and ∠ M > ∠ M′.

TO PROVE: that NO > _____.

PROOF. Place △ M′N′O′ upon △ MNO so that $\overline{M′N′}$ coincides with $\overline{MN}$ and ∠ O′ falls on the same side of $\overline{MN}$ as ∠O. Bisect ∠ OMO′ with $\overline{MR}$. Draw $\overline{O′R}$. (Post. 3)

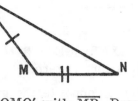 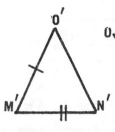 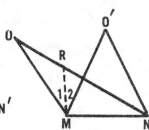

STATEMENTS	REASONS
In ⚠ MRO and MRO′,	
1. MO = _____	1. ....
2. MR = _____	2. .... Property of Equality
3. ∠ 1 = ∠ 2	3. ....
4. Hence △ _____ ≅ △ _____	4. ....
5. Hence RO = _____	5. ....
6. NR + RO′ > NO′	6. Post. ? .... Principle
7. NR + RO > NO′	7. .... Principle
8. ∴ NO > N′O	8. ....
Therefore _____	

THEOREM 47

If two triangles have two sides of one equal respectively to two sides of the other, but the third side of the first greater than the third side of the second, then the angle opposite the third side of the first is greater than the angle opposite the third side of the second. (Proof often optional)

GIVEN: ⚠ ABC and A′B′C′ with AC = A′C′, BC = B′C′, and AB > A′B′.

TO PROVE: that ∠ _____ > ∠ _____.

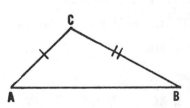 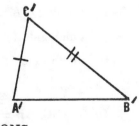

PROOF. (Indirect Method)   STATEMENTS   REASONS

1. Either ∠ C = ∠ C′, or ∠ C < ∠ C′, or ∠ C > ∠ C′.	1. ....
2. If ∠ C = ∠ C′, △ ABC ≅ △ A′B′C′	2. ....
3. Then AB must = A′B′.	3. ....
4. But this is impossible, and therefore ∠ C ≠ ∠ C′.	4. Contradiction of ? ....

85

5. If $\angle C < \angle C'$, then AB must be $< A'B'$.   5. Th. 46 ....

6. But this is impossible, and therefore $\angle C \not< $ 6. ....
$\angle C'$.   ....

7. $\therefore \angle C > \angle C'$.   7. ....

Therefore _____

_____

EXERCISES B

1. Fill each answer-space below with the correct term:

a. In a $\triangle$ having unequal sides, the $\angle$ opposite the greatest of these sides is always the

_____ $\angle$.

b. In a $\triangle$ having unequal $\angle$, the side opposite the greatest of these $\angle$ is always the _____
side.

c. In two $\triangle$ having two sides respectively equal, but the included $\angle$ formed by these sides
unequal, the $\triangle$ having the greater included $\angle$ will have the _____

third _____.

d. In two $\triangle$ having two sides respectively equal, but their third sides unequal, the $\triangle$ having
the greater third side will always have the _____ included _____.

Before answering the following questions, make FREE-HAND DRAWINGS of the conditions given in the space provided for drawings.

DRAWINGS

2. In $\triangle$ ABC, CB $>$ AC and $\angle$ C $= 120°$.

a. Which side is the largest? _____

b. Which side is the smallest? _____

3. In $\triangle$ ABC $\angle$ A $= 70°$ and $\angle$ C $= 25°$.

a. Which side (AB, AC, or BC) is the largest? _____

b. Which side is the smallest? _____

4. In $\triangle$ ABC, AB $= 8$, AC $= 12$, and BC $= 6$.

a. Which angle (A, B, or C) is the largest? _____

b. Which angle is the smallest? _____

5. In △ ABC, ∠ A = 30°, and exterior ∠ ACD (made by extending BC) = 100°. Which side is the largest? _____

6. In rt. △ ABC, ∠ B is the rt. ∠, and ∠ C = 35°. Which side is the shortest? _____

7. In △ ABC, ∠ B > ∠ C and ∠ A = 60°
   a. Which side is the largest? _____

   b. Which side is the shortest? _____

8. In rt. △ ABC, ∠ B is the right ∠. Which side is the longest? _____

9. In △ ABC, median AM makes ∠ AMC obtuse.
   a. Which side, AC or AB, is the longer? _____
   b. Why? _____
   c. Which angle, ∠ B or ∠ C, is the larger? _____
   d. Why? _____

10. In △ RST, ST > RT and median TM is drawn.
    a. Which angle, ∠ RMT or ∠ SMT, is the larger? _____
    b. Why? _____
    c. Is ∠ RMT acute or obtuse? _____

Unit VIII.

BASIC PRINCIPLES ABOUT CIRCLES. LOCUS OF POINTS

A. CIRCLES AND POSTULATES PERTAINING TO CIRCLES

A *circle* is a set of points in a plane at a fixed distance from a given point in that plane called the center. That portion of the plane bounded by the circle is known as the *interior region* of the circle. See shaded part in Fig. 4.*

The distance around a circle corresponding to the perimeter of a polygon, is called its *circumference*. A *diameter* of a circle is a straight line-segment drawn through its center and terminating in the circle. See $\overline{MN}$ in Fig. 1. The *radius* of a circle is a straight line-segment drawn from its center to the circle. See $\overline{OA}$ in Fig. 1. A straight line-segment connecting any two points of a circle is called a *chord*. A diameter is a chord. See $\overline{RS}$ in Fig. 1. A *secant* is a straight line or line-segment which cuts a circle in one or two points. See $\overleftrightarrow{XY}$ in Fig. 1. A *tangent* is a line or line-segment which touches a circle in one and only one point, called the *point of tangency*. See $\overleftrightarrow{CD}$

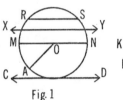 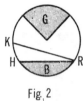 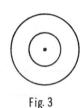

| Fig. 1 | Fig. 2 | Fig. 3 | Fig. 4 |

Fig. 1. One half of a circle is called a *semi-circle*, and one fourth of a circle is called a *quadrant*. A portion of the circumference of a circle is called an *arc*. See KHR in Fig. 2. If an arc of a circle is less than a semi-circle, it is called a *minor arc*. If it is greater than a semi-circle, it is called a *major arc*. An *inscribed angle* is an angle whose vertex touches the circle and whose sides are chords. See ∠HRK in Fig. 2. Minor arc HK is called the *subtended arc* of ∠HRK. An angle formed at the the center of a circle by two radii is called a *central angle*. See ∠AOM in Fig. 1. The portion of the area of a circle that is inclosed by a chord and its arc is called a *segment*. See shaded portion B in Fig. 2. The portion of the area of a circle enclosed by two radii and their intercepted arc is called a *sector*. See shaded portion G in Fig. 2. Unless otherwise specified in a discussion, it is understood that an arc, a segment, or a sector means the MINOR arc, minor segment, or minor sector. Circles that have the same center are said to be *concentric*. See Fig. 3.

The following statements are POSTULATES that pertain to circles. Like previous postulates, they are to be accepted without proof.

30. **Radii or diameters of the same circle or of equal circles are equal.**

31. **Circles having equal radii or equal diameters are equal.**

32. **A diameter of a circle divides it into equal parts.**

33. **A diameter is equal to the sum of two radii.**

34. **One and only one circle can be drawn in a given plane with a given center and given radius.**

35. **A straight line can intersect a circle in two and only two points.**

36. **Points at a radius distance from the center of a line circle lie on the line circle, and conversely.**

37. **Any point within a circle is less than a radius distance from the center, and any point without is greater than a radius distance from the center, conversely.**

---

* A *circle* may also be defined as a closed curve all of whose points are in the same plane and equidistant from a given point within, called the center. Hence the interior region of a circle could be defined as the portion of the plane inclosed within the circle.

38. Arcs (major or **minor**) having equal radii and terminating in the same points are equal (congruent).

39. A central **angle is measured** by its arc, and conversely.

NOTE: Postulate 39 means that a central angle has the same number of angle degrees as its arc has arc degrees.

The symbol $\doteq$ is frequently used in geometry to mean "*is equal in degrees to*".

EXERCISES A.

1. Fill each answer-space below with the correct answer.

_____a. A closed curve all of whose points are in the same plane and equidistant from a given point within called the center.

_____b. A straight line-segment drawn from the center of a circle to the boundary.

_____c. The closed curve that forms the boundary of a circle (or the distance around a circle).

_____d. A straight line-segment drawn through the center of a circle and terminating in its boundary.

_____e. A straight line-segment which connects two points in the boundary of a circle.

_____f. A straight line or line-segment which cuts a line circle in two points.

_____g. A straight line or line-segment which touches a line circle in one point.

_____h. A single point at which a line or line-segment touches a line circle.

_____i. A portion of the circumference of a circle.

_____j. One-half of the circumference of a circle.

_____k. A portion of the circumference of a circle that is greater than a semi-circle.

_____l. A portion of the circumference of a circle that is less than a semi-circle.

_____m. An angle formed at the center of a circle by two radii.

_____n. An angle whose vertex touches a circle and whose sides are chords of the circle.

_____o. A portion of the interior of a circle that is inclosed by two radii and their intercepted arc.

_____p. A portion of the interior of a circle that is inclosed by a chord and its arc.

_____q. Circles in the same plane which have the same center.

_____r. One-fourth of the circumference of a circle.

_____s. A portion of a plane whose boundary is equally distant from a point within.

89

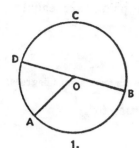
1.

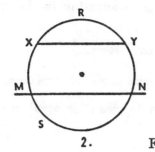
2.

Fig. 4

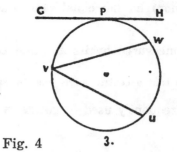
3.

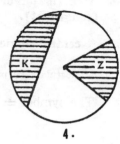
4.

2. Refer to the circles in Fig. 4 above in filling the following answer spaces with correct answers. What term is applied to,

a. Distance ABCDA in ⊙ 1? _____

b. Point O in ⊙ 1? _____

c. OA in ⊙ 1? _____

d. Line-segment BD in ⊙ 1? _____

e. Angle AOD in ⊙ 1? _____

f. Line-segment XY in ⊙ 2? _____

g. Distance XRY in ⊙ 2? _____

h. Distance XSY in ⊙ 2? _____

i. Line-segment MN in ⊙ 2? _____

j. Line-segment GPH in ⊙ 3? _____

k. Point P in ⊙ 3? _____

l. Angle uvw in ⊙ 3? _____

m. Shaded portion K in ⊙ 4? _____

n. Shaded portion Z in ⊙ 4? _____

3. If an arc (or segment, or sector) is not specified, which one is it understood to mean? _____

The operations involved in the following exercises are based upon the postulates pertaining to circles. *Fill the answer-spaces in the usual way.*

4. Given: In Fig. 5 two equal ⊚ O and O'.   **Answers.**

a. Why does OR = O'R'?   a. _____

b. Why does OR = OS?   b. _____

c. Why does MN = M'N'?   c. _____

Fig. 5

5. Given: In Fig. 6 two ⊚ D and D' with DC = D'C' and arc AB = arc A'B'.

a. Why does ⊙ D = ⊙ D'?   a. _____

b. Why does ∠ 1 = ∠ 2?   b. _____

Fig. 6

90

6. Given: In Fig. 7 ⊙ C with point P outside and point E inside the ⊙.

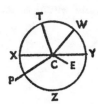

Fig. 7

a. Why does XY = CW + CT?

b. Why does area XYWTX = area XYZX?

c. Why is CP > CE?

a. _____

b. _____

c. _____

B. PROPERTIES OF THE SAME CIRCLE AND PROPERTIES OF EQUAL CIRCLES

THEOREM 48

The diameter of a circle is greater than any other chord.

GIVEN: ⊙ O with diameter AB and any other chord MN.

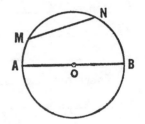

TO PROVE: that _____ > _____.

PROOF. Draw radii MO and _____ as auxiliary lines. (Post. ____)

STATEMENTS	REASONS
1. _____ + _____ > MN	1. Post.? ....
2. _____ = _____ and _____ = _____	2. Post.? about ⊚ ....
3. ∴ _____ + _____ (or AB) > MN	3. ....
Therefore _____	

THEOREM 49

In the same circle, or in equal circles, equal central angles have equal chords and equal arcs.*

GIVEN: Equal ⊛ O and O' with central ∠ AOB = central ∠ A'O'B'.

TO PROVE: (1) that chord AB = chord A'B' and (2) that $\widehat{AB} = \widehat{A'B'}$.

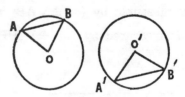

PROOF. STATEMENTS	REASONS
1. △ _____ ≅ △ _____	1. ....
2. ∴ chord AB = chord A'B'.	2. ....
3. So chord AB can be made to coincide with chord A'B'.	3. Post.? ....
4. ∴ $\widehat{AB} = \widehat{A'B'}$.	4. Post.? ....
Therefore _____	

* NOTE: The arcs of equal central angles of UNEQUAL circles are unequal in *length* but equal in degrees.

THEOREM 50

In the same circle, or in equal circles, equal chords have equal central angles and equal arcs.

GIVEN: Equal ⊙ O and O' with chord MN = chord M'N'.

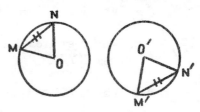

TO PROVE: (1) that ∠ O = ∠ O' and (2) that $\overset{\frown}{MN} = \overset{\frown}{M'N'}$.

PROOF. STATEMENTS	REASONS
1. MO = _____ and NO = _____	1. ....
2. MN = _____	2. ....
3. Hence △ _____ ≅ △ _____	3. ....
4. ∴ ∠ _____ = ∠ _____	4. ....
5. ∴ _____ = _____	5. Th.? ....
Therefore _____	

THEOREM 51

In the same circle, or in equal circles, equal arcs have equal central angles and equal chords.

GIVEN: Equal ⊙ R and R' with $\overset{\frown}{AB} = \overset{\frown}{A'B'}$.

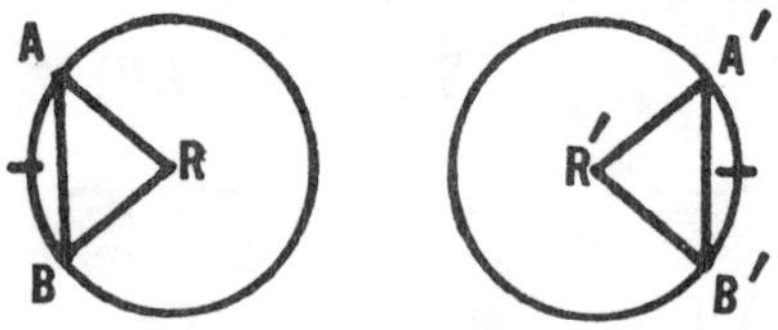

TO PROVE: (1) that ∠ R = ∠ R' and (2) that chord AB = chord A'B'.

PROOF. STATEMENTS	REASONS
1. ∠ R is measured by (or ≐) $\overset{\frown}{AB}$ and ∠ R' is measured by (or ≐) $\overset{\frown}{A'B'}$.	1. Post.? about ⊙ ....
2. But $\overset{\frown}{AB} = \overset{\frown}{A'B'}$	2. ....
3. ∴ ∠ _____ = ∠ _____	3. ....
4. ∴ chord AB = chord A'B'	4. Th.? ....
Therefore _____	

THEOREM 52

In the same circle, or in equal circles, the greater of two unequal central angles has the greater chord and the greater minor arc.

GIVEN: Equal ⊙ O and O' with central ∠ O > central ∠ O'.

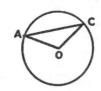

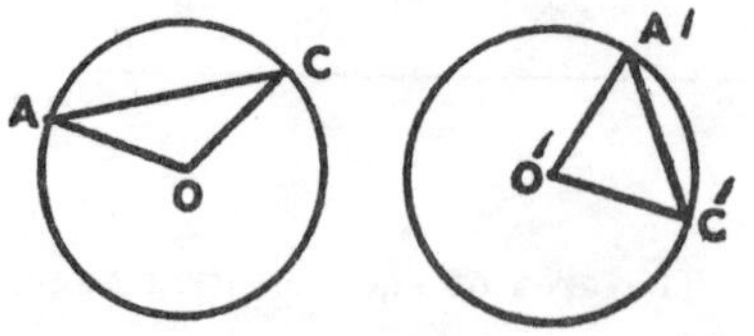

TO PROVE: (1) that chord AC > chord A'C' and (2) that $\overset{\frown}{AC} > \overset{\frown}{A'C'}$.

PROOF.   STATEMENTS   REASONS

In △ OAC and O'A'C',

1. OA = O'A' and OC = O'C'   1. ....

2. ∠ O > ∠ O'   2. ....

3. ∴ chord AC > chord A'C'   3. Th.? ....

4. $\overset{\frown}{AC} \doteq \angle$ O and $\overset{\frown}{A'C'} \doteq \angle$ O'   4. Post.? ....

5. ∴ $\overset{\frown}{AC} > \overset{\frown}{A'C'}$.   5. ....

Therefore _____

THEOREM 53

In the same circle, or in equal circles, the greater of two unequal chords has the **greater central angle** and the **greater minor arc**.

GIVEN: Equal ⊙ C and C' with chord AB> chord A'B'.

TO PROVE: (1) that ∠ C > ∠ C' and (2) that $\overset{\frown}{AB} > \overset{\frown}{A'B'}$.

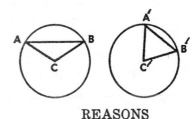

PROOF.   STATEMENTS   REASONS

1. In △ ABC and A'B'C', AB > A'B'   1. ....

2. AC = A'C' and BC = B'C'   2. ....

3. ∴ ∠ C > ∠ C'   3. Unit 7, Th.? ....

4. ∴ _____ > _____   4. Th.? ....

Therefore _____

In Theorem 54 below, provisions are made for proving both parts of each conclusion by the *direct method*, and for proving the first part of each conclusion by the *indirect method* by EX-CLUSION.

THEOREM 54

In the same circle, or in equal circles, the greater of two unequal minor arcs has the **greater central angle** and the **greater chord**.

GIVEN: Equal ⊙ O and O' with $\overset{\frown}{RS} > \overset{\frown}{R'S'}$.

TO PROVE: (1) that ∠ O > ∠ O' and (2) that chord RS > chord R'S'.

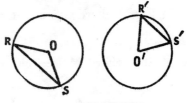

PROOF. (Direct Method) STATEMENTS   REASONS

1. Minor $\overset{\frown}{RS}$ > minor $\overset{\frown}{R'S'}$ 1. ....

2. $\overset{\frown}{RS} \doteq \angle$ _____ and $\overset{\frown}{R'S'} \doteq \angle$ _____   2. ....

3. ∴ ∠ _____ > ∠ _____   3. ....

4. ∴ chord _____ > chord _____   4. Th.? ....

Therefore _____

93

PROOF. (Indirect Method) STATEMENTS

1. Either ∠ O = ∠ O', or _____

_____

2. If ∠ O = ∠ O', then _____

3. But this is impossible, and hence

_____

4. If ∠ O < ∠ O', then _____

5. But _____

_____

6. ∴ ∠O > ∠ O'

7. And ∴ chord _____ > chord _____

   Therefore _____

   _____

REASONS

1. ....

2. Th.? ....

3. Contradiction of? ....

4. ....

5. ....

6. ....

7. Th.? ....

EXERCISES B

Fill each answer-space below with the correct term:

1. In the same circle or in equal circles —

   a. Equal minor arcs have equal _____ and equal _____

   b. Equal central ∡ have equal _____ and equal _____

   c. Equal chords have equal _____ and equal _____

   d. The greater of two minor arcs has the greater _____ and the greater

   _____

   e. The greater of two central ∡ has the greater _____ and the greater

   _____

   f. The greater of two chords has the greater _____ and the greater

   _____

   g. The greater of two *major* arcs has the _____ chord.

2. The longest possible chord that a circle with a 7 inch radius can have is _____ inches long.

3. Given: In Fig. 8 chord MS = chord RN.

   To prove: that chord MN = chord RS.

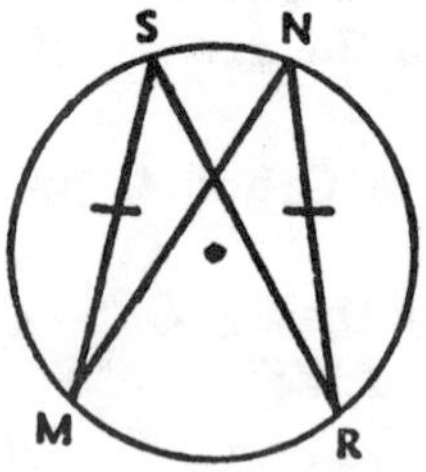

Fig. 8

Proof.   Statements

_____

_____

_____

_____

_____

_____

Reasons

_____

_____

_____

_____

_____

_____

4. Given: In Fig. 9 $\overset{\frown}{MN} = \overset{\frown}{M'N'}$.

To prove: that $\triangle$ MNO $\cong$ $\triangle$ M'N'O.

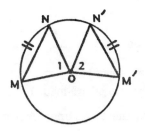

Fig. 9

Proof.   Statements

_____

_____

_____

_____

_____

_____

Reasons

_____

_____

_____

_____

_____

_____

5. Given: In Fig. 10 central $\angle$ AOB = 46° and central $\angle$ AOC = 92°

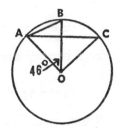

Fig. 10

a. Is chord AC =, > or < 2 chords AB? _____

b. Is arc AC =, >, or < 2 arcs AB? _____

c. How many degrees are there in major arc AC? _____

C. LOCUS OF POINTS

In geometry a locus (lō-kŭs) consists of all the possible places where a point fulfilling a given condition may be located. Hence a *locus* may be defined as the path of a point moving so as constantly to fulfill a given condition. So in geometry, a locus may be regarded as being the set of all points that fulfill a given condition (or set of conditions). For example, the locus of a point that is 2 in. from a given circle of 1 in. radius is a circle of 3 in. radius which is concentric with the given circle. In Fig. 11 the outer circle is the locus. The two conditions that must be proved in the complete proof of a locus problem are these:

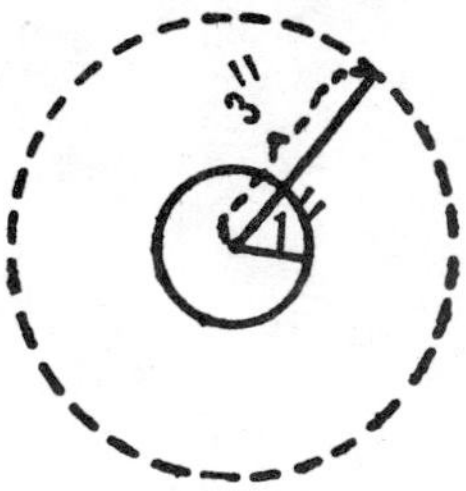

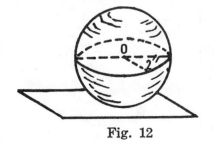

Fig. 11

(1) that every point on the supposed locus fulfills the given condition.

(2) that every point which fulfills the given condition lies on the supposed locus.

The terms "locus", "locus of a point", and "locus of points" all mean the same thing. The plural of locus is loci (lō-sī).

The locus of a point that is 2 in. from a given point O in a given *plane* is a line CIRCLE whose center is at the given point and whose radius is 2 in. Note the circle in Fig. 12. However, the locus of a point that is 2 in. from a given point O in *space* is a SPHERE whose center is at the given point and whose radius is 2 in., as shown in Fig. 12.

Fig. 12

1. Define locus _____

_____

2. What is the plural of locus? _____

3. Enumerate the two conditions which must be proved in the proof of a locus problem.

(1) _____

(2) _____

Answer the following questions with complete statements, and draw a figure in the space provided for illustrations to represent each answer. Represent each locus by means of broken lines or by dots.

4. What is the locus of points equidistant from two parallel lines —   **ILLUSTRATIONS**

a. When all are in one plane? _____

_____

_____

b. When all are in space? _____

_____

5. What is the locus of a point that is 3 in. from a given line —

a. When all are confined to one plane?

_____

_____

b. When all are in space? _____

_____

6. What is the locus equidistant from two concentric circles (in the same plane) having radii of 2 units and 5 units? _____

_____

_____

7. What is the locus of points *within* an angle that is a constant distance c from the vertex? _____

_____

_____

8. What is the locus of a point (in a given plane) equally distant from the the sides of an angle? _____

9. What is the locus of the center of a circle having a radius of 1 unit —

a. Which (when confined to a single plane) touches a fixed line?

_____

_____

b. Which in space touches a fixed line? _____

_____

_____

c. Which (when confined to a single plane) passes through a fixed point? _____

_____

d. Which in space passes through a fixed point? _____

_____

_____

10. What is the locus equally distant from two points —

a. Within a plane? _____

_____

b. Within space? _____

_____

11. Locate a point which is ½ in. from XY and ¾ in. from point C in the accompanying figure.

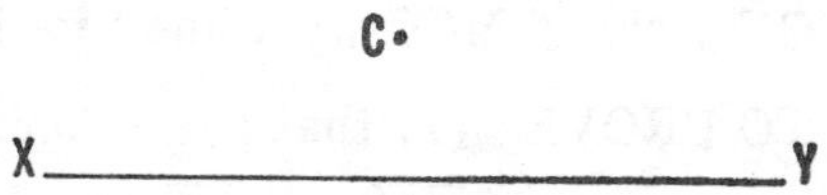

C•

X_____Y

D.   THEOREMS THAT PERTAIN TO LOCUS OF POINTS

THEOREM 55

The locus of points (in a plane) equidistant from two given points is the perpendicular bisector of the line-segment joining them.

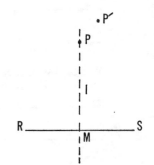

GIVEN: Two points R and S and line l, the ⊥ bisector of $\overline{RS}$.

TO PROVE: (1) that any point on l, such as point P, is equidistant from R and S (i. e. PR = PS) and (2) that any point P′ which *is* equidistant from R and S must lie on l.

PROOF of Part 1. Draw $\overline{PR}$ and $\overline{PS}$. (Post. 3)

STATEMENTS	REASONS
1. △ ——— ≅ △ ———	1. ———————————————
2. ∴ $\overline{PR} = \overline{PS}$, proving that *any* point on line l is equidistant from points R and S.	2. ———————————————

PROOF of Part 2. Connect P′ with M, the midpoint of $\overline{RS}$, and with R and S.

STATEMENTS	REASONS
1. △ ——— ≅ △ ———	1. ....
2. ∠ P′MR = ∠ ———	2. ....
3. Hence $\overline{P'M}$ is the ⊥ bisector of $\overline{RS}$	3. Def. of? ....
4. Hence P′M must coincide with l	4. Th.? ....
5. ∴ line l becomes the required locus.	5. Def. of? ....
Therefore ———————————————————————————	

THEOREM 56

The locus of a point equally distant from the sides of an angle is the bisector of the angle.

GIVEN: ∠ MOC with line l its bisector.

TO PROVE: (1) that P, any point on l, is equally distant from $\overrightarrow{OC}$ and $\overrightarrow{OM}$ (i. e. PR = PS) and (2) that any point P′ which *is* equally distant from $\overrightarrow{OC}$ and $\overrightarrow{OM}$ lies on l.

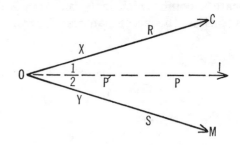

PROOF of part 1. Draw $\overline{PR}$ ⊥ to $\overrightarrow{OC}$ and $\overline{PS}$ ⊥ to $\overrightarrow{OM}$. (Th. 13)

STATEMENTS	REASONS
1. △ ——— ≅ △ ———	1. ———————————————
2. ∴ PR = PS, which proves that any point on l is equidistant from $\overrightarrow{OC}$ and $\overrightarrow{OM}$.	2. ———————————————

PROOF of part 2. Draw $\overrightarrow{P'X} \perp$ to $\overrightarrow{OC}$ and $\overrightarrow{P'Y} \perp$ to $\overrightarrow{OM}$.

STATEMENTS		REASONS
1. $\triangle$ _____ $\cong \triangle$ _____		1. ....
2. Hence $\angle$ XOP' $= \angle$ YOP'		2. ....
3. Hence $\overrightarrow{OP'}$ is the bisector of $\angle$ MOC		3. ....
4. $\therefore \overrightarrow{OP'}$ must coincide with l.		4. Th.? ....
5. $\therefore$ line l is the locus required.		5. ....

Therefore _____

THEOREM 57

The perpendicular bisector of a chord passes through the center of its circle.

GIVEN: $\odot$ O with $\overleftrightarrow{MN}$ the $\perp$ bisector of chord AB.

TO PROVE: that $\overleftrightarrow{MN}$ passes through the center O.

PROOF. Draw radii AO and BO. (Post. 3)

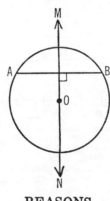

STATEMENTS		REASONS
1. AO $=$ BO		1. ....
2. $\therefore$ Center O lies on $\overleftrightarrow{MN}$.		2. Unit 8, Th.? ....

Therefore _____

CONSTRUCTION EXERCISES D

1-3. *With compass and straightedge find the center of circle A in exercise 1. In exercise 2 construct a circle which shall have M and N as chords. In exercise 3, find the center of the circle having arc CD, and complete the circle. Leave all construction lines .*

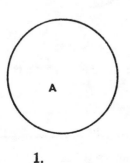

1.

2.

3.

Unit IX.

CIRCLES AND RELATED LINES.
INSCRIBED AND CIRCUMSCRIBED POLYGONS

A. BASIC FACTS AND PRINCIPLES PERTAINING TO CHORDS, ARCS, AND TANGENTS

Two circles which are both tangent to the same line at the same point are known as *tangent circles*. When one of two tangent circles lies wholly outside the other, they are said to be *tangent externally*. See circles C and C' in Fig. 2. When one of two tangent circles lies wholly inside the other, they are said to be *tangent internally*. See circles C' and O in Fig. 2. A line or line-segment passing through the centers of two circles is called the *line of centers* of the circles. See MN in Fig. 1. If a tangent to two circles lies on opposite sides of the circles, it is called a *common internal tangent*. See CD in Fig. 3. If a tangent to two circles lies on the same side of the circles, it is called a *common external tangent*. See AB in Fig. 3.

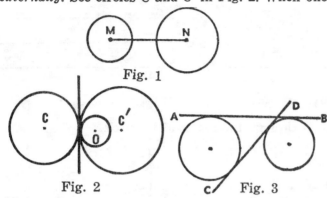

Fig. 1

Fig. 2   Fig. 3

EXERCISES A

1. Fill each of the following answer-spaces with the correct answer.

_____a. Two circles which are both tangent to the same line at the same point.

_____b. Two circles which are both tangent to the same line at the same point when one lies wholly inside the other.

_____c. Two circles which are both tangent to the same line at the same point when one lies wholly outside the other.

_____d. A line which touches two circles.

_____e. A line which touches two circles that lie on opposite sides of the line.

_____f. A line which touches two circles that lie on the same side of the line.

_____g. A line passing through the centers of two circles.

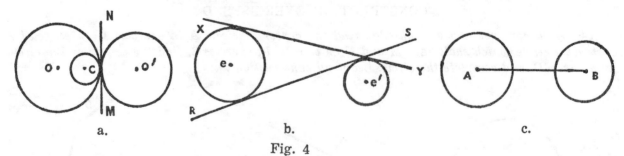

a.   b.   c.

Fig. 4

2. Referring to the circles in Fig. 4 above, fill in the following answer-spaces with correct answers. What is the best term applied to,

a. ⊚ O and O'? _____   d. Line-segment XY? _____

b. ⊚ O and C? _____   e. Line-segment RS? _____

c. Line-segment MN? _____   f. Line-segment AB? _____

THEOREM 58

Through three given points (not in the same straight line) one circle and only one can be drawn.

GIVEN: Points A, B, and C not in the same straight line.

TO PROVE: (1) that a circle can be drawn through A, B, and C, and (2) that only one circle can be drawn through A, B, and C.

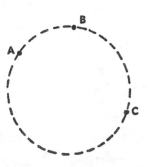

Proof of part 1. Draw $\overline{AB}$ and $\overline{BC}$. (Post. 3) Then draw the $\perp$ bisectors of $\overline{AB}$ and $\overline{BC}$, calling them l and l' respectively. (Const. 1)

STATEMENTS	REASONS
1. Lines l and l' are not ‖ and will intersect at some point O. Connect A, B, and C, with point O.	1. Th. 33, Cor. ? ....
2. AO = BO and CO = BO	2. Th. ? ....
3. Hence AO = BO = CO	3. .... Property of Equality
4. ∴ Points A, B, and C lie on a circle whose center is point O	4. Post. ? ....

PROOF of part 2. Let us assume for the moment that another circle whose center is O' can be drawn through points A, B, and C. Connect points A, B, and C to the *assumed* center O'.

STATEMENTS	REASONS
1. Then AO' = BO' = CO'	1. Post. ? ....
2. Hence O' must lie on l.	2. Unit 8, Th. ? ....
3. Point O' must also lie on l'.	3. ....
4. Hence center O' must coincide with center O.	4. Post. ? ....
5. Hence radius AO' = radius AO.	5. Post. ? ....
6. ∴ only one circle may be passed through points A, B, and C.	6. ....

Therefore _____

_____

THEOREM 59

A diameter perpendicular to a chord bisects the chord and the arcs of the chord.

GIVEN: ⊙ C with diameter AB ⊥ to chord MN.

TO PROVE: (1) that MO = _____ and (2) that $\overset{\frown}{MA}$ = _____ and $\overset{\frown}{MB}$ = _____.

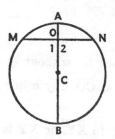

PROOF. Draw radii MC and NC. (Post. 3)

STATEMENTS	REASONS
1. In △ MOC and NOC, MC = _____	1. ....
2. ∠ 1 and ∠ 2 are rt. △	2. ....
3. _____ = _____	3. ....
4. Hence △ _____ ≅ △ _____	4. ....
5. ∴ MO = _____	5. ....
6. ∠ MCO = ∠ _____	6. ....
7. ∴ $\overset{\frown}{MA}$ = _____	7. Unit 8, Th.? ....
8. $\overset{\frown}{MA}$ + $\overset{\frown}{MB}$ = $\overset{\frown}{NA}$ + $\overset{\frown}{NB}$	8. Post.? about ⊙ ....
9. ∴ $\overset{\frown}{MB}$ = _____	9. .... Property of Equality

Therefore _____

THEOREM 60

A diameter that bisects a chord (that is not a diameter) is perpendicular to the chord.

GIVEN: ⊙ O with diameter AB bisecting chord MN.

TO PROVE: that $\overline{AB}$ is ⊥ to $\overline{MN}$.

PROOF. Draw $\overline{MO}$ and $\overline{NO}$. (Post. 3)

STATEMENTS	REASONS
1. △ _____ ≅ △ _____	1. _____
2. Hence ∠ _____ = ∠ _____	2. _____
3. ∴ $\overline{AB}$ is ⊥ to $\overline{MN}$	3. _____

Therefore _____

THEOREM 61

A tangent to a circle is perpendicular to the radius (or diameter) drawn to the point of contact.

GIVEN: ⊙ C with $\overleftrightarrow{XY}$ tangent to the circle at R.

TO PROVE: that $\overleftrightarrow{XY}$ is ⊥ to radius CR at point R.

PROOF. Let O represent *any* point on $\overleftrightarrow{XY}$ except Point R. Draw $\overline{CO}$. Post. _____

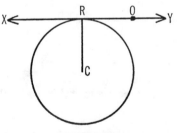

STATEMENTS	REASONS
1. Point O must lie without ⊙ C	1. Def. of ? ....
2. Hence $\overline{CR}$ < $\overline{CO}$, any other distance from C to $\overleftrightarrow{XY}$	2. Post.? about ⊙ ....
3. ∴ $\overline{CR}$ is ⊥ to $\overleftrightarrow{XY}$, or XY is ⊥ to CR	3. Post.? ....

Therefore _____

POSTULATE 40: **If a line (or a line-segment) coincides with another, it will have all the properties of that line (or line-segment).**

INDIRECT PROOF BY COINCIDENCE

In Unit 7 we became familiar with a type of proof known as proof by exclusion. Our next corollary, we are going to prove by another type of indirect proof, which is known as proof by *coincidence*. It works in this manner: In Fig. 5 $\overline{AO}$ is perpendicular to $\overline{MN}$. Now let us suppose that we desire to prove that $\overline{BO}$ is perpendicular to $\overline{MN}$ too. If we can prove that $\overline{BO}$ must coincide with $\overline{AO}$, then $\overline{BO}$ too will be perpendicular to $\overline{MN}$ since, according to postulate 40, a line must have all the properties of a line with which it coincides.

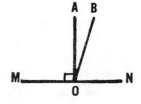

Fig. 5

COR. 1. A line that is perpendicular to a tangent to a circle at the point of contact passes through the center of the circle.

GIVEN: $\odot$ O with $\overleftrightarrow{CP} \perp$ to tangent $\overleftrightarrow{RS}$ at point of contact P.

TO PROVE: that $\overleftrightarrow{CP}$ passes through the center O.

PROOF (By Coincidence). Draw radius OP as shown. (Post. 3)

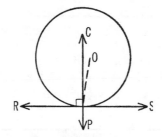

STATEMENTS	REASONS
1. $\overleftrightarrow{CP}$ is $\perp$ to tangent $\overleftrightarrow{RS}$.	1. _____
2. Radius OP is $\perp$ to tangent $\overleftrightarrow{RS}$ too.	2. Th.? about $\circledS$ _____
3. Hence $\overleftrightarrow{CP}$ must coincide with OP	3. Th.? _____
4. $\therefore$ $\overleftrightarrow{CP}$ must pass through point O.	4. Post.? _____

Therefore _____

THEOREM 62

A line perpendicular to a radius of a circle at its outer extremity is tangent to the circle.

GIVEN: $\odot$ O with $\overleftrightarrow{MN} \perp$ to radius OA at point A.

TO PROVE: that $\overleftrightarrow{MN}$ is tangent to $\odot$ O.

PROOF. Let P represent *any* point on $\overleftrightarrow{MN}$ except point A. Draw $\overline{OP}$. (Post. 3)

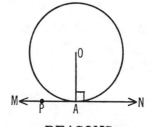

STATEMENTS	REASONS
1. OP > radius OA	1. Post.? _____
2. Hence point P lies without $\odot$ O	2. Post.? about $\circledS$ _____
	_____
3. $\therefore$ $\overleftrightarrow{MN}$ is tangent to $\odot$ O	3. Def. of? _____

Therefore _____

1. Construct a tangent to ⊙ O at point P. Leave all construction lines. State the principle of geometry which justifies your construction.

   _____

   _____

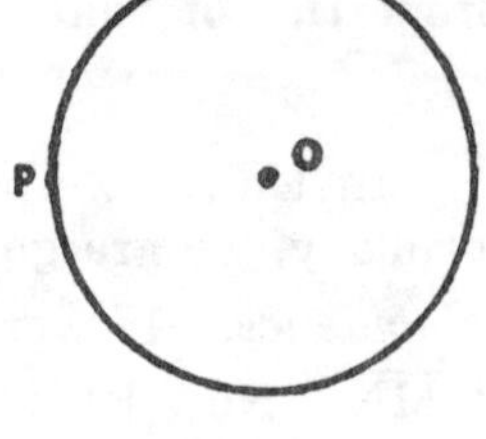

2. With compass and straightedge bisect arc MN. Leave all construction lines. State the principle of geometry which justifies your construction.

   _____

   _____

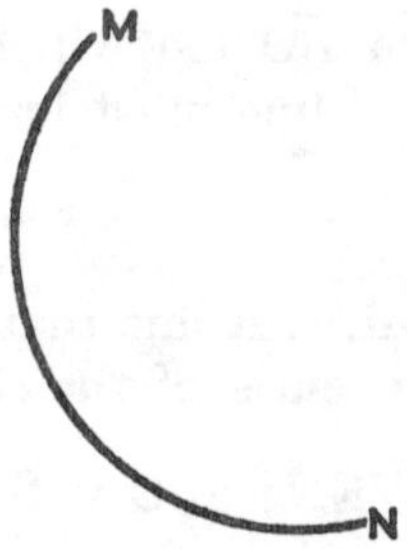

3. Draw four circles of different sizes which will contain line-segment AB as a chord. What is the locus of points of the centers of all circles containing AB as a common chord?

   _____

   _____

A _____ B

THEOREM 63

Tangents to a circle from an external point are equal, and form equal angles with the line joining the point to the center.

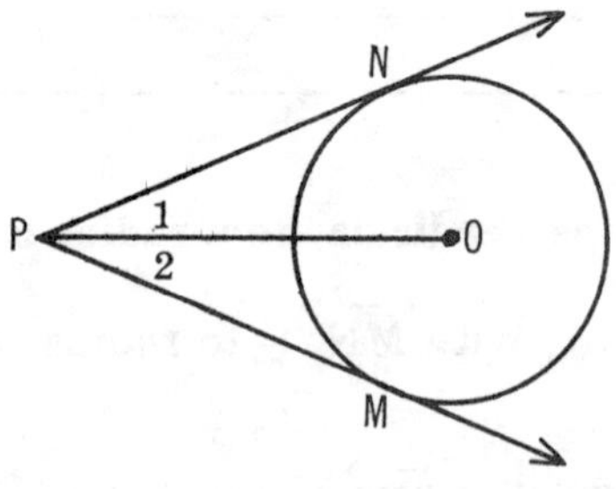

GIVEN: $\overline{PN}$ and $\overline{PM}$, tangents to ⊙ O from external point P.

TO PROVE: (1) that PN = _____ and (2) that ∠ 1 = ∠ _____

PROOF. Draw $\overline{MO}$ and $\overline{NO}$. Post. _____

STATEMENTS	REASONS
1. ∠ _____ and ∠ _____ are rt. ∡	1. Unit 9, Th.? ....
2. PO = _____	2. .... Property of Equality
3. NO = _____	3. ....
4. _____	4. ....
5. ∴ PN = _____ and ∠ 1 = ∠ _____	5. ....
Therefore _____	

THEOREM 64

The arcs of a circle between parallel lines are equal.

CASE 1. In which one parallel line is a tangent and the other, a secant or chord.

GIVEN: $\odot$ O with $\overleftrightarrow{AB}$ tangent to $\odot$ O at point P, and with $\overleftrightarrow{AB}$ ∥ to secant $\overleftrightarrow{MN}$, which intersects the $\odot$ at points X and Y.

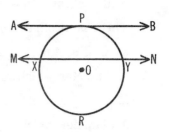

Case 1

TO PROVE: that $\overparen{XP} = \overparen{YP}$.

PROOF. Draw diameter PR. (Post. 3)

STATEMENTS	REASONS
1. $\overleftrightarrow{PR}$ is ⊥ to $\overleftrightarrow{AB}$	1. Unit 9, Th.? ....
2. Hence $\overleftrightarrow{PR}$ is ⊥ to $\overleftrightarrow{MN}$	2. Th. 22, Cor.? ....
3. ∴ $\overparen{XP} = \overparen{YP}$	3. Th.? about ⊚ ....

CASE 2. In which both parallel lines are secants or chords.

GIVEN: $\odot$ O with secant AB ∥ to secant MN and in which $\overleftrightarrow{AB}$ and $\overleftrightarrow{MN}$ intersect the circle at points H and K, and X and Y respectively.

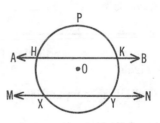

Case 2

TO PROVE: that $\overparen{HX} = \overparen{KY}$

PROOF. Draw tangent $\overleftrightarrow{RS}$ through point P ∥ to $\overleftrightarrow{AB}$. Th. _____

STATEMENTS	REASONS
1. $\overleftrightarrow{RS}$ is ∥ to $\overleftrightarrow{AB}$	1. ....
2. Hence $\overleftrightarrow{RS}$ is ∥ to $\overleftrightarrow{MN}$	2. Unit 4, Th.? ....
3. $\overparen{XP} =$ _____ and $\overparen{HP} =$ _____	3. Case? ....
4. ∴ $\overparen{HX} =$ _____	4. .... Property of Equality

CASE 3. In which both parallel lines are tangents.

GIVEN: $\odot$ O with tangent $\overleftrightarrow{AB}$ ∥ to tangent $\overleftrightarrow{XY}$ and in which points P and P' are the respective points of tangency.

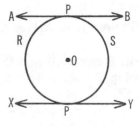

Case 3

TO PROVE: that $\overparen{PRP'} = \overparen{PSP'}$.

PROOF. Draw any chord RS ∥ to $\overleftrightarrow{AB}$. (Th. 9)

STATEMENTS	REASONS
1. $\overparen{RP} = \overparen{SP}$, and $\overparen{RP'} = \overparen{SP'}$	1. ....
2. ∴ $\overparen{PRP'} = \overparen{PSP'}$	2. .... Property of Equality
Therefore _____	

105

Fill each answer-space that follows with the correct term or answer:

1. Three non-colinear points determine a geometric figure called a (n) _____
   as well as the _____ of which this figure is a part.

2. A diameter which is perpendicular to a chord will _____ both the _____
   _____ and its _____.

3. A diameter which bisects a non-diameter chord is _____ to that chord and
   bisects the _____ of that chord.

4. Two tangents to a circle from an external point are _____ and they form
   _____ with the line joining the external point to the _____

5. Arcs of a circle between _____ lines are _____

6. A line that is perpendicular to a (n) _____ of a circle at the point of
   _____ will pass through the _____ of the _____

7. A tangent to a circle is _____ to the diameter or the radius drawn to the
   point of _____.

8. A line which is perpendicular to a radius of a circle at its outer end is _____
   to the circle.

9. A line which is perpendicular to a tangent to a circle at the point of tangency will **always**
   _____.

10. Given: In Fig. 6 ∠ A = 48°, and tangent $\overline{AB}$ = 18 in.

    a. How long is tangent $\overline{AC}$? _____

    b. How many degrees are there in minor arc BC? _____

    Hint: Draw $\overline{OB}$ and $\overline{OC}$.

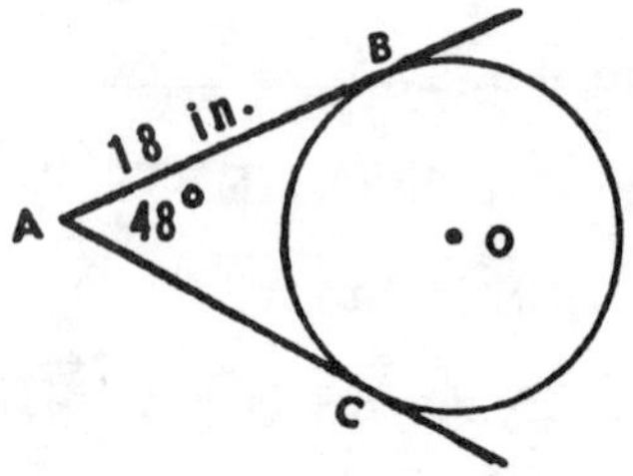

Fig. 6

11. Given: In Fig. 7 $\overline{AB}$ and $\overline{CD}$, common external tangents to ⊙ O and O'.

    To Prove: that AB = CD.

    Proof. Extend $\overline{AB}$ and $\overline{CD}$ until they meet at
    a point P.   (No additional construction is
    needed).

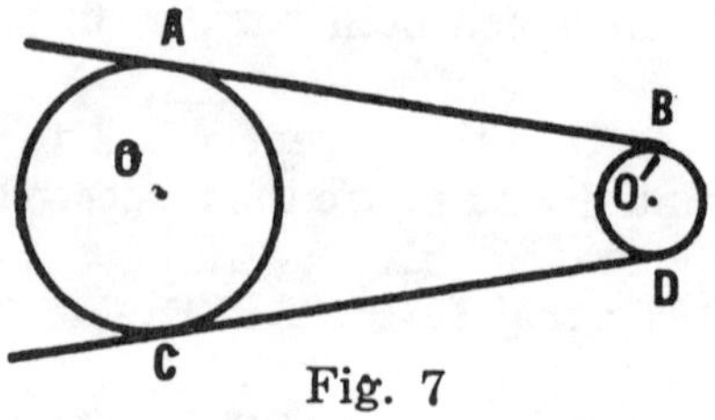

Fig. 7

Statements	Reasons
1. _____	1. _____
2. _____	2. _____
3. ∴ AB = CD	3. _____

12. Given: In Fig. 8 $\overline{MN}$ and $\overline{RS}$, common internal tangents to ⊚ C and C′.

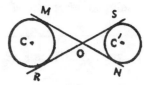

Fig. 8

To Prove: that MN = RS.

Proof. Statements	Reasons
1. _____	1. _____
2. _____	2. _____
3. ∴ MN = RS	3. _____

13. Given: In Fig. 9 $\overline{PS}$ and $\overline{PR}$ are tangent to ⊙ O, and ∠ ROS = 110°

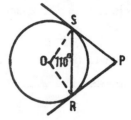

Fig. 9

a. How many degrees are there in ∠ P? _____

b. How many degrees are there in ∠ RSP? _____

B. INSCRIBED AND CIRCUMSCRIBED POLYGONS

A polygon is said to be *inscribed* in a circle, if each of its vertices is tangent to the circle. The circle is said to be *circumscribed* about the polygon. See Fig. 10 and 12. Obviously a circle can be circumscribed about a polygon, if there is a point which is equidistant from all its vertices.

  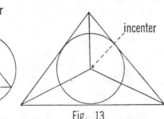 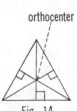 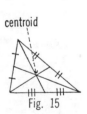

Fig. 10   Fig. 11   Fig. 12   Fig. 13   Fig. 14   Fig. 15

A polygon is said to be circumscribed about a circle, if each of its sides is tangent to the circle. The circle in this case is said to be inscribed in the polygon. See Figs. 11 and 13. We shall prove that the perpendicular bisectors of the sides of a triangle meet in a point called the *circumcenter*. This point is called the circumcenter because it is the center of the circle which may be circumscribed about the triangle. See Fig. 12. We shall prove that the bisectors of the angles of a triangle meet in a point called the *incenter*. This point is called the incenter because it is the center of a circle which may be inscribed in the triangle. See Fig. 13. We shall prove that the altitudes of a triangle are *concurrent* (i. e. meet in a point called the *orthocenter*). See Fig. 14. A *median* of a triangle is a line-segment drawn from a vertex of the triangle to the midpoint of the opposite side. We shall also prove that the medians of a triangle meet in a point called the *centroid* of the triangle. See Fig. 15. The centroid of a triangle is the center of gravity of the triangle, so called because it is the point at which the triangle will BALANCE when it is placed on a mere point as a support.

PRELIMINARY EXERCISES B

1. When is a polygon *inscribed in* a circle? _____

2. When is a polygon *circumscribed about* a circle? _____

_____

3. In Fig. 16 polygon ABCD is said to be _____

_____ _____ circle O, and circle O

is said to be _____ _____
polygon ABCD.

4. In Fig.17 polygon MNOPQ is said to be _____

_____ _____ circle C, and

circle C is said to be _____ _____
polygon MNOPQ.

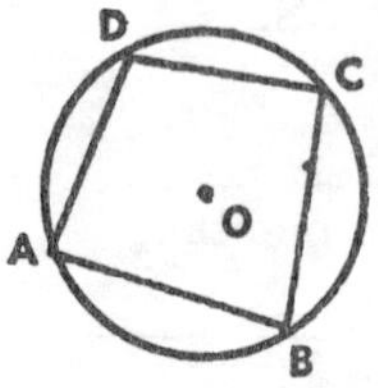

Fig. 16 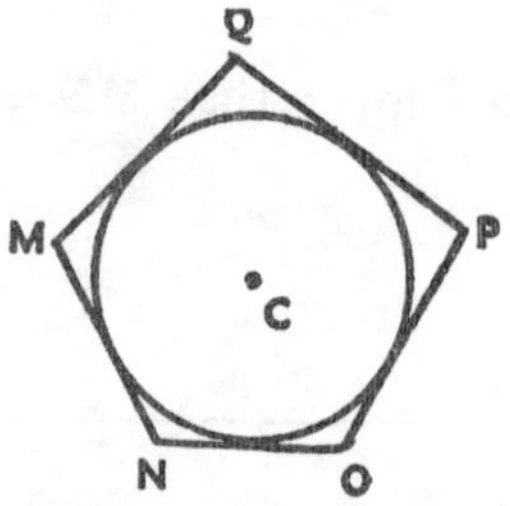   Fig. 17

5. A circle can be *circumscribed about* a polygon, if a point can be found which is _____

from all its _____.

6. A circle can be *inscribed in* a polygon, if a point can be found which is _____

from all its _____.

THEOREM 65

The perpendicular bisectors of the sides of a triangle meet in
a point.

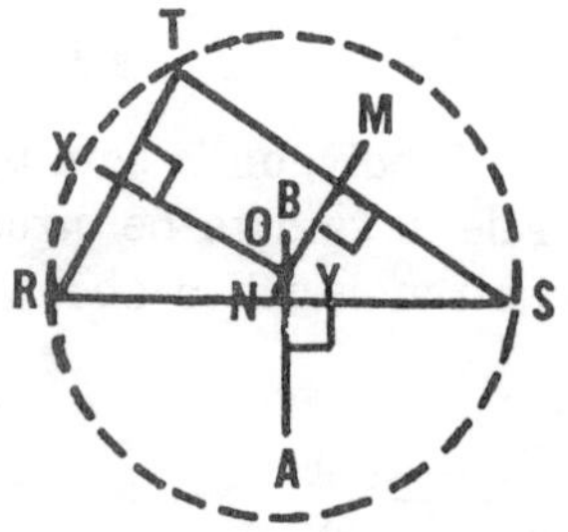

GIVEN: △ RST with $\overline{AB}$, $\overline{MN}$, and $\overline{XY}$ the ⊥ bisectors of sides RS,
ST, and TR respectively.

TO PROVE: that $\overline{AB}$, $\overline{MN}$, and $\overline{XY}$ meet in a point (i. e. that they
are concurrent).

PROOF.   STATEMENTS   REASONS

1. Circumscribe a circle about △ RST calling
   its center O.   (Why is this possible?)   1. Th.? ....

2. $\overline{RS}$, $\overline{ST}$, and $\overline{TR}$ have become chords with
   $\overline{AB}$, $\overline{MN}$, and $\overline{XY}$ as their respective perpendicular bisectors.   2. Def. of? ....

3. ∴ $\overline{AB}$, $\overline{MN}$, and $\overline{XY}$ will each pass through
   O.   3. Unit 8, Th.? ....

   Therefore _____

THEOREM 66

The bisectors of the angles of a triangle meet in a point.

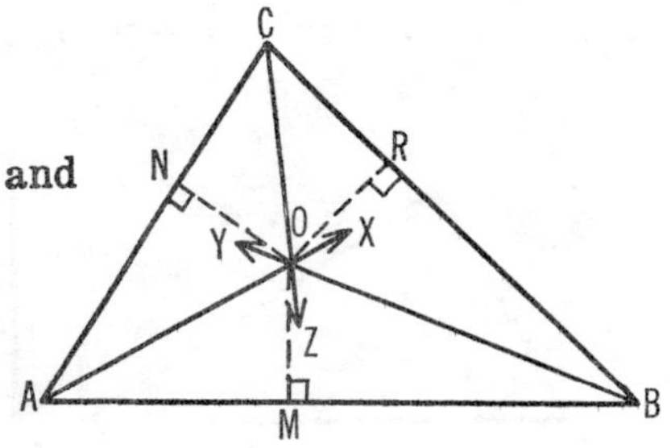

GIVEN: $\triangle$ ABC with $\overrightarrow{AX}$, $\overrightarrow{BY}$, and $\overrightarrow{CZ}$, the bisectors of $\angle$ A, B, and C respectively.

TO PROVE: that $\overrightarrow{AX}$, $\overrightarrow{BY}$, and $\overrightarrow{CZ}$ meet in a point.

PROOF. STATEMENTS	REASONS
1. $\overrightarrow{AX}$ and $\overrightarrow{BY}$ will intersect at some point O.	1. Th. 33, Cor.? ....
2. Draw $\overline{OM}$, $\overline{ON}$, and $\overline{OR}$ $\perp$ to $\overline{AB}$, $\overline{AC}$, and BC respectively.	2. Unit 1, Th.? ....
3. ON = OM and OR = OM	3. Unit 8, Th.? ....
4. Hence ON = OR	4. .... Principle
5. $\therefore$ point O must also lie on $\overrightarrow{CZ}$, making $\overrightarrow{AX}$, $\overrightarrow{BY}$, and $\overrightarrow{CZ}$ concurrent.	5. Unit 8, Th.? ....

Therefore _____

EXERCISES B

1. What is the point of intersection of the *bisectors of the sides* of a triangle called? _____
2. Circumscribe a circle about each of the following triangles:

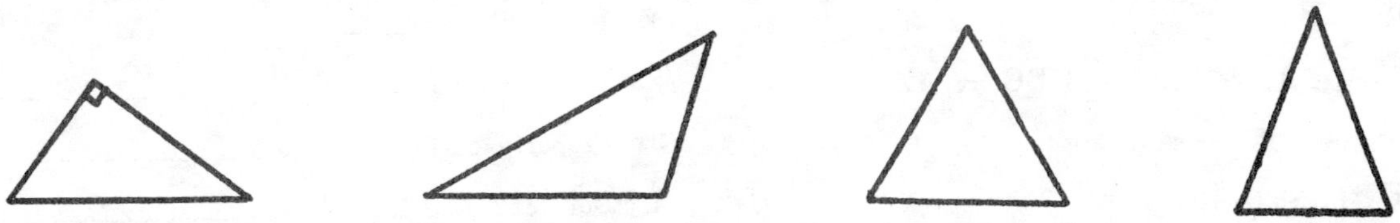

      a.   b.   c.   d.

3. Can a circle be circumscribed about any triangle? _____; about any square? _____; about any rectangle? _____; about any rhombus? _____; about any rhomboid? _____

109

4. What is the point of intersection of the *bisectors of the angles* of a triangle called? _____

5. Inscribe a circle in each of the following triangles:

a.   b.   c.   d.

6. Can a circle be inscribed in any triangle? _____; in any square? _____; in any rectangle? _____; in any rhombus? _____; in any rhomboid? _____.

THEOREM 67

The altitudes of a triangle meet in a point.

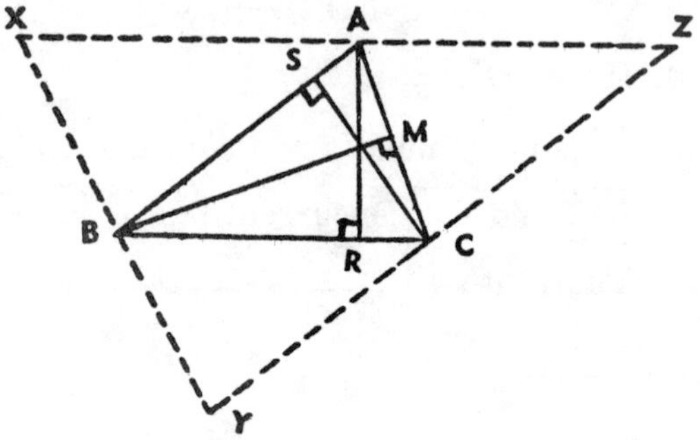

GIVEN: △ ABC with altitudes AR, BM, and CS.

TO PROVE: that _____, _____, and _____ meet in a point.

PROOF. Through the vertices of △ ABC draw lines ∥ respectively to the opposite sides of △ ABC, forming △ XYZ. Th. _____

STATEMENTS	REASONS
1. AXBC and AZCB are ▱ with common side BC	1. Def. of? ....
2. Hence AX = BC and BC = AZ	2. Unit 6, Th.? ....
3. Hence AX = AZ	3. Property of Equality No.? ....
4. $\overline{AR}$ is ⊥ to $\overline{BC}$	4. Def. of? ....
5. So $\overline{AR}$ is ⊥ to $\overline{XZ}$ too.	5. Th. 22, Cor.? ....
6. ∴ $\overline{AR}$ is the ⊥ bisector of side XZ.	6. ....
7. BXAC and BYCA are ▱ with common side AC.	7. ....
8. Hence BX = BY	8. ....
9. $\overline{BM}$ is ⊥ to $\overline{XY}$	9. ....
10. ∴ $\overline{BM}$ is the ⊥ bisector of side XY	10. ....
11. CYBA and CZAB are ▱ with common side AB.	11. ....
12. Hence CY = CZ	12. ....
13. $\overline{CS}$ is ⊥ to $\overline{YZ}$	13. ....
14. ∴ $\overline{CS}$ is the ⊥ bisector of side YZ	14. ....
15. ∴ $\overline{AR}$, BM, and $\overline{CS}$ must meet in a point	15. Unit 9, Th.? ....

Therefore _____

1. What is the point of intersection of the *altitudes* of a triangle called? _____

2. Find the point of intersection of the altitudes of the following triangles:

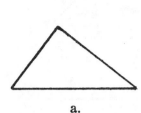 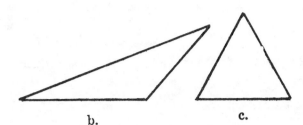 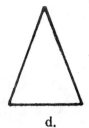

    a.   b.   c.   d.

3. What is the *median* of a triangle? _____
_____

4. What is the point of intersection of the *medians* of a △ called? _____
 Why? _____

5. Find the point of intersection of the medians of each of the following ⧌:

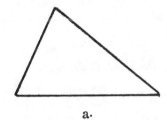 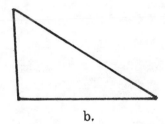 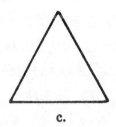

    a.   b.   c.

THEOREM 68

  The medians of a triangle meet in a point which is two-thirds of the distance from each vertex to the midpoint of the opposite side.

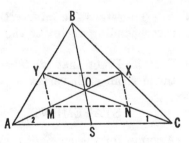

GIVEN: △ ABC with medians AX, CY, and BS.

TO PROVE: that AX, CY, and BS meet in a point O such that AO = 2/3 AX, CO = 2/3 CY, and BO = 2/3 BS.

PROOF. Regard side $\overline{AC}$ as the transversal of medians AX and CY.

Part 1. Proof that any two medians of a △ will intersect.

STATEMENTS	REASONS
1. Medians AX and CY are either intersecting or parallel.	1. Post.? ....
2. If $\overline{AX}$ and $\overline{CY}$ are ∥, then ∠ 1 + ∠ 2 must equal 180°.	2. Th. 22, Cor.? ....
3. But ∠ A + ∠ B + ∠ C = 180°	3. ....

111

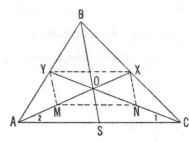

4. Hence ∠ 1 + ∠ 2 cannot equal 180°, **and so** $\overline{AX}$ **and** $\overline{CY}$ **are not ∥.***

    4. Contradiction of Th.? ....

5. ∴ $\overline{AX}$ **and** $\overline{CY}$ **must intersect.**

    5. Post.? ....

      Therefore, any two medians of a △ will intersect.

Part 2. Proof that the intersection point of any two medians of a △ is 2/3 of the distance from each corresponding vertex to the midpoint of the opposite side.

Through M and N, the midpoints of $\overline{AO}$ and $\overline{CO}$ respectively, draw $\overline{MN}$. Also draw $\overline{NX}$, $\overline{XY}$, and $\overline{MY}$. (Post. 3)

STATEMENTS		REASONS
1. In △ ABC, $\overline{YX}$ is ∥ to $\overline{AC}$, and YX = ½ AC	1.	Th. 39, Cor.? ....
2. In △ ACO, $\overline{MN}$ is ∥ to $\overline{AC}$, and MN = ½ AC	2.	....
3. ∴ $\overline{YX}$ is ∥ to $\overline{MN}$	3.	Th.? ....
4. ∴ YX = MN	4.	.... Property of Equality
5. Hence MNXY is a ▱	5.	Unit 6, Th.? ....
6. ∴ MO = XO, and NO = YO	6.	Th.? ....
7. But AM = MO, and CN = NO	7.	....
8. AM = OX and CN = YO	8.	.... Property of Equality
9. ∴ AO = 2/3 AX, and CO = 2/3 CY.	9.	By Definition of Fractional Parts ....

      Therefore the intersection-point of *any two* **medians of a △ is 2/3 of the distance from each corresponding vertex to the midpoint of the opposite side.**

Part 3. Proof that *all three* medians of a △ are concurrent at a point which is 2/3 of the distance from each vertex to the midpoint of the opposite side.

STATEMENTS		REASONS

Assume for the moment that $\overline{BS}$ and $\overline{AX}$ will not intersect in O, but in some other point O′.

1. Then BO′ = 2/3 BS and AO′ = 2/3 AX	1.	Part 2 ....
2. Hence AO′ = AO	2.	.... Property of Equality
3. ∴ O′ must coincide with O, proving that $\overline{BS}$ passes through point O too.	3.	....

Therefore ....

_____

*Do we see that if ∠1 + ∠2 were to equal 180°, then the sum of the three angles of a triangle would EXCEED 180°?

EXERCISES B''

1. Is it ever possible to have a △ in which the *circumcenter, incenter,* and *centroid* coincide? _____ If so, when? _____

Make free-hand drawings of the conditions given in the following exercises in the space provided for drawings. Then solve each exercise.

DRAWINGS

2. The altitude of an equilateral triangle is 18 in. How long is the radius of the circle circumscribed about the triangle?

Ans. _____

3. An equilateral triangle is inscribed in a circle whose radius is 6 in. How long is its altitude?

Ans. _____

4. Trisect line-segment MN by applying the principle of intersecting medians.

M

N

C. DETERMINING OF GEOMETRIC FIGURES

A geometric figure is *determined* if enough conditions are given to FIX it in size, shape, and location (or position). For example, a line-segment is determined by the position of its end points because these two points *fix* both its direction and its length.

EXERCISES C.

1. Enumerate the three conditions that must be satisfied to determine a geometric figure. _____

_____

ILLUSTRATIVE DRAWINGS

2. Is a circle determined —

    a. By the position of three non-colinear points? _____

    b. By the position of its center? _____

    c. By the position of its center and the length of

       its radius? _____

3. Is a triangle determined —

    a. By the position of its vertices? _____

    b. By the length and the position of its base and the
       length of the altitude upon the base? _____

    c. By the position of a vertex and the length of
       the two sides forming the vertex? _____

4. Is a square determined —

    a. By the length and position of one side? _____

    b. By the length and position of a diagonal? _____

5. Is △ RST determined by ∠ R, side RT, and side ST? ____

    Hint: Construct the △ to find out.

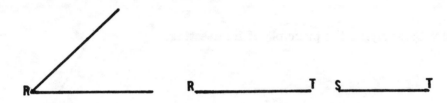

6. Is a rectangular box determined —

    a. By the position and lengths of a pair of intersecting edges? _____

    b. By the position and length of a pair of diagonally opposite edges? _____

Unit X.

INSCRIBED ANGLES. INTERCEPTED ARCS. TANGENTS. INTERSECTING CHORDS

A. INSCRIBED ANGLES • ANGLES FORMED BY CHORDS AND TANGENTS

We are now going to deal with the measurement of inscribed angles. In Unit VIII an *inscribed angle* was defined as an angle whose vertex touches a circle and whose sides form chords of the circle. An *intercepted arc* was shown to be an arc of a circle which extends across the opening of an inscribed (or a central) angle. The symbol $\doteq$ has been defined to mean is *equal in degrees to.*

THEOREM 69

An inscribed angle is measured by one-half its intercepted arc.

CASE 1. In which one side of the inscribed $\angle$ is a diameter.

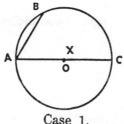

GIVEN: $\angle$ A inscribed in $\odot$ O.

TO PROVE: that $\angle$ A $\doteq$ ½ $\overparen{BC}$.

PROOF. Draw radius BO. Post. _____

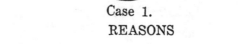

Case 1.

STATEMENTS	REASONS
1. $\overline{OA} = \overline{OB}$	1. Post.? ....
2. $\angle$ A $=$ $\angle$ B	2. Th.? ....
3. $\angle$ X is $\doteq$ $\overparen{BC}$	3. Post.? ....
4. Hence ½ $\angle$ X $\doteq$ _____	4. .... Property of Equality
5. $\angle$ X $=$ $\angle$ ____ $+$ $\angle$ ____	5. Th. 33, Cor.? ....
6. $\angle$ X $=$ 2 $\angle$ A	6. .... Principle
7. Hence $\angle$ A $=$ ½ $\angle$ X	7. ....
8. $\therefore$ $\angle$ A $\doteq$ ½ _____	8. .... Principle

CASE 2. In which the center of the circle is inside the inscribed $\angle$.

GIVEN: $\angle$ A inscribed in $\odot$ O.

TO PROVE: that $\angle$ A $\doteq$ ½ $\overparen{BC}$.

PROOF. Draw diameter AD. (Post. 3)

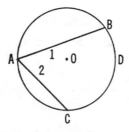

Case 2.

STATEMENTS	REASONS
1. $\angle$ 1 $\doteq$ ½ $\overparen{DB}$	1. Case? ....
2. $\angle$ 2 $\doteq$ ½ $\overparen{DC}$	2. ....
3. $\therefore$ $\angle$ A $\doteq$ ½ $\overparen{DB}$ $+$ ½ $\overparen{DC}$, or ½ $\overparen{BC}$	3. .... Property of Equality

CASE 3. In which the center of the circle is outside the inscribed ∠.

GIVEN: ∠ A inscribed in ⊙ O.

TO PROVE: that ∠ A ≐ ½ $\overset{\frown}{BC}$.

PROOF. Draw diameter AD. (Post. 3)

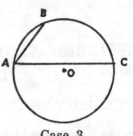

Case 3.

STATEMENTS	REASONS
1. ∠ BAD ≐ ½ _____	1. Case? _____
2. ∠ CAD = ½ _____	2. Case? _____
3. ∴ ∠ BAC ≐ ½ $\overset{\frown}{BC}$	3. _____ Property of Equality

Therefore _____

COR. 1. An angle inscribed in a semicircle is a right angle.

GIVEN: ∠ C inscribed in semicircle ABC.

TO PROVE: that ∠ C = a rt. ∠.

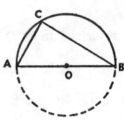

PROOF. STATEMENTS	REASONS
1. ∠ C ≐ ½ arc	1. Th.? _____
2. _____	2. _____
3. _____	3. _____

Therefore _____

COR. 2. Inscribed angles intercepting the same arc or equal arcs are equal.

GIVEN: ∠ 1 and ∠ 2 each intercepting $\overset{\frown}{AB}$ in ⊙ O.

TO PROVE: that ∠ 1 = ∠ 2.

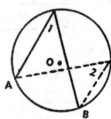

PROOF. STATEMENTS	REASONS
1. ∠ 1 ≐ _____ and ∠ 2 ≐ _____	1. Th.? _____
2. ∴ ∠ 1 = ∠2	2. _____

Therefore _____

CONSTRUCTION 6

To construct a tangent to a circle from an external point.
GIVEN: ⊙ O and point P outside the circle.

REQUIRED: To construct a tangent to ⊙ O from point P.

CONSTRUCTION: Draw $\overline{PO}$. Now construct a ⊙ with $\overline{PO}$ as its diameter. Call the intersection of the two ⊛ above $\overline{PO}$ R and that below $\overline{PO}$ S. Draw $\overline{PR}$ (or $\overline{PS}$).

$\overline{PR}$ (or $\overline{PS}$) is the required tangent to ⊙ O.

PROOF. Draw $\overline{OR}$ (or $\overline{OS}$).

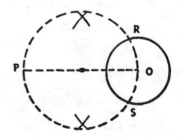

STATEMENTS	REASONS
1. ∠ PRO is a rt. ∠	1. ....
2. ∴ $\overline{PR}$ is tangent to ⊙ O.	2. Unit 9, Th.? ....

CONSTRUCTION EXERCISES A

Make the following constructions with compass and straightedge. Leave all construction lines.

STATEMENTS	CONSTRUCTIONS
1. Construct an arc (i. e. segment) of a circle upon MN as a chord in which ∠ A may be inscribed.	
2. Inscribe a triangle within ⊙ O having ∠ X and ∠ Y. 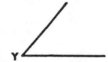	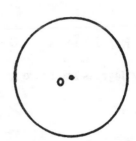
3. Erect a perpendicular to line-segment MN at point N by applying the principle of Cor. 1 under Theorem 69 in this unit. *Do not extend* MN.	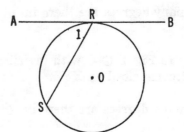

THEOREM 70

An angle formed by a tangent and a chord (drawn from the point of contact) is measured by one-half its arc.

GIVEN: ⊙ O with tangent AB and chord RS, making ∠ 1 at point of contact R.

TO PROVE: that ∠ 1 ≐ ½ $\overset{\frown}{RS}$.

PROOF. Through point S draw chord ST ‖ to tangent AB. (Th. 9)

117

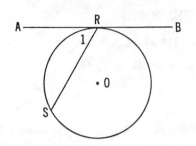

STATEMENTS		REASONS

1. $\angle 1 = \angle RST.$

2. $\overset{\frown}{RT} =$ _____

3. $\angle RST \doteq \frac{1}{2} \overset{\frown}{RT}$

4. $\therefore \angle 1 \doteq \frac{1}{2} \overset{\frown}{RS}$

Therefore _____

1. Unit 4, Th.? ....

2. Th.? ....

3. Th.? ....

4. ....

EXERCISES A

1. Given: In Fig. 1 central $\angle O = 56°$.

   How many degrees are there in $\angle R$? _____

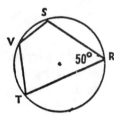

Fig. 1

2. Given: In Fig. 2 $\overset{\frown}{XZ} = 100°$, and $\angle Z = 60°$.

   How many degrees are there in $\overset{\frown}{YZ}$? _____

3. Given: In Fig. 3 $\angle R = 50°$.
   How many degrees are there in $\angle V$? _____

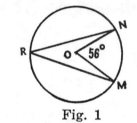

Fig. 2   Fig. 3

4. Given: In Fig. 4 tangent AB and minor arc AC = 125°.

   How many degrees are there in $\angle A$? _____

5. Given: In Fig. 5 $\odot$ O with inscribed $\triangle$ ABC and circumscribed $\triangle$ XYZ.

   How many degrees are there in $\angle X$? _____

   in $\angle Y$? _____; in $\angle Z$? _____

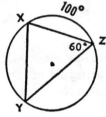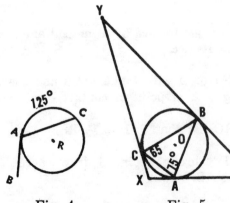

Fig. 4   Fig. 5

B. ANGLES FORMED BY INTERSECTING CHORDS AND BY TANGENTS AND SECANTS

THEOREM 71

An angle formed by two chords intersecting within a circle is measured by one-half the sum of its intercepted arc and the intercepted arc of its vertical angle.

GIVEN: $\odot$ O with chords AB and RS intersecting at point M.

TO PROVE: that $\angle 1 \doteq \frac{1}{2} (\overset{\frown}{AR} + \overset{\frown}{SB})$.

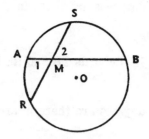

PROOF. Draw auxiliary line RB. Post. _____

STATEMENTS	REASONS
1. $\angle 1 = \angle$ _____ $+ \angle$ _____	1. Th. 33, Cor.? ....
2. But $\angle B =$ _____ and $\angle R =$ _____	2. Th.? ....
3. $\therefore \ \angle 1 \doteq \frac{1}{2} \overset{\frown}{AR} + \frac{1}{2} \overset{\frown}{SB}$, or $\frac{1}{2} (\overset{\frown}{AR} + \overset{\frown}{SB})$	3. ....

Therefore _____

THEOREM 72

An angle formed outside a circle (1) by two secants, (2) by a secant and a tangent, or (3) by two tangents, is measured by one-half the difference between the intercepting arcs.

GIVEN: $\circledS$ O_1, O_2, and O_3 having in Case 1 two secants, in Case 2 a tangent and a secant, and in Case 3 two tangents, which form in each case external $\angle$ P.

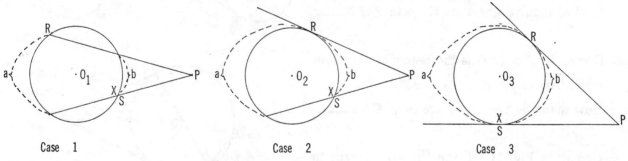

Case 1   Case 2   Case 3

TO PROVE: that $\angle P \doteq \frac{1}{2} (\overset{\frown}{a - b})$

PROOF. Draw auxiliary line RS for each case. Post. _____

	REASONS
1. In each case $\angle P + \angle R = \angle x$	1. Th. 33, Cor.? ....
2. Hence $\angle P = \angle x - \angle R$	2. .... Property of Equality
3. In Cases 1 and 2 $\angle x \doteq \frac{1}{2} \overset{\frown}{a}$	3. Th.? ....
4. In Case 3 $\angle x \doteq \frac{1}{2}$ _____	4. Th.? ....
5. In Case 1 $\angle R \doteq \frac{1}{2} \overset{\frown}{b}$	5. Th.? ....
6. In Cases 2 and 3 $\angle R \doteq \frac{1}{2}$ _____	6. ....
7. $\therefore \ \angle P \doteq \frac{1}{2} \overset{\frown}{a} - \frac{1}{2} \overset{\frown}{b}$ or $\frac{1}{2} (\overset{\frown}{a - b})$	7. ....

Therefore _____

1. Given: In Fig. 6 chords AB and MN intersecting at O.

   How many degreees are there in ∠ x? _____

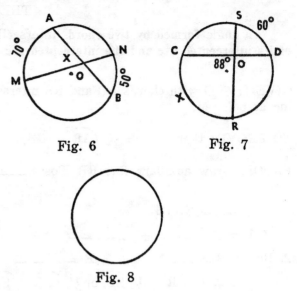

Fig. 6   Fig. 7

2. Given: In Fig. 7 chords CD and RS intersecting at O.

   How many degrees are there in arc x? _____

3. Three consecutive sides of a quadrilateral inscribed in a circle have (subtend) arcs of 76° 130°, and 60° respectively. Using the circle in Fig. 8, make a free-hand drawing of the conditions given.

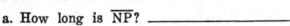

Fig. 8

   a. What is the value of each ∠ of the quadrilateral? _____

   b. What is the value of each ∠ at the intersection of its diagonals? _____

4. Given: In Fig. 9 tangents from point P drawn to ⊙ O at points M and N. MP = 20. Major arc MN = 240°

   a. How long is $\overline{NP}$? _____

   b. How many degrees are there in ∠ P? _____

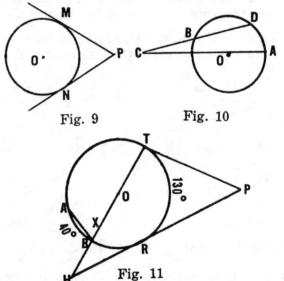

Fig. 9   Fig. 10

5. Given: In Fig. 10 O is the center of the ⊙ in which $\overarc{AD}$ = 60° and $\overarc{DB}$ = 98°.

   How many degrees are there in ∠ C? _____

6. Given: In Fig. 11 $\overline{PT}$ and $\overline{PH}$ are tangent to ⊙ O. HT passes through center O. $\overarc{AB}$ = 40° and $\overarc{RT}$ = 130°.

   a. ∠ P = _____   **b.** ∠ X = _____   **c.** ∠ H = _____

Fig. 11

C. DISTANCES OF EQUAL AND UNEQUAL CHORDS FROM THE CENTERS OF CIRCLES

THEOREM 73

In the same circle, or in equal circles, equal chords are equally distant from the center.

GIVEN: Equal ⊙ O and O′ with chord MN = chord M′N′, and with $\overline{OA}$ ⊥ to $\overline{MN}$, and $\overline{O'A'}$ ⊥ to $\overline{M'N'}$.

TO PROVE: that OA = O′A′.

PROOF. Draw $\overline{OM}$ and $\overline{O'M'}$. Post. _____

STATEMENTS	REASONS
1. OM = _____	1. Post.? ....
2. MA = ½ MN and M′A′ = ½ M′N′	2. Unit 9, Th.? ....
3. $\overline{MA}$ = _____	3. .... Perperty of Equality
4. Hence △ MAO _____	4. ....
5. ∴ _____ = _____	5. ....

Therefore _____

THEOREM 74

In the same circle, or in equal circles, chords equally distant from the center are equal.

GIVEN: Equal ⊙ C and C′ with distance CA = distance C′A′, and with $\overline{AC}$ and $\overline{A'C'}$ ⊥ respectively to chords MN and M′N′.

TO PROVE: that _____ = _____ .

PROOF. Draw $\overline{CM}$ and $\overline{C'M'}$. Post. _____

STATEMENTS	REASONS
1. _____ = _____	1. ....
2. CA = _____	2. ....
3. Hence △ _____ ≅ △ _____	3. ....
4. ∴ MA = _____	4. ....
5. But MA = ½ MN and M′A′ = ½ M′N′	5. ....
6. Hence ½ MN = ½ M′A′	6. .... Principle
7. ∴ MN = M′N′	7. .... Property of Equality

Therefore _____

POSTULATE 41: **The distance between any two non-adjacent points is greater than zero.**

Do we see that the Principle underlying Postulate 41 is implied in the order of property of numbers on the **real** number line? (See Unit II)

THEOREM 75

In the same circle, or in equal circles, the greater of two unequal chords is nearer the center.

GIVEN: ⊚ O and O′ with chord MN > chord M′N′, $\overline{OY} \perp \overline{MN}$, and $\overline{O'Y'} \perp \overline{M'N'}$.

TO PROVE: that $\overline{OY} < \overline{O'Y'}$.

PROOF. In ⊙ O draw chord NR = to chord M′N′. Draw $\overline{OX} \perp$ to $\overline{NR}$. Th. _____

STATEMENTS	REASONS
1. OX = O′Y′	1. Th.. _____
2. OA > OY	2. Post.? _____
3. AX > 0	3. Post.? _____
4. OA + AX > OY	4. Property of Equality No.? _____
5. But OA + AX = OX	5. Post.? _____
6. Hence OX > OY	6. Substitution _____
	7. _____

Therefore _____

THEOREM 76

In the same circle, or in equal circles, if two chords are unequally distant from the center, the chord nearer the center is the greater.

GIVEN: ⊙ O with chords MN and XY, with $\overline{OA}$ and $\overline{OB}$ their respective distances from the center, and with OB < OA.

TO PROVE: that $\overline{XY} > \overline{MN}$.

PROOF. (Indirect Method) STATEMENTS

	REASONS
1. Either XY = MN, or XY < MN, or XY > MN	1. The _____ Principle ____
2. If XY = MN, then ____ must = ____	2. Th.? _____
3. But this is impossible, and ∴ XY ≠ MN	3. Condradiction of? _____
4. If XY < MN, then ____ must be > ____	4. Th.? _____
5. But this is impossible, and ∴ XY ≮ MN	5. _____
6. ∴ XY > MN	6. _____

Therefore _____

EXERCISES C

1-4. In the same ⊙ or in equal ⊚ : two equal chords are (1) _____ from the center, two chords equidistant from the center are (2) _____, and two chords unequally distant from the center are (3) _____, the (4) _____ chord being nearer the center.

Unit XI.

AREA AND VOLUME. THEOREM OF PYTHAGORAS. HERO'S FORMULA

A. AREAS OF PARALLELOGRAMS AND TRIANGLES ● VOLUMES OF RECTANGULAR SOLIDS

Just ordinary numbers like 2, 2/3, 5¾, and 6.4 are classified as *real* and *rational*. *Rational numbers* are those which can be expressed as common fractions (or ratios) of two integers (whole numbers). For example, we may write 2 as: 4/2, 6/3, etc. 2/3 is already expressed as a common fraction of two integers (2 and 3). We may express 5¾ as 23/4, and 6.4 as 64/10, 32/5, etc. When a rational number is expressed as a common fraction (a ratio) its numerator and its denominator have a COMMON unit of measure contanied in each an integral number of times. Quantities that have a common unit of measure contained in each an integral number of times are said to be commensurable. Those without such a common unit of measure are said to be *incommensurable*. The numerator and the denominator of a rational number (expressed in common fractional form) are commensurable.*

The number of square units of measure contained in a surface is called the *area* of that surface. Polygons that have the same area are said to be *equivalent*. Figures 1 and 2 are equivalent, since each one has an area of 16 square units.

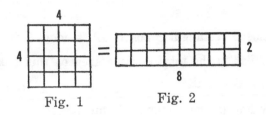

Fig. 1   Fig. 2

POSTULATE 42: **The total area of a polygon is equal to the sum of the areas of its parts.** (THE — AREA ADDITION POSTULATE)

The number of cubic units of space that a body contains is known as its *volume*. The rectangular box in Fig. 3 contains 2×2×2 or 8 cubic units and the box in Fig. 4 contains 4×2×2 or 16 cubic units. We will note that each layer one unit deep contains as many cubic units of volume as there are square units of area in its base.

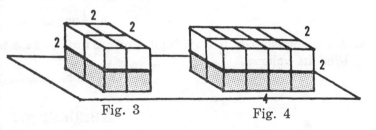

Fig. 3   Fig. 4

The principle for finding the area of a rectangle (**principle II**) is as follows:

The area of a rectangle is equal to the product of its base and altitude. Or A. of ▭ = b·h

The principle for finding the volume of a rectangular box (**principle III**) may be stated in the following two forms:

1. **The volume of a rectangular box is equal to the product of the AREA of its base and its height.**
   Or V = B · h

2. **The volume of a rectangular box is equal to the product of its length, width and height.**
   Or V = l · W · h

EXERCISES A

1. Fill each answer-space below with the correct term.

_____a. Two quantities that have a common unit of measure contained in each a whole number of times.

_____b. Any number that can be expressed as a ratio of two integers.

_____c. The number of square units of measure contained in a surface.

_____d. The number of cubic units of measure in a container.

_____e. Polygons that have equal areas.

* A non-ending and non-repeating decimal number like the square root of 3 (which is 1.73205 . . .) and 𝜋 (which is 3.14159 . . .) is called an *irrational number.* An irrational number can neither be expressed completely in decimal figures nor as a common fraction (or ratio) of two integers.

2. Place a C before each of the following pairs of commensurable quantities and an I before each pair of incommensurable quantities and an R before each rational number.

_____a. A 10 in. string and a 2 in. string.   _____d. $\sqrt{2}$ ft. and 7 ft.   _____g. ¾

_____b. 4⅛ ft. and 2½ ft.   _____e. 13 rds. and 2 rds.   _____h. π

_____c. The diagonals and side of a square.   _____f. The circumference and diameter of a circle.

3. What is the area of a rectangle,

  a. Which is 30 ft. long and 5 ft. wide? _____

  b. Which is 6 yds long and 6 ft. wide? _____

4. What is the length of a rectangle having a width of 5 in. and an area 200 sq. in.?

                                                Ans. _____

5. What is the perimeter of the rectangle in problem 4?

                              Ans. _____

6. A closed rectangular box is 12 ft. long, 3 ft. wide, and 8 ft. deep.

  a. What is the total surface area of this box?

                              Ans. _____

  b. What is the volume of this box?

                              Ans. _____

7. What is the volume of a cube the edge of which is 4 in.?

                              Ans. _____

8. A rectangular box is 5 in. high. The area of its base is 15 sq. in. Find its volume.

                              Ans. _____

THEOREM 77

The area of any parallelogram is equal to the product of its base and altitude.

GIVEN: $\square$ ABCD with base b and altitude h.

TO PROVE: that the area of $\square$ ABCD = b · h.

PROOF. Draw $\overline{AR}$ ∥ to $\overline{SB}$ and extend $\overline{CD}$ to R. (Th. 9 and Post. 23 respectively)

STATEMENTS

1. ABSR is a rectangle

2. Area of $\square$ ABSR (or △ ADR + △ ABSD) = b · h.

3. △ ADR ≅ △ BCS

4. ∴ area of $\square$ ABCD (or △ BCS + △ ABSD) = b · h.

Therefore _____

REASONS

1. Def. of a (n)? ....

2. Principle. ....

3. ....

4. Substitution Principle. ....

124

COR. 1. Parallelograms with equal bases and equal altitudes are equivalent.

GIVEN: ▱ A and B with b = b′ and h = h′.

TO PROVE: that area of ▱ A = area of ▱ B.

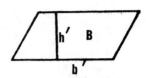

PROOF. STATEMENTS

1. Area of ▱ A = _____

2. Area of ▱ B = _____

3. But b = b′ and h = h′

4. Hence b · h = b′ · h′

5. ∴ area of ▱ A = area of ▱ B

   Therefore _____

REASONS

1. Th.? ....

2. Th.? ....

3. ....

4. .... Property of Equality

5. ....

EXERCISES A′

Solve the following exercises. (You may have to draw auxiliary lines.)

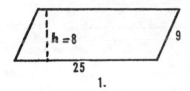

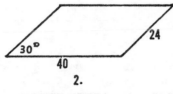

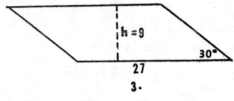

1.

a. Area = _____

b. Perimeter = _____

2.

a. Area = _____

b. Perimeter = _____

3.

a. Area = _____

b. Perimeter = _____

THEOREM 78

The area of a triangle is equal to one-half the product of its base and altitude.

GIVEN: △ RST with base b and altitude h.

TO PROVE: that the area of △ RST = ½ b · h.

PROOF. Draw TW ∥ RS and SW ∥ to RT. (Th. _____)

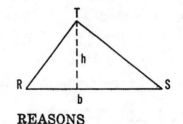

STATEMENTS

1. RSWT is a parallelogram.

2. △ _____ ≅ △ _____

3. Area of ▱ RSWT (or △ RST + △ WTS)
   = b · h.

4. Hence area of 2 △ RST = b · h.

5. ∴ area of △ RST = ½ b · h.

   Therefore _____

REASONS

1. ....

2. ....

3. Th.? ....

4. Substitution ....

5. .... Property of Equality

COR. 1. Triangles with equal bases and equal altitudes are equivalent.

GIVEN: △ A and B with base b = base b′ and
altitude h = altitude h′.

TO PROVE: that area of △ A = area of △ B.

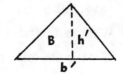

PROOF.   STATEMENTS

1. Area of △ A = _____ and area of △ B = _____

2. b • h = _____

3. Hence ½ _____ = ½ _____

4. ∴ area of △ A = area of △ B

Therefore _____

REASONS

1. Th.? _____

2. _____ Property of Equality

3. _____ Property of Equality

4. _____ Principle

COR. 2. A parallelogram is equivalent to two triangles having equal bases and equal altitudes.

GIVEN: ⟂ ABCD and △ RST with h = h′ and AB = RS.

TO PROVE: that ⟂ ABCD = 2 △ RST.

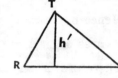

PROOF.   STATEMENTS

1. ⟂ ABCD = AB · h

2. △ RST = ½ RS · h′

3. Hence △ RST = ½ AB · h

4. 2 △ RST = AB · h

5. ∴ ⟂ ABCD = 2 △ RST

Therefore _____

REASONS

1. Th.? _____

2. Th.? _____

3. _____ Principle

4. _____ Property of Equality

5. _____ Principle

EXERCISES A″

1. What is the area of a triangle,

    a. Whose base is 12.5″ and whose altitude is 6.4″? _____

    b. Whose base is 4.5 yd. and whose altitude is 2 ft? _____

2. Find the altitude of a triangle whose area is 52.7 sq. in. and whose base is 6.2 in.

    Ans. _____

3. What is the area of rt. △ ABC in Fig. 5? _____

    _____

4. What is the area of the rt. isosceles △ in Fig. 6? _____

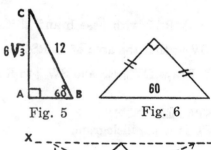

Fig. 5   Fig. 6

5. In Fig. 7 $\overline{XY}$ is ∥ to $\overline{RS}$. Do the three △ with base $\overline{RS}$ and vertices on $\overline{XY}$ have the same area? _____ Explain _____

_____

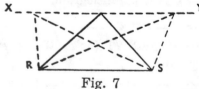

Fig. 7

6. Fig. 8 represents a box whose ends are right triangles.

    a. What is the volume of a *layer* of the box one unit deep? _____

    b. What is the total volume of the box? _____

    c. What is its total surface area? _____

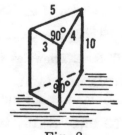

Fig. 8

STATEMENTS	CONSTRUCTIONS
1. Construct a rt. △ which will be equivalent to △ RST upon the same base, $\overline{RS}$. Shade the right triangle with pencil. Leave all construcion lines.	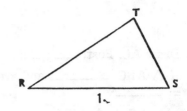
2. Construct a △ which will be equivalent to ▱ WXYZ upon the same base, $\overline{WX}$. Shade the triangle with pencil. Leave all construction lines.	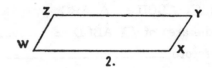
3. Construct a parallelogram which will be equivalent to △ MNO upon the same base, $\overline{MN}$. Shade the parallelogram with pencil.	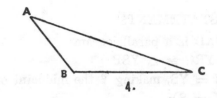
4. Transform (by construction) △ ABC into an equivalent parallelogram having the same altitude. Shade the parallelogram with pencil.	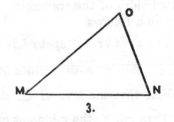
5. Transform △ ABC into an equivalent triangle AB'C' whose altitude from C' to $\overline{AB'}$ is h. *Hint*: Upon $\overline{AC}$ locate C' at a distance h above $\overline{AB}$. Draw $\overline{C'B}$. Upon the extension of $\overline{AB}$ locate B' so that △ C'BB' will be equivalent to △ CC'B.	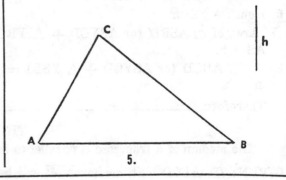

B. TRAPEZOIDS
THEOREM 79
The area of a trapezoid is equal to one-half the product of its altitude and the sum of its bases.

GIVEN: Trapezoid ABCD with bases b and b' and altitude h.

TO PROVE: that the area of ▱ ABCD =

½ h (b + b'), or h $\dfrac{(b + b')}{2}$.

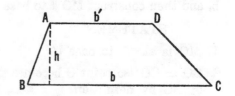

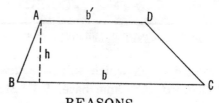

PROOF. Draw $\overline{AC}$. Post. ———— STATEMENTS

1. Area of $\triangle$ ABC = ———— and area of $\triangle$ ACD = ————

2. Hence $\triangle$ ABC + $\triangle$ ACD = ———— + ————, or ½ h (b + b′)

3. But $\square$ ABCD = $\triangle$ ABC + $\triangle$ ACD

4. ∴ the area of $\square$ ABCD = ————

Therefore ————————————————————

REASONS

1. Th.? ....

2. .... Property of Equality

3. Post.? ....

4. .... Principle

The *median* of a trapezoid is defined as the line-segment which joins the midpoints of the non-parallel sides of the trapezoid. We are going to deal with the median of a trapezoid in Corollary I which follows.

COR. 1. The area of a trapezoid is equal to the product of its altitude and its median.

GIVEN: $\square$ ABCD with altitude h and median m.

TO PROVE: that the area of $\square$ ABCD = m · h.

PROOF. Through Y, the midpoint of $\overline{BC}$, draw $\overline{RS}$ ‖ to $\overline{AD}$, and extend $\overline{DC}$ to R.

STATEMENTS

1. ASRD is a parallelogram.
2. $\triangle$ YRC $\cong$ $\triangle$ YSB.
3. YR = YS, making Y the midpoint of $\overline{RS}$.
4. AX = SY.
5. Hence ASYX is a parallelogram.
6. Hence AS = m
7. Area of $\square$ ASRD (or ASYCD + $\triangle$ YRC) = AS · h.
8. ∴ $\square$ ABCD (or ASYCD + $\triangle$ YSB) = m · h.

Therefore ————————————————————

REASONS

1. ....
2. ....
3. ....
4. .... Property of Equality
5. Unit 6, Th.? ....
6. Unit 6, Th.? ....
7. Th.? ....

8. ....

THEOREM 80

The median of a trapezoid is parallel to both bases and equal to one half the sum of the bases.

GIVEN: $\square$ ABCD with median $\overline{MM'}$ and bases b and b′.

TO PROVE: (1) that $\overline{MM'}$ is ‖ to bases b and b′ and (2) that median MM′ = ½ (b + b′)

PROOF: Let us assume for the moment that $\overline{MM'}$ is not ‖ to base b, and then construct $\overline{MO}$ ‖ to base b.

STATEMENTS

1. $\overline{MO}$ is also ‖ to base b′

2. BO = CO; so point O becomes the midpoint of BC by definition.

REASONS

1. Unit 4, Th.? ....

2. Unit 6, Th.? ....

3. But point M' is the midpoint of $\overline{BC}$.

4. Hence point O and point M' must coincide.

5. So $\overline{MM'}$ must coincide with $\overline{MO}$.

6. ∴ $\overline{MM'}$ is ‖ to bases b and b'

   Connect points A and C, calling the intersection of $\overline{AC}$ with $\overline{MM'}$ "X." (Post. 3)

7. In △ ADC MX = ½ b' and in △ ABC M'X = ½ b.

8. But MM' = MX + M'X

9. ∴ MM' = ½ b' + ½ b or ½ (b + b')

   Therefore _____

3. Def. of? _____

4. Post.? _____

5. Post.? _____

6. Post.? _____

7. Th. 39, Cor.? _____

8. Post.? _____

9. _____

EXERCISES B

1. What is the length of the median MM' of the trapezoid in Fig. 9? _____

2. What is the area of the trapezoid in Fig. 9?

   Ans. _____

3. An isoceles trapezoid has a perimeter of 250 and a median of 60. What is the length of each non-parallel side?

   Ans. _____

4. What is the area of the trapezoid in Fig. 10?

   Ans. _____

5. How many degrees are there in ∠ R if ∠ MAB contains 80°?

   Ans. _____

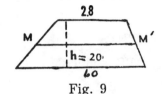

Fig. 9

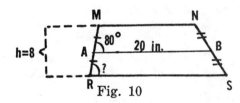

Fig. 10

6. The base of the pyramid in Fig. 11 is a 10″ by 10″ square. The slant height (altitude of each triangular side) is 15″. What is the *lateral area* (the sum of the areas of the triangular sides)?

7. In Fig. 11, what is the *total area* (the lateral area + the area of the base) of the pyramid?

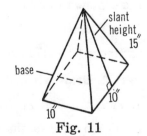

Fig. 11

The lateral area of a pyramid with a REGULAR polygon as its base is the combined area of its SLOPING congruent triangular sides. So if b = one side of the base, P = its perimeter, and l = its slant height, then the lateral area of the pyramid, A_l, becomes:

$$A_l = ½lb + ½lb + ½lb \ldots = ½l (b + b + b \ldots) = ½lP$$

8. What is the lateral area of a pyramid whose slant height is 6″ and whose base has a perimeter of 20″?

129

The square on the hypotenuse of any right triangle is equal in area to the sum of the areas of the squares on the other two sides (or legs).

GIVEN: RT. $\triangle$ RST with rt. $\angle$ T and with squares SXYT, TBAR, and RMNS constructed upon sides a, b, and c respectively.

TO PROVE: that $c^2 = a^2 + b^2$.

PROOF. From T draw $\overline{TH}$ ∥ to $\overline{RM}$, intersecting $\overline{RS}$ at O and $\overline{MN}$ at H. (Th. _____) Draw $\overline{AS}$ and $\overline{MT}$. Post. _____

OVER-ALL PLAN. Show that:
▭ RMHO = ▭ ARTB and ▭ SNHO = ▭ XSTY

STATEMENTS

Part 1. In $\triangle$ ARS, and TRM,

1. $\angle$ ARS = $\angle$ TRM

2. AR = RT and RS = RM

3. Hence $\triangle$ ARS $\cong$ $\triangle$ TRM

4. STB is a straight line-segment.

Taking $\overline{AR}$ as the common base and $\overline{RT}$ as the common altitude of ▭ ARTB and $\triangle$ ARS,

5. ▭ ARTB = 2 $\triangle$ ARS

Taking $\overline{RM}$ as the common base and _____ as the common altitude of ▭ RMHO and $\triangle$ TRM,

6. ▭ RMHO = 2 $\triangle$ TRM

7. Hence ▭ ARTB, or b^2, = ▭ RMHO

Part 2. Draw $\overline{XR}$ and $\overline{NT}$.

1. $\triangle$ _____ $\cong$ $\triangle$ _____

2. RTY is a straight line-segment.

Taking $\overline{SX}$ as the common base and _____ as the common altitude of ▭ _____ and $\triangle$ _____,

3. ▭ _____ = 2 $\triangle$ _____

4. Taking _____ as the common base and _____ as the common altitude, ▭ _____ = 2 $\triangle$ _____

REASONS

1. .... Property of Equality

2. Def. of? ....

3. ....

4. Because it forms the exterior sides of? ....

5. Th. 78, Cor.? ....

6. Th.? Cor.? ....

7. .... Principle

REASONS

1. ....

2. ....

3. ....

4. ....

5. Hence □ —————, or a², = □ —————   **5.** .... Principle

Part 3.

1. □ RMNS = □ SNHO + □ RMHO   **1.** Post.? ....

2. ∴ □ RMNS = □ XSTY + □ ARTB,
    or $c^2 = a^2 + b^2$ **2.** ....

Therefore _____

_____

COR. 1. The square on one side (or leg) of a right triangle is equal to the difference between the squares on the hypotenuse and the other side (or leg).

GIVEN: RT. △ ABC with sides a and b, and hypotenuse c.

TO PROVE: that $a^2 = c^2 - b^2$.

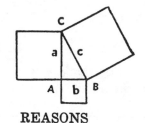

PROOF.   STATEMENTS   REASONS

1. ——— + ——— = ———   **1.** Th.? ....

2. $b^2 =$ ———   **2.** .... Property of Equality

3. ∴ $a^2 = c^2 - b^2$ **3.** .... Property of Equality

Therefore _____

_____

EXERCISES C

Solve the following exercises. (Auxiliary lines are sometimes required.)

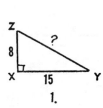
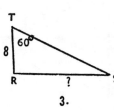
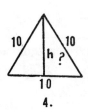
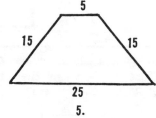

1.   **2.**   **3.**   **4.**   **5.**

YZ = ————   Area = ————   Area = ————   h = ————   Area = ————

Area = ————   AC = ————   Area = ————   RS = ————

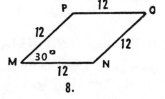

6.   **7.**   **8.**   **9.**

Area = ————   Area = $5\sqrt{3}$ Area = ————   Area = ————

S = ————

10. In trapezoid ABCD, base AB = 60, base CD = 40, non-parallel side AD = 10, and ∠ A = 60°. What is the area of the trapezoid?

Ans. _____

11. What is the area of an isosceles trapezoid whose bases are 30 and 50, and whose non-parallel sides are 20 each?

Ans. _____

12. What is the area of a rhombus whose diagonals are 6 and 30?

Ans. _____

CONSTRUCTION EXERCISES C

Make the following constructions accurately with compass and straightedge in the corresponding space provided for constructions.

STATEMENTS	CONSTRUCTIONS
1. Construct a square equal to the sum of the areas of squares A and B. 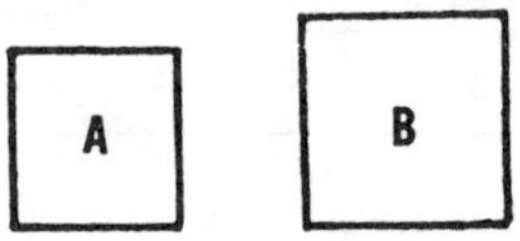 A B	 1.
2. Construct a square whose area is three times the area of square C. C 	 2.
3. Construct a square whose area is equal to the difference between the areas of squares R and S. R S 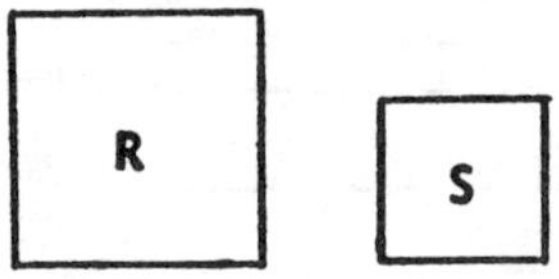	 3.

D. PROJECTION AND HERO'S FORMULA

The *projection of a point* upon a given line (or line-segment) is defined as the foot of the perpendicular drawn from the point to the line. In Fig. 11 point X is the projection of point O upon $\overline{MN}$. The portion of a line (or line-segment) included between the projections of the end points of a line-segment upon the line is called the *projection of that line-segment* upon the line. In Fig. 12 $\overline{CD}$ is the projection of $\overline{AB}$ upon $\overline{MN}$.

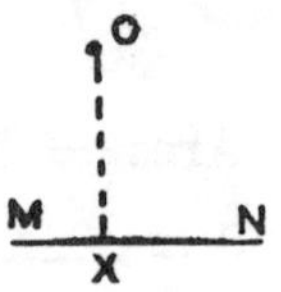

Fig. 11 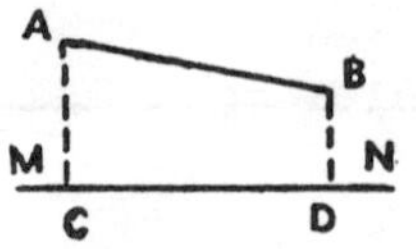   Fig. 12

1. Fill the following answer-spaces with correct answers.

   a. The foot of the _____ drawn from a point to a given line is called the _____ _____ of that *point* upon the given line.

   b. The segment of a line included between the _____ of the end points of a line-segment upon a given line is called the _____ of that *line-segment* upon the given line.

2. Find the projection of point P upon $\overline{AB}$ in Fig. a below, and the projection of $\overline{mn}$ upon $\overline{xy}$ in the other figures.

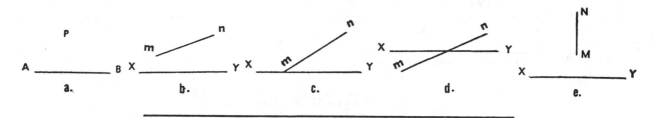

a.   b.   c.   d.   e.

The area of a triangle in terms of its sides. (Hero's Formula).

GIVEN: $\triangle$ RST with sides a, b, and c, and an altitude h.

To Prove: that $A = \sqrt{s(s-a)(s-b)(s-c)}$, in which $s = \dfrac{a+b+c}{2}$.

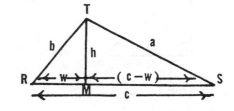

Proof.   Steps   Reasons

1. $a^2 = (c-w)^2 + h^2$ 1. _____

2. But $h^2 = b^2 - w^2$ 2. _____

3. Hence $a^2 = (c-w)^2 + b^2 - w^2$ 3. _____

   Solving step 3 for w:

   $a^2 = c^2 - 2cw + w^2 + b^2 - w^2$
   $2cw = c^2 + b^2 - a^2.$
   $w = \dfrac{c^2 + b^2 - a^2}{2c}.$

4. Hence $h^2 = b^2 - \left(\dfrac{c^2 + b^2 - a^2}{2c}\right)^2.$ 4. _____

Changing the form of step 4:

$$h^2 = \left(b + \frac{c^2 + b^2 - a^2}{2c}\right)\left(b - \frac{c^2 + b^2 - a^2}{2c}\right) = \left(\frac{2bc + c^2 + b^2 - a^2}{2c}\right)\left(\frac{2bc - c^2 - b^2 + a^2}{2c}\right)$$

$$= \left(\frac{b^2 + 2bc + c^2 - a^2}{2c}\right)\left(\frac{a^2 - (b^2 - 2bc + c^2)}{2c}\right) = \frac{[(b+c)^2 - a^2][a^2 - (b-c)^2]}{4c^2}$$

$$= \frac{(a+b+c)(a+b+c-2a)(a+b+c-2c)(a+b+c-2b)}{4c^2}$$

5. But since a + b + c = 2s,

$$h^2 = \frac{2s\,(2s-2a)\,(2s-2c)\,(2s-2b)}{4c^2} = \frac{16s\,(s-a)\,(s-b)\,(s-c)}{4c^2}$$

$$= \frac{4s\,(s-a)\,(s-b)\,(s-c)}{c^2}$$

5. ....

6. $h = \dfrac{2\sqrt{s\,(s-a)\,(s-b)\,(s-c)}}{c}$

6. Property of Equality No.? ....

7. But A = ½ c · h

7. Th.? ....

8. ∴ A = ½ c·2 $\dfrac{\sqrt{s\,(s-a)\,(s-b)\,s-c)}}{c}$,

8. ....

Or A = $\sqrt{s\,(s-a)\,(s-b)\,(s-c)}$

EXERCISES D′

Solve each of the following exercises by use of **Hero's Formula.**

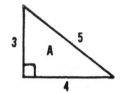

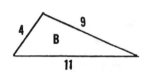

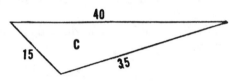

1. Area = _____

2. Area = _____

3. Area = _____

5. Verify your answer in △ A by use of the formula:

A = ½ b · h

A = _____

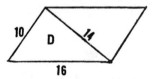

4. Area = _____

E. TRANSFORMING A POLYGON INTO AN EQUIVALENT TRIANGLE.
CONSTRUCTION 7

To transform a polygon into an equivalent triangle.

GIVEN: Polygon ABCDE.

REQUIRED: To construct a △ equivalent to polygon ABCDE.

Construction: Draw diagonal AD connecting the first and third of three consecutive vertices. Through E, the second of the three vertices, draw $\overline{EM}$ ∥ to $\overline{AD}$, and extend $\overline{AB}$ to meet $\overline{EM}$. Draw $\overline{DM}$. Continue this process until a △ is formed.

△ MND is equivalent to polygon ABCDE.

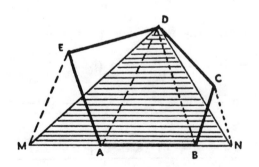

PROOF. STATEMENTS

1. △ MAD = △ EAD
2. Polygon ABCDE = △ EAD + polygon ABCD
3. Hence polygon ABCDE = △ MAD + polygon ABCD, or polygon MBCD
4. △ NBD = △ CBD
5. Polygon MBCD = △ CBD + polygon MBD
6. Hence polygon MBCD = △ NBD + polygon MBD, or △ MND
7. ∴ polygon ABCDE = △ MND

REASONS

1. Th. 78, Cor.? ....
2. Post.? ....
3. ....
4. ....
5. ....
6. ....
7. ....

CONSTRUCTION EXERCISES E

Make the following constructions accurately with compass and straightedge in the corresponding space provided for constructions.

1. Transform each of the following polygons into an equivalent △. Shade each △ with pencil.

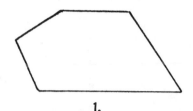

1.

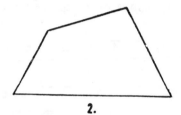

2.

EXERCISES F

By a simple experiment, let us discover the formula for finding the volume of a pyramid:

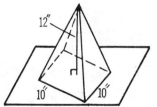

1. EQUIPMENT: An empty water-tight rectangular box and an empty water-tight pyramid that have congruent bases and equal heights (altitudes). (The altitude of each container is the perpendicular distance from the top to the base.) A container of water or sand.

2. PROCEDURE: Determine the number of pyramids of water (or sand) that are required to fill the rectangular box.

3. CONCLUSION: It takes _____ pyramids of water (or sand) to fill the box. So the volume of the pyramid, expressed in terms of the volume of the box (which is: $V = l \, W \, h$ or $B \, h$)
becomes: $V_p = \underline{\quad} l \, W \, h$ or $V_p = \underline{\quad} B \, h$

_____

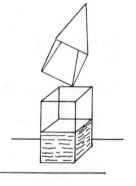

1. In Fig. 14, the base of the pyramid is a 10″ by 10″ square. Its altitude is 12″. What is its volume?   Fig. 14

_____

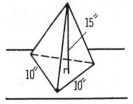

2. In Fig. 15, the base of the pyramid is an equilateral triangle with each side 10″ long. The altitude is 15″. Find its volume.   Fig. 15

_____

Unit XII.

COORDINATE GEOMETRY

A. THE FORMULA FOR THE DISTANCE BETWEEN TWO POINTS ● THE FORMULA FOR THE MID-POINT OF A LINE-SEGMENT

Coordinate geometry deals with the representation of geometric figures as graphs of algebraic equations on graph paper, using the familar rectangular coordinate system.

Let us find the distance D between points P_1 (2, 1) and P_2 (6, 4) in Fig. 1. We shall observe these relationships in right $\triangle P_1 A P_2$:

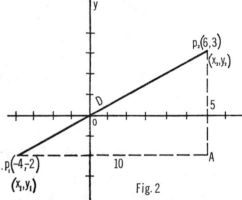

Fig. 1

a. Hortizontal leg $P_1 A$ is 6 – 2 or 4 units long.

b. Vertical leg $P_2 A$ is 4 – 1 or 3 units long.

c. Hence $D^2 = 4^2 + 3^2 = 16 + 9$ or 25 (Pythagoras)

d. $\therefore \sqrt{D^2} = \sqrt{25}$ (Square root property of equality)

e. Or D = 5

The above relationships expressed as indicated processes, become:

$$D = \sqrt{(6 - 2)^2 + (4 - 1)^2} = \sqrt{4^2 + 3^2}$$

Similarly, in Fig. 2, we have:

$$D = \sqrt{(6 - (-4))^2 + (3 - (-2))^2} = \sqrt{10^2 + 5^2}$$
$$= \sqrt{100 + 25} = \sqrt{125} = \sqrt{25 \times 5} = 5\sqrt{5}$$

THEOREM 82

The distance D between two points (x_1, y_1) and (x_2, y_2) is:

$$D = \sqrt{(x_2 - x_1)^2 + (y_2 - y_1)^2} \text{ (Pythagoras)}$$

Bear in mind that these distances are always considered to have absolute values.

THEOREM 83

The coordinates of the midpoint of the line-segment whose end-points are (x_1, y_1) and (x_2, y_2) is the point where $x_m = \dfrac{x_1 + x_2}{2}$ and $y_m = \dfrac{y_1 + y_2}{2}$.

GIVEN: Line-segment $P_1 P_2$ with point P_m its midpoint.

TO PROVE: that $x_m = \dfrac{x_1 + x_2}{2}$ and $y_m = \dfrac{y_1 + y_2}{2}$

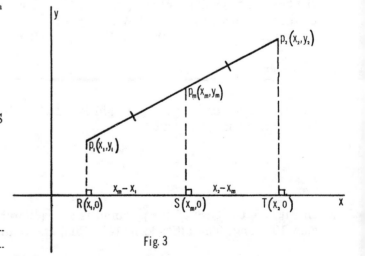

Fig. 3

PROOF   STATEMENT   REASONS

1. From points P_1, P_m, and P_2 draw $P_1 R$, $P_m S$, and $P_2 T$ perpendicular respectively to the x-axis.   1. Th.? ....

2. $P_1 R \parallel P_m S \parallel P_2 T$ 2. Th. 23, Cor.? ....

136

3. $P_1P_m = P_mP_2$ 3. Given ....

4. $RS = ST$ 4. Th.? ....

5. $x'_m - x_1 = x_2 - x'_m$ 5. Why? ....

6. $2 x'_m = x_1 + x_2$ 6. Why? ....

7. $\therefore x_m = \dfrac{x_1 + x_2}{2}$ 7. Why? ....

Similarly, we may prove $y_m = \dfrac{y_1 + y_2}{2}$ by drawing $\perp$s from points P_1, P_m, and P_2 to the y-axis.

EXERCISES A

Compute the distance between each of the following pairs of points and verify your answers by graphic interpretation.

1. The point (0, 5) and the point (0, -6).

2. The point (3, 0) and the point (-4, 0).

3. The point (5, 2) and the point (7, 6).

4. The point (-3, 0) and the point (1, -3).

5. Show that the points (2, 5), (5, 0), and (-1, 0) are the vertices of an isosceles triangle.

6. Find the length of the sides of a triangle whose vertices are at the following points: (-1, 0), (7, 6), and (-4, 4).

7. What are the coordinates of the midpoint of a line-segment which joins the points (6, 0) and (10, 0) ?

_____

8. What are the coordinates of the midpoint of a line-segment which joins the points (2, 4) and (6, 8) ?

_____

9. What are the coordinates of the midpoint of a line-segment which joins the points (0, 4) and (0, 8) ?

_____

10. What are the coordinates of the midpoint of a line-segment which joins the points (-2, 6) and (6, -4) ?

_____

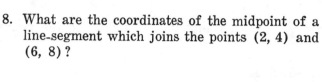

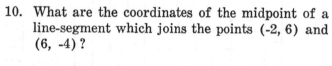

B. THE SLOPE FORMULA FOR A STRAIGHT LINE ● SLOPES OF LINES PARALLEL TO THE x-AXIS ● LINES PERPENDICULAR TO THE x-AXIS

In Mathematics, the **slope of a line** is the ratio of its change in the y value ($\triangle y$) between any two points to its corresponding change in x value ($\triangle x$) between those two points. Then as a formula, in which m = the slope of a line l, we have:

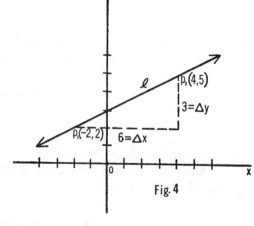

Fig. 4

THEOREM 84

$$m = \frac{y_2 - y_1}{x_2 - x_1}, \text{ or } \frac{\triangle y}{\triangle x}$$

For the line in Fig. 4 we have:

$$m = \frac{5 - 2}{4 - (-2)} = \frac{3}{6} \text{ or } \frac{1}{2}$$

We will observe that the slope of the above line l, is POSITIVE. **All lines which slant UPWARD toward the right have positive slopes.**

Of course, the slope of a given straight line is the same or constant all along that line.

In Fig. 5 the slope of line l, which contains points (2, 1) and (-4, 4), is:

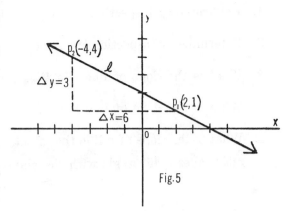

Fig.5

$$m = \frac{y_2 - y_1}{x_2 - x_1} \text{ or } \frac{\triangle y}{\triangle x} = \frac{4 - 1}{-4 - 2}$$

$$= \frac{3}{-6} = -\frac{1}{2}$$

We will observe that the slope of the line in Fig. 5 is NEGATIVE. **All lines which slant DOWNWARD toward the right have negative SLOPES.**

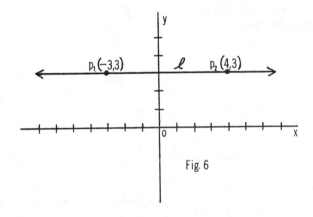

Fig. 6

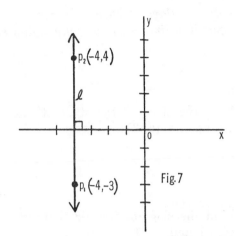

Fig.7

Fig. 6, the slope of line 1, which contains points (-3, 3) and (4, 3), is:

$$m = \frac{y_2 - y_1}{x_2 - x_1} = \frac{3 - 3}{4 - (-3)} = \frac{0}{7} = 0 \; *$$

We will observe that the slope of the above line l is 0. **All lines PARALLEL to the x-axis have a slope of zero.**

In Fig. 7 the slope of line 1, which contains points (-4, -3) and (-4, 4), is:

$$m = \frac{x_2 - y_1}{x_2 - x_1} = \frac{4 - (-3)}{-4 - (-4)} = \frac{4 + 3}{-4 + (+4)} = \frac{7}{0} \; *$$

This is meaningless since we cannot divide by zero. **All lines PERPENDICULAR to the x-axis have no slopes.**

EXERCISES B

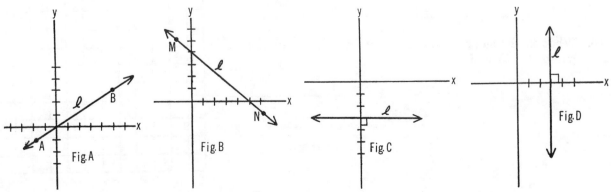

Fig.A   Fig.B   Fig.C   Fig.D

* Do we see that it does not matter which one of the two points we take as P_1?

139

1. Determine by inspection the slope of line AB in Fig. A above.   _____

2. Determine by inspection the slope of line MN in Fig. B above.   _____

3. What is the slope of line l in Fig. C above?   _____

4. What is the slope of line l in Fig. D above?   _____

5. What is the slope of a line that slants upward toward the right and makes a 45° angle with the x-axis?   _____

Compute the slope of each of the lines that contains the given pair of points. Then sketch each corresponding line in the accompanying squared region.

6. Find the slope of the straight line that contains points (0, 0) and (6, 3).

    _____

7. Find the slope of the straight line that contains points (2, 3) and (5, 1).

    _____

8. What is the slope of the straight line that contains the points (-4, 2) and (2, 5)?

    _____

9. What is the slope of the straight line that contains points (3, 5) and (-5, 5)?

    _____

10. What is the slope of the straight line that contains the points (3, 5) and (3, -4)?

    _____

C. PARALLEL LINES AND PERPENDICULAR LINES •
THE SLOPE - INTERCEPT EQUATION

THEOREM 85

If two non-vertical lines are parallel, then they have equal slopes.

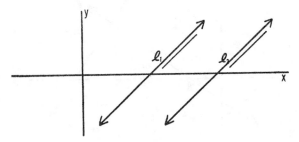

GIVEN: Parallel lines l_1 and l_2.

TO PROVE: slope m_1 = slope m_2

PROOF   STATEMENTS

1. Measure any convenient distance BA along l_1 and an equal distance SR along l_2.
2. Drop perpendiculars $\overline{AC}$ from A to the x-axis and $\overline{RT}$ from R to the x-axis.
3. $\angle ABC = \angle RST$
4. Rt. $\triangle ABC \cong$ Rt. $\triangle RST$
5. Hence AC = RT and BC = ST
6. $\dfrac{AC}{BC} = \dfrac{RT}{ST}$
7. But $\dfrac{AC}{BC} = m_1$ and $\dfrac{RT}{ST} = m_2$
8. $\therefore m_1 = m_2$

1. Construction ....
2. Th.? ....
3. Why? ....
4. Why? ....
5. Why? ....
6. .... Property of Equality
7. Definition of slope
8. Substitution Principle.

THEOREM 86

If two non-vertical lines have equal slopes, then the lines are parallel.

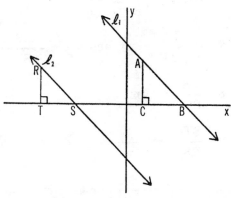

GIVEN: Lines l_1 and l_2 with slope m_1 or $\dfrac{CA}{CB}$ = slope m_2

or $\dfrac{TR}{TS}$

TO PROVE: that l_1 is $\parallel$ to l_2.

PROOF   STATEMENTS

1. CB = TS and CA = TR
2. $\angle T = \angle C$
3. $\therefore \triangle ABC \cong \triangle RST$
4. Hence $\angle ABC = \angle RST$
5. $\therefore l_1$ is $\parallel$ to l_2

REASONS

1. Corr. distances of = slopes are =
2. All rt. $\angle$ are =
3. Why? ....
4. Why? ....
5. If corr. $\angle$ of ls cut by a transv. are =, the ls are $\parallel$.

THEOREM 87

If two non-vertical lines are perpendicular, then the slope of the one is the negative reciprocal of the slope of the other (i.e. the products of their slopes is –1).

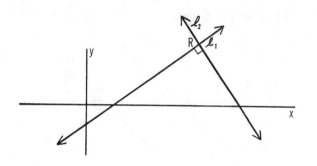 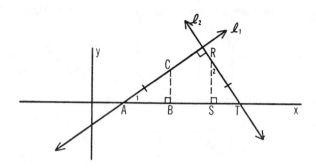

GIVEN: Lines l_1 and l_2 intersecting and perpendicular at point R and with m_1 and m_2 their respective slopes.

TO PROVE: $m_1 = -\dfrac{1}{m_2}$ or $m_1 \cdot m_2 = -1$

PROOF   STATEMENTS

REASONS

1. Measure any distance AC along l_1 and an equal distance TR along l_2, as shown.

   1. By what authority? ....

2. Drop a perpendicular $\overline{CB}$ from point C to the x-axis and $\overline{RS}$ from point R to the x-axis.

   2. Theorem? ....

3. $\angle 1 = \angle 2$

   3. Unit 5, Th.? ....

4. Hence $\triangle ABC \cong \triangle RST$

   4. Why? ....

5. $BC = ST$ and $AB = RS$

   5. Why? ....

6. Hence $\dfrac{BC}{AB} = \dfrac{ST}{RS}$

   6. .... Property of Equality

7. $+\dfrac{BC}{AB} = m_1$ and $m_2 = -\dfrac{RS}{ST}$

   7. Definition of a slope to a line, where l_1 and l_2 have opposite slopes. Also Th. 84.

8. $\dfrac{RS}{ST} = -m_2$

   8. Multiplying $(-\dfrac{RS}{ST} = m_2)$ by -1 in step 7.

9. $\dfrac{ST}{RS} = -\dfrac{1}{m_2}$

   9. Inverting each side of step 8

10. $\therefore m_1 = -\dfrac{1}{m_2}$, or $m_1 \cdot m_2 = -1$

   10. Substituting m_1 for $\dfrac{BC}{AB}$ and $-\dfrac{1}{m_2}$ for $\dfrac{ST}{RS}$ in step 6.

THEOREM 88

The slope-intercept equation is: $y = mx + b$
In this equation the value of y is expressed in terms of m (the slope of the line), the value

of x, and b, the value of y where the graph crosses the y-axis. This equation may be derived in the following manner:

Let us consider the *general* slope formula: $\dfrac{y - y_1}{x - x_1} = m$ *

Now let us call the y-distance where the graph of this equation crosses the y-axis "*b*". The corresponding x distance at this point is 0. So this is the point (0, b).

By substitution, we have:

$$\frac{y - b}{x - 0} = m. \quad \text{Or} \quad \frac{y - b}{x} = m$$

Multiplying through by x, we get: $y - b = m x$

$\therefore y = m x + b$ (Addition property of equality)

* We will observe that it is permissible to replace (x_2, y_2) with (x, y) in Theorem 84 because (x_2, y_2) may represent *any* point on a line other than point (x_1, y_1).

EXERCISES C

Give the best answer to each of the following questions.

1. If two non-vertical lines have equal slopes, the lines are always ? _____

2. If two non-vertical lines are parallel, then they have equal ? .... _____

3. If two non-vertical lines are perpendicular, then the slope of the one is the ? of the other. .... _____

4. GIVEN: that non-vertical line l_1 is parallel to l_2. The slope of l_1 is 3/5. What is the slope of l_2? .... _____

5. GIVEN: that l_1 passes through points (2, 3) and (-3, -1). l_2 passes through points (3, 0) and (8, 4). Are l_1 and l_2 parallel? Why? .... _____

6. GIVEN: that l_1 passes through points (0, 0) and (4, 3). l_2 passes through points (3, -1) and (5, 3). Are the lines parallel? _____ Why? _____

7. GIVEN: that line l_1 is $\perp$ to line l_2. The slope of line l_1 is 2/3. What is the slope of line l_2? .... _____

8. GIVEN: that line l_1 passes through points (2, 3) and (3, 5). Line l_2 passes through points (5, 2) and (3, 3). Are these lines (1) parallel (2) perpendicular (3) neither? .... _____

9. GIVEN: that line l_1 passes through points (2, 5) and (-3, -2). Line l_2 passes through points (3, 2) and (-3, 3). Are l_1 and l_2 (1) parallel (2) perpendicular (3) neither? .... _____

10. GIVEN: that line l_1 is $\perp$ to line l_2. What is the product of their slopes? .... _____

    GIVEN: The equation $y = 3x + 5$

11. What is the slope of the graph of this equation? .... _____

12. What is the y-intercept of the graph of this equation? .... _____

13. Will the graph of this equation pass through the origin? .... _____

    GIVEN: The equation $3y + 2x = 6$

14. What is the slope of this equation? .... _____

15. What is the y-intercept of the graph of this equation? .... _____

16. What is the x-intercept of the graph of this equation? .... _____

17. Two points on the graph of a linear equation are (5, 4) and (-5, 0). Express the equation in simplest form. (Hint: Determine the slope and make use of the slope formula.) .... _____

18. What is the value of the y-intercept of the graph in question 17? _____

19. GIVEN: The y-intercept of an equation is -3 and its slope is -¾. Write the equation in simplest form. .... _____

20. The slope of l_1 is 2/3. What is the slope of l_2 which is perpendicular to l_2? .... _____

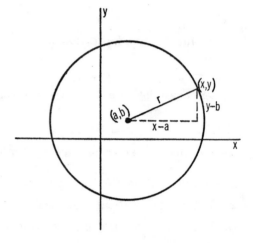

D. EQUATIONS OF THE CIRCLE

The general equation for the circle is a special formula for the distance between two points in which one of the points (a, b) or the center remains fixed, while the other point (x, y) may lie any place on the circle. So for each particular circle, a and b are constants, whereas x and y are variables.

If we substitute a for x_1, b for y_1, x for x_2, y for y_2 and r for D in the formula

$\sqrt{(x_2 - x_1)^2 + (y_2 - y_1)^2} = D$, we obtain the following equation:

$\sqrt{(x - a)^2 + (y - b)^2} = r$. Squaring each member of this equation, we get the *general equation of the circle*, which appears in Theorem 89 that follows:

THEOREM 89

The equation of the circle with center (a,b) and radius r is: $(x - a)^2 + (y - b)^2 = r^2$

COROLLARY I: The equation of the circle with center at the origin (0,0) is: $x^2 + y^2 = r^2$

Do we see that the equation in corollary I is obtained by substituting 0 for a and 0 for b in the equation of Theorem 89?

EXAMPLE EXERCISES INVOLVING THE USE OF THE EQUATIONS OF THE CIRCLE

1. Write the equation of the circle with its center at the point (3, 2) and with radius 5.
   SOLUTION: Substituting in the equation of the circle in Theorem 89 we get:
   $(x - 3)^2 + (y - 2)^2 = 25$

2. Write the equation of the circle with its center at the origin and with radius 3.
   SOLUTION: Substituting in the equation of the circle in Corollary I above, we get:
   $x^2 + y^2 = 9$

Write the equation of each of the following circles and draw its graph.

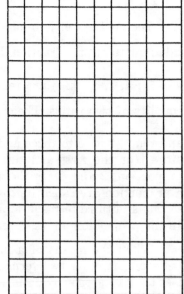

1. The equation of the circle with its center at point (2, 5) and with radius 2.

   _____

2. The equation of the circle with its center at point (-3, -2) and with radius 3.

   _____

3. The equation of the circle with its center at the origin and with a radius of 4.

   _____

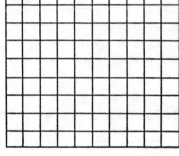

Determine the center and the radius of each of the following circles.

4. $(x + 2)^2 + (y - 5)^2 = 36$

   _____

5. $x^2 + y^2 = 25$

   _____

Unit XIII.

RATIO AND PROPORTION. PROPORTIONAL LINE-SEGMENTS

A. RATIO AND PROPORTION

The quotient of two numbers of like kind is called a *ratio*. A ratio may be regarded as an indicated quotient or a fraction. Examples of rations are $\frac{2}{3}$ and $\frac{5}{4}$, which may also be written as 2 : 3 and 5 : 4, and which are read "two to three" and "five to four" respectively. A *proportion* is an equality of two ratios. The expression $\frac{2}{3} = \frac{4}{6}$ is a proportion. It may also be written 2 : 3 = 4 : 6, and read "two is to three as four is to six". The parts of a proportion are its *terms*. The numerators, (or the first and third terms) of a proportion are called its *antecedents*. In the above proportion, 2 and 4 are the antecedents. The denominators (or the second and fourth terms) of a proportion are called its *consequents*. In the above proportion 3 and 6 are the consequents. The second and third terms of a proportion are its *means*, while the first and last terms are its *extremes*. In the proportion above, 3 and 4 are the means, and 2 and 6 the extremes.

When the means of a proportion are alike, either mean is known as the *mean proportional* between the other two terms. In the proportion 8 : 4 = 4 : 2, 4 is the mean proportional. The last term of a proportion in which the means are ALIKE is known as the *third proportional* to the other two terms. In the proportion just given, 2 is the third proportional to 8 and 4. The fourth term of a proportion, in which the means are not the same, is called a *fourth proportional*. In the proportion 9 : 3 = 6 : 2, 2 is the fourth proportional to 9, 3, and 6.

EXERCISES A

1. Fill each answer-space below with the correct answer.

_____ a. The (indicated) quotient of two numbers of like kind.

_____ b. The equality of two ratios.

_____ c. The numerators, or first and third terms, of a proportion.

_____ d. The parts of a proportion.

_____ e. The, denominators, or second and fourth terms, of a proportion.

_____ f. The second and third terms of a proportion.

_____ g. The first and last (fourth) terms of a proportion.

_____ h. Either mean of a proportion in which the means are alike.

_____ i. The fourth (last) term of a proportion.

_____ j. The last term of a proportion in which the means are alike.

2. Fill the following answer-spaces with correct answers.

a. The fraction $\frac{3}{4}$ or 3 : 4 is called a (n) _____. In this fraction, the 3 is known as

the _____ and the 4 as the _____.

b. The expression 2 : 5 = 6 : x is called a (n) _____. In this expression, the 2, 5, 6,

and x are known as the _____; the 2 and 6 are called the _____, and the 5 and

x, the _____. x is also called the _____ to 2, 5, and 6.

The 2 and x are called the _____ and the 5 and 6 the _____.

c. In the proportion $3:7 = 7:y$, the 7 is known as the _____ between the 3 and y, and the y as the _____ _____ to 3 and 7.

3. Answer the following questions.

   a. Is the expression 3 ft. : 12 ft. = 3 mi. : 12 mi. a proportion? _____

   b. Hence which of the following factors determines the value of a ratio, the *number* of units or the *size* of the units? _____

B. FUNDAMENTAL THEOREMS ON PROPORTION.

90. **In any proportion, the product of the means is equal to the product of the extremes.**

GIVEN: $\dfrac{a}{b} = \dfrac{c}{d}$ TO PROVE that $a \cdot d = b \cdot c$.

PROOF.   STATEMENTS   REASONS

1. ___ $\cdot \dfrac{a}{b} = $ ___ $\cdot \dfrac{c}{d}$, or $a \cdot d = b \cdot c$ 1. .... Property of equality

91. **If the product of two quantities is equal to the product of two other quantities, either pair may be made the means and the other pair the extremes of a proportion.**

GIVEN: $a \cdot d = b \cdot c$ TO PROVE: that $a:b = c:d$. .

PROOF.   STATEMENTS   REASONS

1. $\dfrac{a \cdot d}{\quad} = \dfrac{b \cdot c}{\quad}$, or $\dfrac{a}{b} = \dfrac{c}{d}$ 1. .... Property of equality

92. **In any proportion, the ratios may be inverted. (prop. by inversion).**

GIVEN: $\dfrac{a}{b} = \dfrac{c}{d}$ TO PROVE: that $\dfrac{b}{a} = \dfrac{d}{c}$.

PROOF.   STATEMENTS   REASONS

1. $a \cdot d = b \cdot c$ 1. Th.? ....

2. $\therefore b:a = d:c$ 2. Th.? ....

93. **In any proportion, the first term is to the third term as the second term is to the fourth. (prop. by alternation).**

GIVEN: $\dfrac{a}{b} = \dfrac{c}{d}$ TO PROVE: that $\dfrac{a}{c} = \dfrac{b}{d}$.

PROOF.   STATEMENTS   REASONS

1. $a \cdot d = b \cdot c$ 1. Th.? ....

2. $\therefore a:c = b:d$ 2. Th.? ....

94. **In any proportion, the sum of the first two terms is to the second term as the sum of the last two terms is to the last. (prop. by addition).**

GIVEN: $\dfrac{a}{b} = \dfrac{c}{d}$ TO PROVE: that $\dfrac{a+b}{b} = \dfrac{c+d}{d}$

PROOF.   STATEMENTS   REASONS

1. $\dfrac{a}{b} + 1 = \dfrac{c}{d} + 1$ or $\dfrac{a}{b} + \dfrac{b}{b} = \dfrac{c}{d} + \dfrac{d}{d}$ or $\therefore \dfrac{a+b}{b} = \dfrac{c+d}{d}$ 1._____ Property of equality

95. In any proportion, the difference between the first two terms is to the second as the difference between the last two terms is to the last. (prop. by subtraction).

GIVEN: $\dfrac{a}{b} = \dfrac{c}{d}$ TO PROVE: that $\dfrac{a-b}{b} = \dfrac{c-d}{d}$

PROOF.   STATEMENTS   REASONS

1. $\dfrac{a}{b} - 1 = \dfrac{c}{d} - 1$,, or $\dfrac{a}{b} - \dfrac{b}{b} = \dfrac{c}{d} - \dfrac{d}{d}$, or $\therefore \dfrac{a-b}{b} = \dfrac{c-d}{d}$ 1._____
                                                                                                          Property of equality

96. If any three terms of one proportion are equal respectively to three corresponding terms of another proportion, the other two terms are equal.

GIVEN: $\dfrac{a}{b} = \dfrac{x}{c}$ and $\dfrac{m}{n} = \dfrac{y}{d}$ in which a = m, b = n, and c = d.

TO PROVE: that x = y.

PROOF.   STATEMENTS   REASONS

1. bx = ac and ny = md   1. ....

2. $x = \dfrac{ac}{b}$ and $y = \dfrac{md}{n}$ 2. ....

3. But m = a, d = c, and n = b.   3. ....

4. Hence $y = \dfrac{ac}{b}$ 4. .... Principle

5. $\therefore$ x = y   5. ....

97. In any series of equal ratios, the sum of the antecedents is to the sum of the consequents as any one of the antecedents is to its consequent.

GIVEN: $\dfrac{a}{b} = \dfrac{c}{d} = \dfrac{e}{f}$.   TO PROVE: that $\dfrac{a+c+e}{b+d+f} = \dfrac{a}{b}$

PROOF.   STATEMENTS   REASONS

Let $\dfrac{a}{b} = r$

1. Then $\dfrac{c}{d} = r$ and $\dfrac{e}{f} = r$ 1. .... Principle

2. a = b·r, c = d·r, and e = f·r   2. Th.? ....

3. a + c + e = _____ + _____ + _____,
   or r (_____ + _____ + _____)   3. .... Property of Equality

4. Hence $\dfrac{a+c+e}{b+d+f} = r$ 4. .... Property of Equality

5. $\therefore$ $\dfrac{a+c+e}{b+d+f} = \dfrac{a}{b}$ 5. ....

148

EXERCISES B

In the exercises that follow, complete the statements and give the NUMBER of the *theorem on proportions* which applies in each exercise.

Statements

Statements

Theorem No.

Theorem No.

1. Given $\dfrac{r}{s} = \dfrac{a}{b}$ $\therefore$ $r:a =$ —— : —— —— 5. Given: $m:c = r:s$ $\therefore$ $r:m =$ —— : —— ——

2. Given: $m:x = y:n$ $\therefore$ $m \cdot n =$ —— —— 6. Given: $\dfrac{w}{a} = \dfrac{n}{b}$ $\therefore$ $\dfrac{w-a}{a} =$ —— ——

3. Given: $\dfrac{m}{a} = \dfrac{c}{d}$ $\therefore$ $\dfrac{a}{m} =$ —— —— 7. Given: $\dfrac{m}{a} = \dfrac{n}{b}$ $\therefore$ $\dfrac{m+n}{a+b} =$ —— ——

4. Given: $a:x = b:d$ $\therefore$ $\dfrac{a+x}{x} =$ —— —— 8. Given: $\dfrac{a}{x} = \dfrac{b}{c}$ and $\dfrac{a}{y} = \dfrac{b}{c}$ $\therefore$ $x =$ —— ——

Find x in the following proportions.

9. $\dfrac{x}{50} = \dfrac{5}{20}$ 10. $\dfrac{30}{x} = \dfrac{50}{25}$ 11. $8:14 = 3:x$ 12. $\dfrac{x+12}{4} = \dfrac{7}{2}$

Ans. _____   Ans. _____   Ans. _____   Ans. _____

Solve the following exercises by proportion.

13. The ratio of two complementary angles is 7 to 11. How large is each angle?

Ans. _____

14. The ratio of two supplementary angles is 1 to 5. How large is each angle?

Ans. _____

15. A line-segment 72 in. long is divided into two parts whose ratio is 3 to 5. How long is each part?

Ans. _____

16. What is the *mean proportional,*

   a. Between 25 and 9? _____   b. Between 12 and 75? _____

17. What is the *third proportional,*

   a. To 4 and 12? _____   b. To 12 and 4? _____

18. What is the *fourth proportional,*

   a. To 5, 15, and 4? _____   b. To 2, 3, and 8? _____

C. PROPORTIONAL LINE-SEGMENTS

If any two parts of one line-segment have the same ratio as the corresponding parts of another line-segment, the two line-segments are said to be *divided proportionally*. In Fig. 1 $\overline{MN}$ and $\overline{RS}$ are divided proportionally by transversal $\overline{AB}$ because $8 : 4 = 6 : 3$. A line segment is said to be *divided internally*, if its point of division lies between its end points. In Fig. 2 $\overline{XY}$ is divided internally at R. If its point of division lies upon its extension, a line-segment is said to be *divided externally*. In Fig. 2 $\overline{XY}$ is said to be divided externally at S. A line-segment which is divided internally and externally into the same ratio is said to be *divided harmonically*. In Fig. 3 $\overline{CD}$ is divided internally at P into the ratio $\dfrac{CP}{PD}$ or $\dfrac{5}{3}$. $\overline{CD}$ is divided externally at P′ into the ratio $\dfrac{CP'}{P'D}$ or $\dfrac{20}{12}$ which reduces to $\dfrac{5}{3}$. Hence $\overline{CD}$ is divided harmonically.

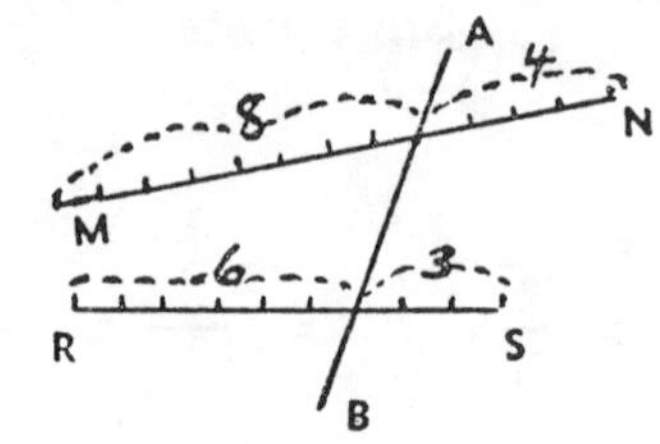

Fig. 1

Fig. 2

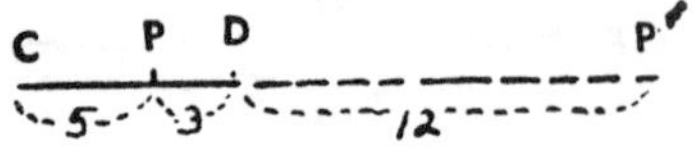

Fig. 3

EXERCISES C.

1. Fill the following answer-spaces with correct answers: Two line-segments are said to be divided _____, if any two parts of the one have the same _____ as the corresponding parts of the other.

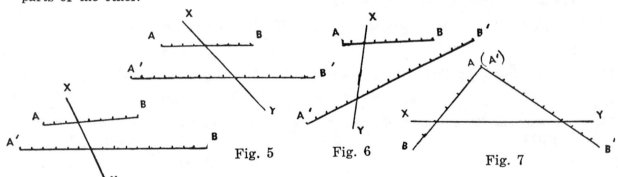

Fig. 4

Fig. 5

Fig. 6

Fig. 7

2. Answer the following questions, referring to the above figures. Are $\overline{AB}$ and $\overline{A'B'}$ divided proportionally by $\overline{XY}$,

   a. In Fig. 4? _____ b. In Fig. 5? _____ c. In Fig. 6? _____ d. In Fig. 7? _____

3. Fill the following answer-spaces with correct answers.

   a. If its point of division lies between its end points, a line-segment is said to be divided ____

   b. If its point of division lies upon its extension, a line-segment is said to be divided _____

   c. If a line-segment is divided internally and externally in the same ratio, it is said to be divided _____

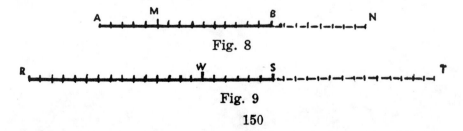

Fig. 8

Fig. 9

150

4. Refer to Fig. 8 above in filling the following answer-spaces.

a. AB is divided internally at _____ and externally at _____.

b. AB is divided internally into the ratio of _____ and externally into the ratio of _____.

c. Hence is AB divided harmonically? _____

5. Refer to Fig. 9 above in filling the following answer-spaces.

a. RS is divided internally at _____ and externally at _____.

b. RS is divided internally into the ratio of _____ and externally into the ratio of _____.

c. Hence is RS divided harmonically? _____.

THEOREM 98

If a line is drawn through two sides of a triangle parallel to the third side, it divides the two sides proportionally.

GIVEN: $\triangle$ RST with $\overline{MN}$ ∥ to $\overline{RS}$.

TO PROVE: that $\dfrac{TM}{MR} = \dfrac{TN}{NS}$.

Assume that TM and MR are commensurable.

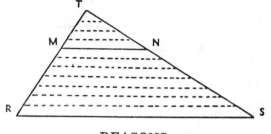

PROOF.   STATEMENTS

1. Let a = some common unit of measure of $\overline{MT}$ and $\overline{RM}$. (Why is this possible?)

2. Then let a be contained into $\overline{MT}$ x times, and into $\overline{MR}$ y times. (Why is this possible?)

3. Through the points of division of RT draw lines ∥ to $\overline{MN}$. These are ∥ to each other (Why?)

4. Then $\overline{TN}$ is divided into ____ equal segments, or TN = x, and $\overline{NS}$ is divided into ____ equal segments, or NS = ____

5. Hence $\dfrac{MT}{MR} = \dfrac{x}{y}$ and $\dfrac{TN}{NS} = \dfrac{x}{y}$

6. ∴ $\dfrac{TM}{MR} = \dfrac{TN}{NS}$

Therefore _____

REASONS

1. MT and RM are commensurable ....

2. ....

3. Unit 4, Th.? ....

4. Unit 6, Th.? ....

5. Quantities are proport. to their numerical measure (Division Property of Equality) ....

6. ....

COR. 1. If a line is drawn through two sides of a triangle parallel to the third side, either side is to one of its segments as the other side is to its corresponding segment.

GIVEN: $\triangle$ ABC with RS ∥ to AB.

TO PROVE: that $\dfrac{CA}{RA} = \dfrac{CB}{SB}$.

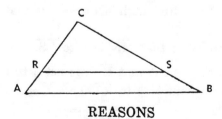

PROOF   STATEMENTS

1. $\dfrac{CR}{RA} = \dfrac{CS}{SB}$

2. $\dfrac{CR + RA}{RA} = \dfrac{CS + SB}{SB}$

REASONS

1. Th.? ....

2. Th.? About Proportion ....

3. However, CR + RA = CA and CS + SB = CB.

   3. Post.? ....

4. $\therefore \dfrac{CA}{RA} = \dfrac{CB}{SB}$

   4. ....

   Therefore ....

   ....

COR. 2. Corresponding segments cut off by three or more parallels on any two transversals are proportional.

GIVEN: ‖s $\overline{AB}$, $\overline{CD}$, and $\overline{EF}$ cut by transversals XY and RS.

TO PROVE: that $\dfrac{OM}{MG} = \dfrac{KN}{NH}$.

PROOF. Draw .... Th.? .....

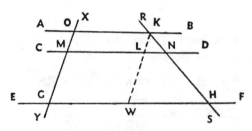

STATEMENTS

1. $\dfrac{KL}{LW} = \dfrac{KN}{NH}$

2. But KL = ... and LW = ...

3. $\therefore$ ..... = ...

   Therefore ....

   ....

REASONS

1. Th.? ....

2. Unit 6, Th.? Cor.? ....

3. ....

EXERCISES C′

Solve the following exercises.

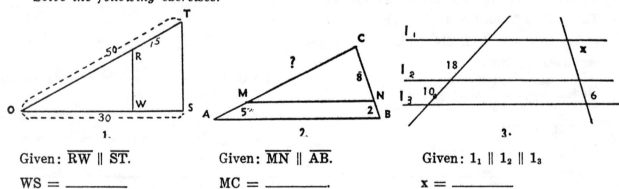

1.

Given: $\overline{RW} \parallel \overline{ST}$.

WS = ...

2.

Given: $\overline{MN} \parallel \overline{AB}$.

MC = ...

3.

Given: $1_1 \parallel 1_2 \parallel 1_3$

x = ...

THEOREM 99

If a line divides two sides of a triangle proportionally, it is parrallel to the third side.

GIVEN: $\triangle$ RST with MN drawn so that $\dfrac{TR}{TM} = \dfrac{TS}{TN}$.

TO PROVE: that $\overline{MN}$ is ‖ to $\overline{RS}$.

PROOF. Assume that $\overline{MN}$ is not ‖ to $\overline{RS}$. Draw $\overline{MN'}$ through point M ‖ to $\overline{RS}$. Th. ....

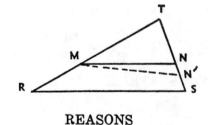

STATEMENTS

1. $\dfrac{TR}{TM} = \dfrac{TS}{TN}$

REASONS

1. ....

152

2. $\dfrac{TR}{TM} = \dfrac{TS}{TN'}$

3. Hence TN = TN′

4. Hence point N must coincide with point N′

5. Hence $\overline{MN}$ must coincide with $\overline{MN'}$

6. ∴ $\overline{MN}$ is ∥ to $\overline{RS}$

   Therefore _____

1. ....

2. ....

3. Th.? About Proportion ....

4. Post.? ....

5. Post.? ....

6. Post.? ....

CONSTRUCTION 8

To construct the fourth proportional to three given line-segments.

GIVEN: the three line-segments a, b, and c.

REQUIRED: To construct a line-segment x such that a:b = c:x.

Construction: Draw $\overrightarrow{OR}$ and $\overrightarrow{OS}$ making any convenient angle O.

On $\overrightarrow{OR}$ mark off $\overline{OM}$ = a and MN = b. On $\overrightarrow{OS}$ mark off $\overline{OW}$ = c.

Draw $\overline{MW}$. Then draw $\overline{NK}$ ∥ to $\overline{MW}$. Line-segment x is the fourth proportional to a, b, and c.

PROOF.   STATEMENTS

1. ∴ a : b = c:x

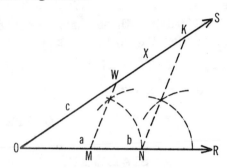

REASONS

1. Th.? ....

CONSTRUCTION EXERCISES C.

Make the following constructions accurately with compass and straightedge in the corresponding spaces provided for constructions.

STATEMENTS	CONSTRUCTIONS
1. Construct the fourth proportional to line-segments **r**, **s**, and **t**. r s t	1.
2. Construct the third proportional to line-segments **m** and **n**. m n	2.
3. Construct a rectangle that will have length l and that will be equivalent to square A. A S l	3.

To divide a line-segment into parts that are proportional to any number of given line-segments.

GIVEN: Line-segment AB and the three line-segments a, b, and c.

REQUIRED: To divide $\overline{AB}$ into three line-segments x, y, and z, such that a:b:c = x:y:z.

Construction: Draw $\overrightarrow{AR}$ making any convenient $\angle$ BAR with $\overline{AB}$.

On $\overrightarrow{AR}$ mark off AM = a, MN = b, and NW = c. Draw $\overline{BW}$. Then through points N and M draw line-segments to $\overline{AB} \parallel$ to $\overline{BW}$.

$\overline{AB}$ is divided into three parts x, y, and z, that are proportional to a, b, and c.

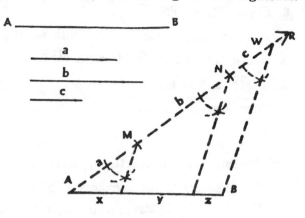

PROOF.   STATEMENTS

1. ∴ a:b:c = x:y:z

REASONS

1. Th.? Cor.? ....

CONSTRUCTION EXERCISE C'.

STATEMENT	CONSTRUCTION
1. Divide line-segment MN into four parts which are proportional to line-segments a, b, c, and d. a b c d	M ———————————— N 1.

THEOREM 100

The bisector of an (interior) angle of a triangle divides the opposite side into segments that are proportional to the other two sides.

GIVEN: $\triangle$ ABC with $\overline{CM}$ bisecting $\angle$ C.
TO PROVE: that AM:MB = AC:CB.

PROOF: Through A draw $\overline{AR} \parallel$ to CM and extend $\overline{BC}$ to their intersection R.

STATEMENTS

1. $\overline{AR}$ and $\overline{BC}$ extended must intersect.

2. $\angle 2 = \angle 3$

3. $\angle 1 = \angle 2$

4. $\angle 4 = \angle 3$

5. Hence $\angle 1 = \angle 4$

REASONS

1. Th.? ....

2. ....

3. Th.? ....

4. ....

5. .... Principle

6. Hence AC = RC   6. ....

7. AM:MB = RC:CB   7. Th.? ....

8. ∴ AM:MB = AC:CB   8. ....

    Therefore _____

THEOREM 101

    If the bisector of an exterior angle of a triangle meets the opposite side extended, it will divide the side externally into segments that are proportional to the adjacent sides.

GIVEN: △ RST with $\overline{TC}$ bisecting exterior ∠ STA.

TO PROVE: that RC:CS = RT:TS

PROOF. Draw $\overline{SN}$ ∥ to $\overline{TC}$. (Th. ____)

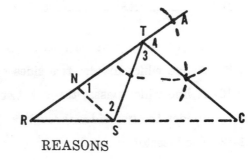

STATEMENTS	REASONS
1. ∠ 3 = ∠ 4	1. ....
2. ∠ ____ = ∠ 3	2. Alt. int. ∠ of ∥ ls. are = ...
3. ∠ ____ = ∠ 4	3: Corres. ∠ of ∥ ls. are = ...
4. Hence ∠ ____ = ∠ ____	4. Substitution Principle ....
5. Hence TN = ____	5. ....
6. RC:CS = ____ : ____	6. ....
7. ∴ RC:CS = RT:TS	7. ....

    Therefore _____

EXERCISES C″

1. Will the bisector of ∠ NOR meet the extension of base MN?   _____

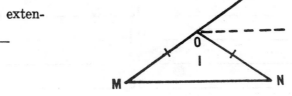

    Explain. _____

---

2. Would this situation occur if ∠ M and ∠ N were unequal? _____

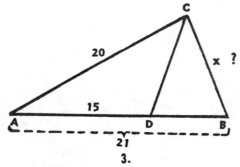

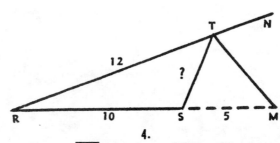

3. Given: $\overline{CD}$ bisects ∠ C. x = ____   4. Given: $\overline{TM}$ bisects ∠ STN. ST = ____

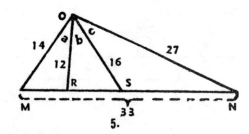 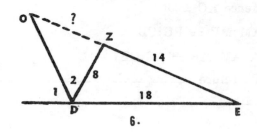

5. Given: ∠ a = ∠ b = ∠ c.

MR = _____ RS = _____ SN = _____

6. Given: ∠ 1 = ∠ 2

OZ = _____

Fill each corresponding answer-space below with the correct answer.

7-8. A line which divides two sides of a △ proportionately is ____ 7 ____ to the ____ 8 ____

9-10. A line which passes through two sides of a △ and which is ___ 9 ___ to the third side divides the two sides through which it passes ___ 10 ___

11-12. The bisector of any interior ∠ of a △ divides the opposite side into segments that are ____ ___ 11 ___ to the ___ 12 ___ sides.

13-14. Corresponding line-segments that are cut off by a series of parallel lines on any two ___ 13 ___ are ___ 14 ___

15-17. The bisector of an exterior ∠ formed at the vertex ∠ of a (n) ____ 15 ____ △, or at each ∠ of a (n) ___ 16 ___ △ is ___ 17 ___ to the opposite side.

18-20. The bisector of an exterior ∠ of a △, in which the ∡ opposite the exterior ∠ that is being bisected are unequal, will intersect the ___ 18 ___ side extended and will divide it ___ 19 ___ into parts which are ___ 20 ___ to the other two sides.

ANSWERS TO QUESTIONS 7-20

7. _____	12. _____	17. _____
8. _____	13. _____	18. _____
9. _____	14. _____	19. _____
10. _____	15. _____	20. _____
11. _____	16. _____	

Unit XIV.

SIMILAR POLYGONS AND RELATED LINES

A. NATURE OF SIMILAR POLYGONS

Similar polygons are polygons which have the same number of sides and angles, whose corresponding sides are proportional and whose corresponding angles are equal.

Corresponding sides of similar polygons always lie in the same RELATIVE POSITION with respect to the other sides of the polygons. In the accompanying figures, squares A, B, and C are similar. Parallelograms D and E are similar, and so are triangles F and G.

The ratio of any two corresponding sides of similar polygons is the same, and it is known as the *ratio of similitude* of the polygons. The ratio similitude of parallelograms D

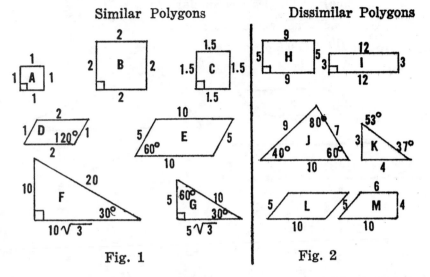

Similar Polygons   Dissimilar Polygons

Fig. 1   Fig. 2

and E, for instance, is 1/5 or 5/1; that of squares B and C is 4/3 or 3/4. The symbol for similar is ~.

PRELIMINARY EXERCISES. A.

1. Define the following terms:

   a. Similar polygons _____

   _____

   b. Corresponding sides of similar polygons _____

   c. Ratio of similitude _____

   _____

2. Answer the following questions correctly with *yes* or *no*.

   Are two polygons necessarily similar,

   a. If they have same size? _____

   b. If they have the same shape? _____

   c. If one is a mere enlargement or magnification of the other? _____

   d. If one is a mere reduction of the other? _____

3. Write the symbol for *similar* _____

4. Underline correct words in parentheses in the following statements. Also make free-hand drawings in the space provided for illustrations, to justify each answer.

   ILLUSTRATIONS

   a. (All, some) equilateral triangles are similar.

   b. (All, some) similar triangles are congruent.

   c. (All, some) congruent triangles are similar.

157

d. (All, some) equivalent triangles are similar.

e. (All, some) right triangles are similar.

f. (All, some) isosceles right triangles are similar.

g. (All, some) isosceles triangles are similar.

h. (All, some) squares are similar.

i. (All some) rectangles are similar.

j. (All, some) rhombuses are similar.

Solve the following exercises.

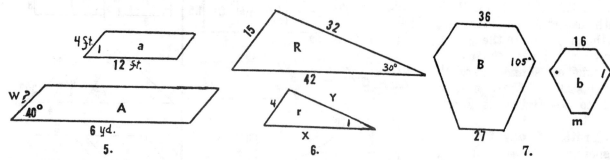

5.

Given: ▱ a ~ ▱ A

W = _____ yd.

∠1 = _____

Ratio of similitude = _____

6.

Given: △ R ~ △ r

x = _____

y = _____

∠ 1 = _____

7.

Given: Polygon B ~ polygon b

m = _____

∠ 1 = _____

Ratio of similitude = _____

8. The three sides of a certain triangle are 20 in., 28 in., and 36 in. respectively. If the triangle is diminished in size but not in shape until the 20 in. side becomes 4 in., what will be the lengths of the other two sides?

Ans._____

THEOREM 102

The perimeters of two similar polygons have the same ratio as the ratio of any two corresponding sides.

GIVEN: Similar polygons R and R′ with a and a′, b and b′, c and c′, d and d′ etc, as their corresponding sides respectively.

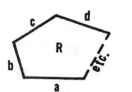

TO PROVE: that $\dfrac{a+b+c+d \text{ etc.}}{a'+b'+c'+d' \text{ etc.}} = \dfrac{a}{a'}$

STATEMENTS

1. $\dfrac{a}{a'} = \dfrac{b}{b'} = \dfrac{c}{c'} = \dfrac{d}{d'}$ etc.

2. ∴ $\dfrac{a+b+c+d. \text{ etc.}}{a'+b'+c'+d' \text{ etc.}} = \dfrac{a}{a'}$

Therefore _____

_____

REASONS

1. Corres. sides of ~ polygons are? ....

2. Th.? About Proportion ....

EXERCISES A.

1. One side of a certain polygon is 5 and its perimeter is 75. What is the perimeter of a similar polygon whose corresponding side is 14?

Ans._____

2. The perimeters of two similar polygons are 160 and 20 respectively. If one side of the first polygon is 7.2, what is the corresponding side of the second?

Ans._____

B. SIMILAR TRIANGLES
THEOREM 103

If two triangles have three angles of one equal respectively to the three angles of the other, the triangles are similar. (AAA)

GIVEN: △ ABC and RST with ∠ A = ∠ R, ∠ B = ∠ S, and ∠ C = ∠ T.

TO PROVE: that △ ABC ~ △ RST.

PROOF. Place △ ABC upon △ RST so that ∠ C coincides with its equal, ∠ T, and so that AB takes the position A′B′ as shown.

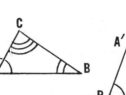
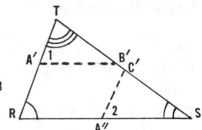

STATEMENTS

1. ∠R = ∠ 1

2. Hence A′B′ is ‖ to RS

3. Hence TA′:TR = TB′:TS

4. Or CA:TR = CB:TS
   Similarly, place △ ABC upon △ RST so that ∠ B coincides with its equal, ∠ S, and so that AC takes the position A″C′ as shown.

5. ∠R = ∠ _____

6. Hence _____ is ‖ to _____

7. Hence SA″:RS = SC′:TS

8. Or AB:RS = CB:TS

9. Hence CA:TR = CB:TS = AB:RS

10. ∴ △ ABC ~ △ RST

   Therefore _____

REASONS

1. Substitution of ∠1 for ∠? ....

2. Th. 23, Cor.? ....

3. Th. 98, Cor.? ....

4. .... Principle

5. ....

6. ....

7. ....

8. ....

9. Substitution or .... Property

10. ....

COR. 1. If two triangles have the two angles of one equal respectively to the two angles of the other, the triangles are similar. (AA)

GIVEN: △ ABC and A′B′C′ with ∠

____ = ∠ ____ and ∠ ____ = ∠ ____

TO PROVE: that △ ____ ~ △ ____

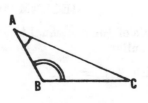
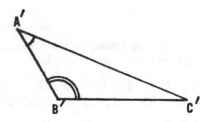

PROOF. STATEMENTS

1. ∠ ____ = ∠ ____ and ∠ ____ = ∠ ____

2. Hence ∠ _____ = ∠ _____

REASONS

1. ....

2. Th. 33, Cor.? ....

159

3. ∴ △ ABC∼ △ A'B'C'   3. _____

Therefore _____

_____

COR. 2 Triangles similar to the same triangle are similar to each other.

GIVEN: △ M'N'R' ∼ △ MNR.
and △ M"N"R" ∼ △ MNR.

TO PROVE: that △ M'N'R' ∼ △ M"N"R"

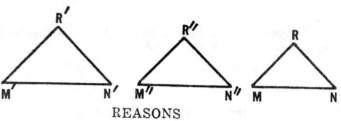

PROOF.   STATEMENTS

1. ∠M' = ∠M, ∠N' = ∠N and
   ∠R' = ∠R

2. ∠M" = ∠M, ∠N" = ∠N and ∠R"
   = ∠R

3. So ∠M' = ∠M", ∠N' = ∠N", and ∠R'
   = ∠R"

4. ∴ △ M'N'R' ∼ △ M"N"R"

Therefore _____

REASONS

1. ....

2. ....

3. .... Property of Equality, or ....

4. ....

COR. 3. Corresponding altitudes of similar triangles have the same ratio as any pair of corresponding sides.

GIVEN: △ ABC ∼ △ A'B'C' with altitudes $\overline{CM}$
and $\overline{C'M'}$ respectively.

TO PROVE: that CM:C'M' = AC:A'C'.

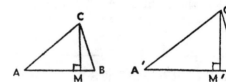

PROOF.   STATEMENTS

1. ∠A = ∠A'

2. ∠AMC = ∠A'M'C'

3. △AMC ∼ △ A'M'C'

4. ∴ CM:C'M' = AC:A'C'

Therefore _____

REASONS

1. ....

2. Th.? ....

3. ....

4. ....

THEOREM 104

If two triangles have an angle of the one equal to an angle of the other and the including sides proportional, the triangles are similar.

GIVEN: △ ABC and A'B'C' with ∠ C = ∠ C'
and with AC:A'C' = BC:B'C'.

TO PROVE: that △ ABC ∼ △ A'B'C'.

PROOF. Place △ ABC upon △ A'B'C' so that ∠C
coincides with its equal, ∠C', and so that side
AB takes the position MN as shown.

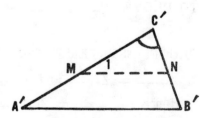

160

STATEMENTS	REASONS
1. AC:A'C' = BC:B'C'	1. ....
2. Hence MC':A'C' = NC':B'C'	2. Substitution ....
3. Hence MN is ‖ to _____	3. ....
4. Hence ∠1 = ∠ _____	4. ....
5. ∠C' = ∠ _____	5. Reflexive? ....
6. Hence △ MNC' ~ △ A'B'C'	6. A A ....
7. ∴ △ ABC ~ △ A'B'C'	7. ....

Therefore _____

THEOREM 105

If two triangles have their corresponding sides proportional, the triangles are similar.

GIVEN: △ ABC and A'B'C' in which

$$\frac{AB}{A'B'} = \frac{CB}{C'B'} = \frac{CA}{C'A'}.$$

TO PROVE: that △ _____ ~ △ _____

PROOF. Mark off CM = C'A' and CN = C'B'.
 Draw $\overline{MN}$. Post. _____.

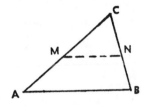

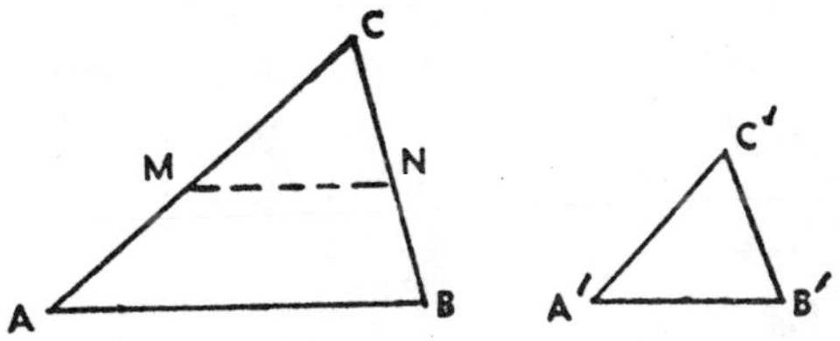

STATEMENTS	REASONS
1. ∠C = ∠C	1. ....
2. $\dfrac{CA}{C'A'} = \dfrac{CB}{C'B'}$	2. ....
3. Hence $\dfrac{CA}{CM} = \dfrac{CB}{CN}$	3. A Double? ....
4. ∴ △ ABC ~ △ _____	4. Th.? ....
5. ∴ $\dfrac{CA}{CM} = \dfrac{AB}{MN}$	5. What Property of ~ △ ? ....
6. $\dfrac{CA}{C'A'} = \dfrac{AB}{A'B'}$	6. ....
7. But CM = C'A'	7. Construction ....
8. Hence (from steps 5 and 6) MN = A'B'	8. Th.? About Proportion ....
9. ∴ △ _____ ≅ △ A'B'C'	9. ....
10. ∴ △ _____ ~ △ _____	10. ....

Therefore _____

LIST I.   LIST II.

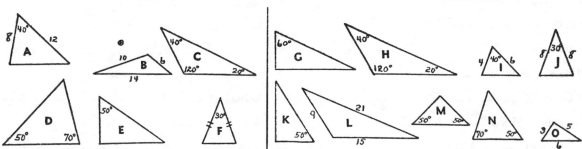

Select from LIST II the triangles that are similar to those in LIST I.

1. △ A ∼ △ ____   Why? _____

2. △ B ∼ △ ____   Why? _____

3. △ C ∼ △ ____   Why? _____

4. △ D ∼ △ ____   Why? _____

5. △ E ∼ △ ____   Why? _____

6. △ F ∼ △ ____   Why? _____

THEOREM 106

Two similar polygons can be divided into the same number of triangles which are similar each to each and similarly placed by diagonals drawn from corresponding vertices.

GIVEN: Polygon ABCDE ∼ polygon A'B'C'D'E'.

TO PROVE: that ABCDE and A'B'C'D'E' can be divided into the same number of △ similar each to each and similarly placed.

PROOF. Draw all possible diagonals from any two corresponding vertices such as A and A'.

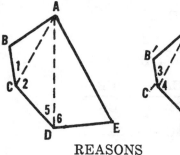

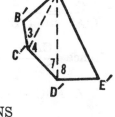

STATEMENTS

1. Both polygons have the same no. of sides, n.

2. ∴ each polygon is divided into _____ △
   In △ ABC and A'B'C',

3. ∠B = ∠ _____

4. $\dfrac{AB}{A'B'} = \dfrac{BC}{B'C'}$

5. ∴ △ _____ ∼ △ _____
   In △ ACD and A'C'D',

6. $\dfrac{AC}{A'C'} = \dfrac{BC}{B'C'}$

7. $\dfrac{CD}{C'D'} = \dfrac{BC}{B'C'}$

8. Hence $\dfrac{AC}{A'C'} = \dfrac{CD}{C'D'}$

REASONS

1. ....

2. ....

3. What property of ∼ polygons? ....

4. What property of ∼ polygons? ....

5. Th.? ....

6. What property of ∼ △? ....

7. ....

8. .... Property of Equality or ....

162

9. $\angle C = \angle$ _____   9. ....

10. $\angle 1 = \angle$ _____   10. ....

11. Hence $\angle$ _____ $= \angle$ _____   11. .... Property of Equality

12. $\therefore \triangle$ _____ $\sim \triangle$ _____   12. Th. ....

13. Finally $\dfrac{AE}{AE'} = \dfrac{DE}{D'E'}$ 13. ....

14. And $\angle E = \angle E'$ 14. ....

15. $\therefore \triangle ADE \sim \triangle A'D'E'$ 15. ....

Therefore _____

THEOREM 107

If two polygons are composed of the same number of triangles similar each to each and similarly placed, the polygons are similar.

GIVEN: Polygons ABCDE and A'B'C'D'E'
with $\triangle$ ABC $\sim \triangle$ A'B'C', $\triangle$ ACD $\sim$
$\triangle$ A'C'D' ... and finally $\triangle$ ADE $\sim \triangle$ A'D'E'

TO PROVE: that ABCDE $\sim$ A'B'C'D'E'.

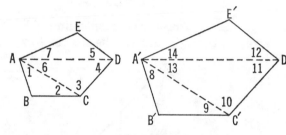

PROOF.   STATEMENTS

REASONS

Proving that the corresponding angles of the polygons are equal:

1. $\angle B = \angle$ _____   1. Property of $\sim \triangle$ ....

2. $\angle 2 = \angle$ _____ and $\angle 3 = \angle$ _____   2. ....

3. Hence $\angle C = \angle$ _____   3. ....

4. Similarly, $\angle D = \angle$ _____   4. ....

5. $\angle E = \angle$ _____   5. ....

6. Finally $\angle A = \angle$ _____   6. .... Property of Equality

Proving that the corresponding sides of the polygons are proportional:

7. $\dfrac{AB}{A'B'} = \dfrac{BC}{B'C'}$ 7. ....

8. $\dfrac{BC}{B'C'} = \dfrac{AC}{A'C'}$ 8. ....

9. $\dfrac{CD}{C'D'} = \dfrac{AC}{A'C'} = \dfrac{AD}{A'D'}$ 9. ....

10. Hence $\dfrac{BC}{B'C'} = \dfrac{CD}{C'D'}$ (from steps 8 and 9)   10. ....

11. Finally $\dfrac{DE}{D'E'} = \dfrac{EA}{E'A'} = \dfrac{AD}{A'D'}$

11. ....

12. Hence $\dfrac{AB}{A'B'} = \dfrac{BC}{B'C'} = \dfrac{CD}{C'D'} =$

12. Transitive ....
    or Multiple ....

$\dfrac{DE}{D'E'} = \dfrac{EA}{E'A'}$

13. ∴ polygon ABCDE ~ polygon A'B'C'D'E'

13. ....

Therefore ....

....

CONSTRUCTION EXERCISES C.

Make the following constructions accurately with compass and straightedge in the corresponding spaces provided for constructions.

STATEMENTS	CONSTRUCTIONS
1. Upon $\overline{MN}$ as the base corresponding to $\overline{RS}$, construct a triangle that will be similar to △ RST.	M_____N
2. Upon $\overline{R'S'}$ as the base corresponding to $\overline{RS}$, construct a polygon that will be similar to polygon RSTW. 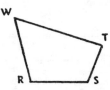	R'_____S'

3. Construct a △ R'S'T' which will be similar to △ RST and which will have as its perimeter line-segment m.

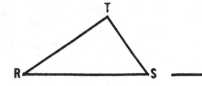

THEOREM 108

If two chords intersect within a circle, the product of the segments of the one is equal to product of the segments of the other.

GIVEN: ⊙ O with chords MN and RS intersecting at C.

TO PROVE: that MC · NC = RC · SC.

PROOF. Draw RM and NS. (Post. 3)

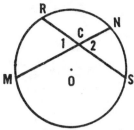

STATEMENTS	REASONS
1. ∠ 1 = ∠ _____	1. ....
2. ∠ M ≐ _____ and ∠ S ≐ _____	2. Unit 10, Th.? ....
3. So ∠ M = ∠ S	3. ....
4. Hence △ MCR ~ △ SCN	4. ....
5. Hence MC : _____ = _____ : _____	5. ....
6. ∴ MC · NC = RC · SC	6. Th.? about Proportion ....

Therefore _____

_____

EXERCISES C

1. Fill the following answer-spaces with correct answers.

1. Except for _____, similar polygons are always alike in every respect. Their corresponding sides are _____ __ and their corresponding angles are _____. Their perimeters have the same _____ as a pair of corresponding _____.

2. Two △ are similar: (1) if each is _____ to the _____, (2) if they are mutually _____, (3) if they have two _____ of the one equal to two _____ of the other, (4) if their corresponding sides are _____ _____, and (5) if two sides of the one are _____ to two sides of the other and the _____ angles are _____.

3. Corresponding _____, corresponding _____, and the _____ of similar △ have the same ratio.

4. Polygons are similar if they are composed of the same number of_____ which are _____ each to each and _____ placed.

5. If within a circle two chords intersect, the _____ of the _____ of the one equals the _____ of the of the other.

6. In a certain circle chords AB and CD intersect at point P within the circle, making AP = 8, BP = 9, and CP twice as long as DP. Using the circle in Fig. 3, make a free hand drawing of the conditions given. How long is chord CD?

ANS. _____

Fig. 3

7. Given: In Fig. 4 ⊙ O whose radius = 25, with OR = 20, and $\overline{MN}$ ⊥ to $\overline{OR}$. How long is $\overline{MN}$?

ANS. _____

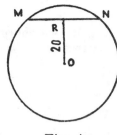

Fig. 4

Unit XV.

USE OF MEAN PROPORTIONALS. EXTREME AND MEAN RATIO

A. SOME APPLICATIONS OF MEAN PROPORTIONAL LINE-SEGMENTS

THEOREM 109

The altitude (perpendicular) drawn from the vertex of the right angle of a right triangle to the hypotenuse forms two triangles which are similar to the given triangle and to each other.

GIVEN: Rt. △ XYZ in which altitude $\overline{ZN}$ is drawn from right ∠ Z to hypotenuse XY.

To PROVE: that △ A ~ △ B ~ △ XYZ.

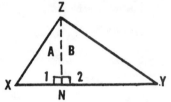

PROOF   STATEMENTS

1. In △ A and △ XYZ, ∠ 1 = ∠ Z
2. And ∠ X = ∠ X
3. ∴ △ A ~ △ XYZ
4. In △ B and △ XYZ, ∠ 2 = ∠ ____
5. Also ∠ Y = ∠ ____
6. ∴ △ B ~ △ XYZ
7. ∴ △ A ~ △ B

Therefore _____

REASONS

1. Unit 1, Th.? ....
2. ....
3. ....
4. ....
5. ....
6. ....
7. Th. 103, Cor.? ....

COR. 1. The altitude drawn from the vertex of the right angle of a right triangle to the hypotenuse is the mean proportional between the segments of the hypotenuse.

GIVEN: Right △ XYZ with altitude $\overline{ZN}$ in the figure for Theorem 109.

TO PROVE: XN: ZN = ZN: NY

PROOF   STATEMENTS

1. △ A ~ △ B
2. ∴ XN : ZN = ZN : NY

REASONS

1. _____
2. _____

Therefore _____

COR. 2. Each leg of a right triangle is the mean proportional between the hypotenuse and the adjacent segment of the hypotenuse formed by the altitude upon the hypotenuse.

166

GIVEN: Right △ XYZ in the figure for Theorem 109 with altitude $\overline{ZN}$ drawn from right ∠ Z to hypotenuse $\overline{XY}$.

TO PROVE: that XN : XZ = XZ : XY and that YN : YZ = YZ : XY

PROOF STATEMENTS	REASONS
1. △ A ~ △ XYZ	1. _____
2. ∴ XN : XZ = XZ : XY	2. _____
3. Also △ B ~ △ XYZ	3. _____
4. ∴ YN : YZ = YZ : XY	4. _____

Therefore _____

EXERCISES A

1. In Fig. 1, △ ABC ~ △ _____ and △ _____
2. In △ ADC, ∠ 3 = _____°
3. In △ BDC, ∠ 1 = _____°
4. In △ ABC, AC = _____, CD = _____, and

BC = _____

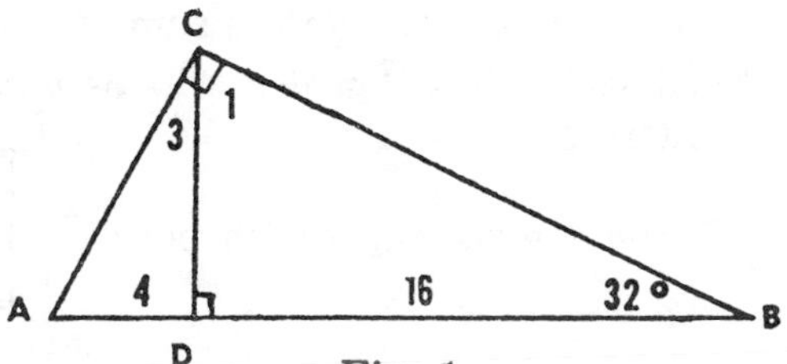

Fig. 1

COR. 3.   **A perpendicular, drawn from any point on a circle to its diameter, is the mean proportional between the segments of the diameter.**

GIVEN: ⊙ O with diameter MN, and $\overline{AB}$ ⊥ to $\overline{MN}$

TO PROVE: that MB: _____ = _____ : _____

PROOF: Draw $\overline{MA}$ and $\overline{NA}$. (Post. ___)

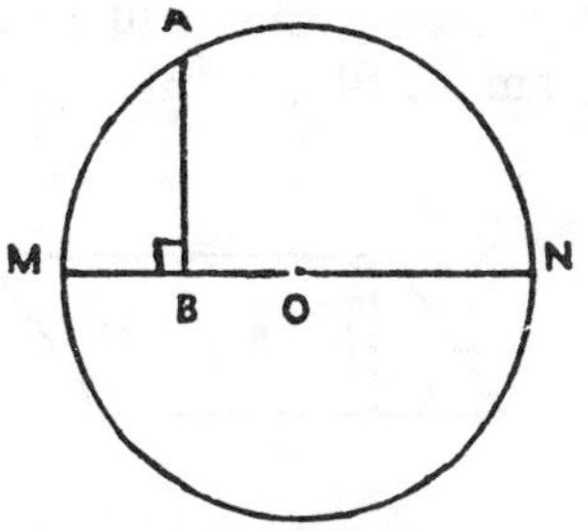

STATEMENTS	REASONS
1. ∠ MAN is a rt. ∠, making △ MAN a rt. △	1. Th. 69, Cor.? _____
2. ∴ MB : _____ = _____ : _____	2. _____

Therefore _____

CONSTRUCTION 10
To construct a mean proportional between two given line-segments.

GIVEN: Line-segments **m** and **n**.

REQUIRED: To construct a mean proportional between **m** and **n** so that **m:x = x:n**.

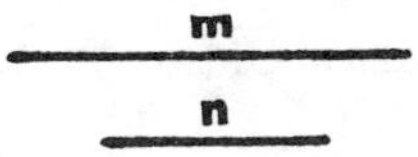

Construction: On **r** mark off a line-segment equal to **m + n**. Locate the midpoint of the line-segment **m + n**, and draw a semicircle with line-segment **m + n** as the diameter. Erect a perpendicular **x** to line-segment **m + n** at the point where **m** and **n** meet, and extend it to the circle.

x is the mean proportional between **m** and **n**.

PROOF. STATEMENTS	REASONS
1. **m:x = x:n**	1. _____

CONSTRUCTION EXERCISES A.

Make the following constructions accurately with compass and straightedge in the corresponding spaces provided for constructions.

	CONSTRUCTIONS
1. Construct a line-segment which will be $\sqrt{10}$ times line-segment **a**. —— a ——	1
2. Construct a rectangle the sum of whose length and width is $\overline{AB}$ which will be equivalent to square N. Shade the rectangle with pencil. N A———————B	2
3. Construct a square that will be equivalent to parallelogram A. Shade the square with pencil. h A / b	3

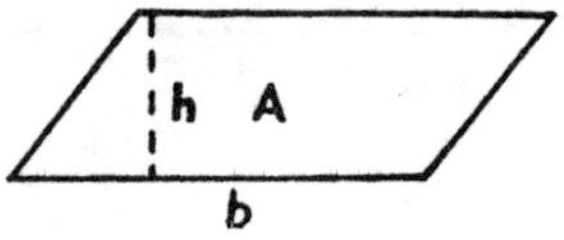

THEOREM 110

The square of the hypotenuse of a right triangle is equal to the sum of the squares of the other two sides.

GIVEN: Rt. $\triangle$ ABC whose rt. $\angle$ is $\angle$ C.

TO PROVE: that $c^2 = a^2 + b^2$.

PROOF. From the vertex C draw $\overline{CM} \perp$ to $\overline{AB}$.

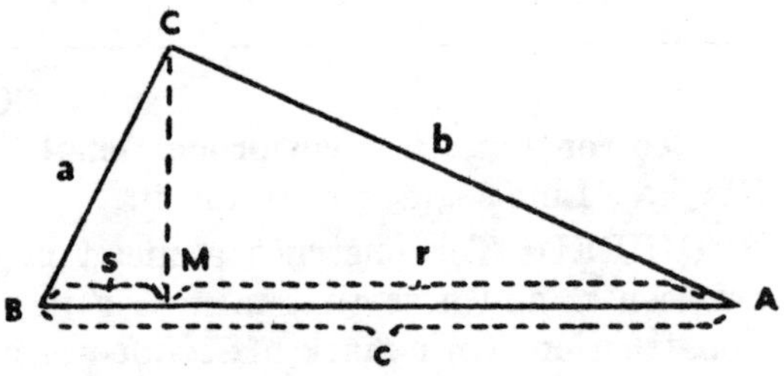

STATEMENTS

1. $c:b =$ _____ $: r$, or $cr =$ _____

2. $c :$ _____ $=$ _____ $: s$, or $cs =$ _____

3. Hence $cr + cs$ or $c(r + s) =$ ___ $+$ ___

4. However, $r + s = c$

5. $\therefore c^2 = a^2 + b^2$

REASONS

1. ....

2. ....

3. .... Property of Equality

4. Postulate 17 ....

5. ....

168

Therefore _____

THEOREM 111

If from a point without a circle a secant and a tangent are drawn, the tangent is the mean proportional between the whole secant and its external segment.

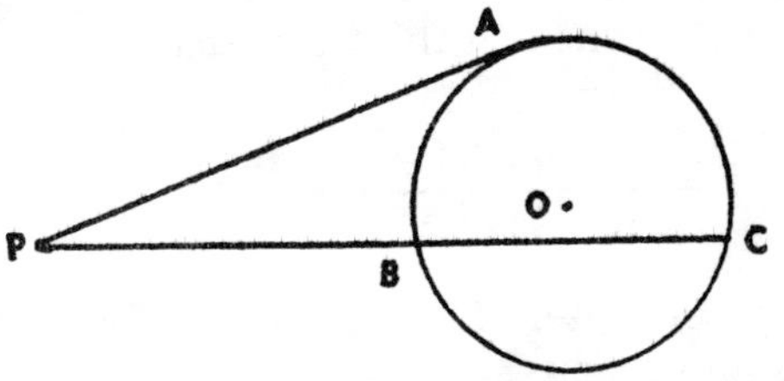

GIVEN: ⊙ O with secant PC and tangent PA drawn from point P outside ⊙ O.

TO PROVE: that PB : PA = PA : PC.

PROOF. Draw $\overline{AB}$ and $\overline{AC}$. Post. _____

STATEMENTS	REASONS
1. ∠ PAB $\doteq$ ½ arc _____	1. Unit 10, Th.? ....
2. ∠ C $\doteq$ ½ arc _____	2. Unit 10, Th.? ....
3. ∠ PAB = ∠ _____	3. .... or .... Prop. of Eq.
4. ∠ _____ = ∠ _____	4. ....
5. Hence △ PBA ~ △ PAC	5. ....
6. ∴ PB : PA = PA : PC	6. ....

Therefore _____

EXERCISE A′

1. Given: In Fig. 2 ⊙ r with tangent PT = 10, and PA = one-third of AM. How long is secant PM?

ANS. _____

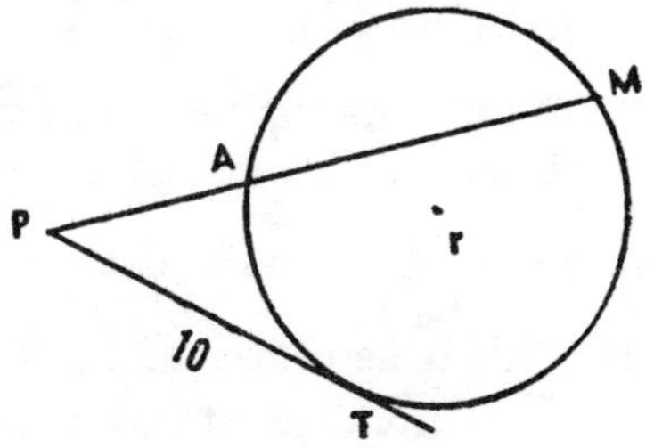

Fig. 2

B. EXTREME AND MEAN RATIO

A line segment is said to be divided into *extreme and mean ratio*, if its larger part is the mean proportional between the whole line-segment and its shorter part. It is said that rectangles which are the most pleasing to the eye are those whose dimensions are in extreme and mean ratio.

EXERCISES B

1. Fill the following answer-spaces with correct answers.

   a. A line-segment is said to be divided into *extreme and mean ratio*, if its larger part is the _____ _____ between the whole line-segment and its shorter part.

   b. The division of a line-segment into extreme and mean ratio may be expressed in the form of the following proportion: _____ part : _____ part = _____ part : both parts.

   c. Rectangles said to be the *most pleasing to the eye* are those whose dimensions are in_____ _____ and _____ ratio.

169

d. The dimensions of rectangle R are in extreme and mean ratio. Write the proportion in term of W and L that expresses this relationship.

W : _____ = _____ : _____.

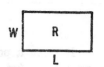

2. Line-segment MN is 12 units long. If $\overline{MN}$ were divided into extreme and mean ratio, what would be the length of each part?

M _____ 12 _____ N

Ans. _____

3. The perimeter of rectangle A is 16, and its dimensions are in extreme and mean ratio. What are its dimensions?

A

Ans. _____

CONSTRUCTION 11

To divide a line-segment into extreme and mean ratio.

GIVEN: Line-segment RS.

REQUIRED: To divide $\overline{RS}$ into extreme and mean ratio, i. e. to find point P on $\overline{RS}$ such that RS:RP = RP:PS.

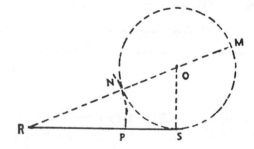

Construction:

1. At S draw $\overline{SO} \perp$ to $\overline{RS}$ and equal to ½ $\overline{RS}$.

2. With O as center and $\overline{OS}$ as radius, draw a circle.

3. Through R and O draw $\overline{RM}$ cutting the circle at N and M.

4. With R as center and $\overline{RN}$ as radius, mark off $\overline{RP}$ on $\overline{RS}$ equal to $\overline{RN}$.
   $\overline{RS}$ is divided into extreme and mean ratio at point P.

PROOF.   STATEMENTS   REASONS

1. $\dfrac{RM}{RS} = \dfrac{RS}{RN}$

   1. Th.? ....

2. $\dfrac{RM - RS}{RS} = \dfrac{RS - RN}{RN}$

   2. Th.? about Proportion ....

3. RS = NM and RN = RP

   3. ....

4. Hence $\dfrac{RM - NM}{RS} = \dfrac{RS - RP}{RP}$

   4. .... Principle ....

5. Or $\dfrac{RP}{RS} = \dfrac{PS}{RP}$

   5. ....

6. $\dfrac{RP}{RS} = \dfrac{PS}{RP}$

   6. ....

7. ∴ $\dfrac{RS}{RN} = \dfrac{RP}{PS}$

   7. Th.? about Proportion ....

170

Make the following constructions with compass and straightedge in the corresponding space provided for construction.

STATEMENTS	CONSTRUCTIONS
1. Divide line-segment AB into extreme and mean ratio.	A●————————————●B 1.
2. Construct the rectangle that shall be most pleasing to the eye, having $\overline{AB}$ in exercise 1 as the sum of its length and width.	2.

Unit XVI.

RATIOS OF AREAS OF POLYGONS

A. RATIOS OF AREAS OF PARALLELOGRAMS

THEOREM 112

The areas of any two parallelograms are to each other (have the same ratio) as the products of their bases and altitudes.

GIVEN: ▱ MNRS and M′N′R′S′.

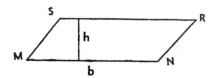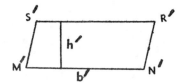

TO PROVE: that $\dfrac{A}{A'} = \dfrac{b \cdot h}{b' \cdot h'}$

PROOF. STATEMENTS

1. A = _____ and A′ = _____

2. ∴ _____ = _____

Therefore _____

_____

REASONS

1. Unit 11, Th.? ....

2. .... Prop. of Equality

COR. 1. The areas of any two parallelograms having equal bases are to each other as their altitudes.

GIVEN: ▱ CDEG and C′D′E′G′ with b = b′.

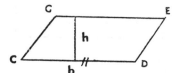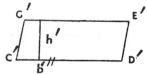

TO PROVE: that $\dfrac{A}{A'} =$ ———.

PROOF. STATEMENTS

1. $\dfrac{A}{A'} = \dfrac{b \cdot h}{b' \cdot h'}$

2. ∴ $\dfrac{A}{A'} = \dfrac{b \cdot h}{b \cdot h'} = \dfrac{h}{h'}$

Therefore _____

_____

REASONS

1. Th.? ....

2. .... and cancellation

COR. 2. The areas of any two parallelgrams having equal altitudes are to each other as their bases.

GIVEN: ▱ RBCD and R′B′C′D′ with h = h′.

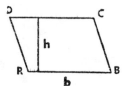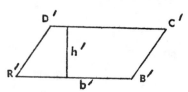

TO PROVE: that _____ = _____.

PROOF. STATEMENTS

1. $\dfrac{A}{A'} =$ _____

2. ∴ _____ = _____ = _____

REASONS

1. ....

2. ....

Therefore _____

EXERCISES A

Solve the following exercises.

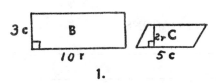 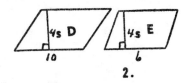 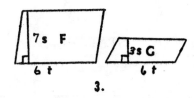

1.

Given: ⌱ B and C with
Area of ⌷ B = 75

Area of ⌷ C = _____

2.

Given: ⌱ D and E with
Area of ⌷ E = 24

Area of ⌷ D = _____

3.

Given: ⌱ F and G with
Area of ⌷ F = 42

Area of ⌷ G = _____

B. RATIOS OF AREAS OF TRIANGLES

THEOREM 113

The areas of any two triangles are to each other as the products of their bases and altitudes.

GIVEN: △ MNR and M'N'R'.

TO PROVE: that $\dfrac{A}{A'} = \dfrac{b \cdot h}{b' \cdot h'}$.

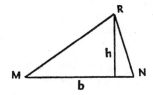

PROOF. STATEMENTS	REASONS
1. A = _____ and A' = _____	1. Th.? _____
2. ∴ $\dfrac{A}{A'} = $ _____ $= \dfrac{b \cdot h}{b' \cdot h'}$	2. _____ Prop. of Equality and ____

Therefore _____

COR. 1. **The areas of any two triangles having equal bases are to each other as their altitudes.**

GIVEN: △ RST and R'S'T' with b = b'.

TO PROVE: that $\dfrac{A}{A'} = \dfrac{h}{h'}$.

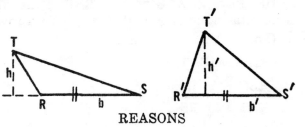

PROOF. STATEMENTS	REASONS
1. $\dfrac{A}{A'} = \dfrac{b \cdot h}{b' \cdot h'}$	1. Th.? _____
2. ∴ $\dfrac{A}{A'} = \dfrac{b \cdot h}{b \cdot h'} = \dfrac{h}{h'}$	2. _____

Therefore _____

COR. 2. The areas of any two triangles having equal altitudes are to each other as their bases.

GIVEN: $\triangle$ BCD and B'C'D' with h = h'.

TO PROVE: that $\dfrac{A}{A'} = \underline{\qquad}$

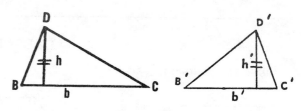

PROOF.   STATEMENTS

1. $\underline{\quad\quad} = \underline{\quad\quad}$

2. $\therefore \ \underline{\quad\quad} = \underline{\quad\quad} = \underline{\quad\quad}$

Therefore $\underline{\qquad\qquad\qquad\qquad}$

REASONS

1. $\underline{\qquad\qquad\qquad\qquad}$

2. $\underline{\qquad\qquad\qquad\qquad}$

EXERCISES B.

Solve the following exercises.

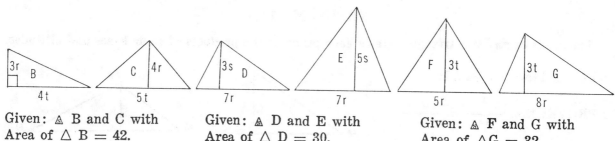

Given: $\triangle$ B and C with
Area of $\triangle$ B = 42.

Area of $\triangle$ C = $\underline{\qquad}$

Given: $\triangle$ D and E with
Area of $\triangle$ D = 30.

Area of $\triangle$ E = $\underline{\qquad}$

Given: $\triangle$ F and G with
Area of $\triangle$G = 32

Area of $\triangle$ F = $\underline{\qquad}$

THEOREM 114

The areas of two triangles having an angle of one equal to an angle of the other are to each other as the products of the sides forming the equal angles.

GIVEN: $\triangle$ ABC and RST with $\angle$ A = $\angle$ R.

TO PROVE: that $\dfrac{\triangle\,ABC}{\triangle\,RST} = \dfrac{AB \cdot AC}{RS \cdot RT}$.

PROOF. Place $\triangle$ ABC upon $\triangle$ RST so that it will take the position of $\triangle$ RBC as shown. Draw $\overline{CS}$. (Posts. $\underline{\quad}$ and $\underline{\quad}$)

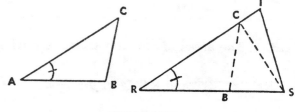

STATEMENTS

1. $\dfrac{\triangle\,RBC}{\triangle\,RSC} = \dfrac{RB}{RS}$ *

2. $\dfrac{\triangle\,RSC}{\triangle\,RST} = \dfrac{RC}{RT}$ **

3. $\dfrac{\triangle\,RBC}{\triangle\,RSC} \cdot \dfrac{\triangle\,RSC}{\triangle\,RST} = \dfrac{RB\cdot}{RS\cdot}$

REASONS

1. Th.?, Cor.? $\underline{\qquad\qquad\qquad}$

2. $\underline{\qquad\qquad\qquad\qquad}$

3. $\underline{\qquad\qquad}$ Prop. of Equality $\underline{\qquad}$

* Consider $\overline{RB}$ to be the base of $\triangle$ RBC and $\overline{RS}$ to be the base of $\triangle$ RSC.

** Consider $\overline{RC}$ to be the base of $\triangle$ RSC and $\overline{RT}$ to be the base of $\triangle$ RST.

4. Or $\dfrac{\triangle RBC}{\triangle RST} = \dfrac{RB \cdot RC}{RS \cdot RT}$

5. $\therefore \dfrac{\triangle ABC}{\triangle RST} = \dfrac{AB \cdot AC}{RS \cdot RT}$

4. Simplifying step 3 by cancellation

5. ....

Therefore _____

_____

EXERCISES B′

Solve the following exercises.

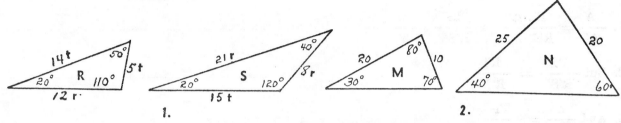

1.

2.

Given: ⟁ R and S with
Area of △ R = 48.

Area of △ S = _____

Given: ⟁ M and N with
Area of △ M = 16

Area of △ N = _____

C. RATIOS OF AREAS OF SIMILAR POLYGONS
PRELIMINARY EXERCISES C.

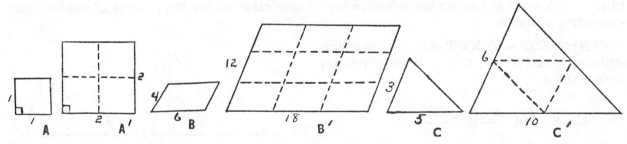

1. Given: In the above polygons A ~ A′, B ~ B′, and C ~ C′. Referring to these polygons, fill in the following table with correct answers.

Polygons	Ratio of corresponding sides	Ratio of areas
a. A and A′		
b. B and B′		
c. C and C′		

2. The following conclusion may be drawn from the preceding table: The areas of two similar polygons have the same ratio as _____

3. Was the above conclusion formed by *inductive* or by *deductive* thinking? _____

The areas of two similar triangles are to each other as the squares of any two corresponding sides.

GIVEN: $\triangle RST \sim \triangle R'S'T'$

TO PROVE: that $\dfrac{A}{A'} = \dfrac{\overline{RT^2}}{\overline{R'T'^2}}$

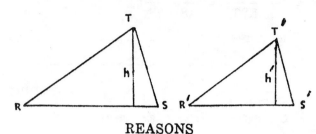

PROOF STATEMENTS

REASONS

1. $\dfrac{A}{A'} = \dfrac{RS \cdot h}{R'S' \cdot h'}$ or $\dfrac{RS}{R'S'} \cdot \dfrac{h}{h'}$

1. ....

2. But $\dfrac{RS}{R'S'} = \dfrac{RT}{R'T'}$

2. ....

3. And $\dfrac{h}{h'} = \dfrac{RT}{R'T'}$

3. Th. 103, Cor.? ....

4. $\therefore \dfrac{A}{A'} = \dfrac{RT}{R'T'} \cdot \dfrac{RT}{R'T'} = \dfrac{\overline{RT^2}}{\overline{R'T'^2}}$

4. .... Principle

Therefore _____

COR. 1. The areas of two similar triangles are to each other as the the squares of any two corresponding altitudes.

GIVEN: $\triangle RST \sim \triangle R'S'T'$ with corresponding altitudes h and h' and a pair of corresponding sides s and s'.

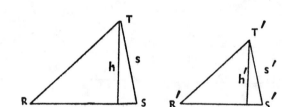

TO PROVE: that $\dfrac{A}{A'} = $ ————

PROOF. STATEMENTS

REASONS

1. $\dfrac{A}{A'} = \dfrac{s^2}{s'^2}$

1. Th.? ....

2. But $\dfrac{s}{s'} = \dfrac{h}{h'}$

2. ....

3. Hence $\dfrac{s^2}{s'^2} = $ ——

3. .... Prop. of Equality

4. $\therefore \dfrac{A}{A'} = \dfrac{h^2}{h'^2}$

4. ....

Therefore _____

THEOREM 116

The areas of any two similar polygons are to each other as the squares of any two corresponding sides.

GIVEN: Polygon P ~ polygon P'.

TO PROVE: that $\dfrac{A}{A'} = \dfrac{s^2}{s'^2}$

PROOF. From any two corresponding vertices, as v and v', draw all possible diagonals. (Post. 3)

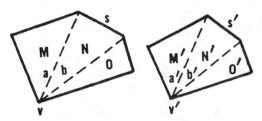

STATEMENTS	REASONS
1. $\triangle\,M \sim \triangle\,$____, $\triangle\,N \sim \triangle\,$____, and $\triangle\,O \sim \triangle\,$____	1. Unit 14, Th.? ....
2. $\dfrac{\triangle M}{\triangle M'} = \dfrac{a^2}{}$ and $\dfrac{\triangle N}{\triangle} = \dfrac{a^2}{}$	2. Th.? ....
3. Hence $\dfrac{\triangle M}{\triangle M'} = \dfrac{\triangle}{\triangle}$	3. ....
4. Similarly $\dfrac{\triangle}{\triangle} = \dfrac{b^2}{b'^2}$, and $\dfrac{\wedge}{\triangle} = \dfrac{b^2}{b'^2}$	4. Same as step ? ....
5. Hence $\dfrac{\triangle}{\triangle} = \dfrac{\triangle}{\triangle}$	5. Same as step ? ....
6. $\therefore\ \dfrac{\triangle}{\triangle} = \dfrac{\triangle}{\triangle} = \dfrac{\triangle}{\triangle}$	6. .... Prop. of equality
7. $\dfrac{\triangle+\triangle+\triangle}{\triangle+\triangle+\triangle} = \dfrac{\triangle N}{\triangle N'}$	7. Th.? about Proportion ....
8. But $\dfrac{\triangle N}{\triangle N'} = \dfrac{s^2}{s'^2}$	8. Th.? ....
9. Hence $\dfrac{\triangle+\triangle+\triangle}{\triangle+\triangle+\triangle} = \dfrac{s^2}{s'^2}$	9. ....
10. $A = \triangle\,M + \triangle\,N + \triangle\,O$ and $A' = \triangle\,M' + \triangle\,N' + \triangle\,O'$	10. Post.? ....
11. $\therefore\ \dfrac{A}{A'} = \dfrac{s^2}{s'^2}$	11. ....

Therefore _____

COR. 1 The areas of any two similar polygons are to each other as the squares of their perimeters.

GIVEN: Polygon R ~ polygon R' with perimeters p and p' and a pair of corresponding sides s and s' respectively.

TO PROVE· that $\dfrac{A}{A'} = \dfrac{p^2}{p'^2}$

PROOF. STATEMENTS	REASONS
1. $\dfrac{A}{A'} = \dfrac{s^2}{s'^2}$	1. Th.? ....
2. $\dfrac{s}{s'} = \dfrac{p}{p'}$	2. Th.? ....
3. Hence $\dfrac{s^2}{s'^2} = \dfrac{p^2}{p'^2}$	3. ....
4. $\therefore \dfrac{A}{A'} = \dfrac{p^2}{p'^2}$	4. ....

Therefore ....

COR. 2. If *similar* polygons are constructed on the three sides of a right triangle, the area of the polygon on the hypotenuse is equal to the sum of the areas of the polygons on the other two sides.

GIVEN: Polygon A ∼ polygon A′ ∼ polygon A″ having corresponding sides **c, a,** and **b** respectively.

TO PROVE: that A = A′ + A″.

PROOF. STATEMENTS	REASONS
1. $\dfrac{A'}{A} = \dfrac{a^2}{c^2}$ and $\dfrac{A''}{A} = $ ——	1. Th.? ....
2. $\dfrac{A'+A''}{A} = $ —— + ——	2. .... Prop. of Equality
3. But $a^2 + b^2 = c^2$	3. ....
4. Hence $\dfrac{A'+A''}{A} = \dfrac{c^2}{c^2} = 1$	4. .... Substitution Principle
5. $\therefore A' + A'' = A$	5. ....

Therefore ....

EXERCISES C

Fill the following answer-spaces with correct answers.

1. The relationships between areas and corresponding dimensions of similar polygons are as follows:

   a. The areas of similar polygons are to each other as the _____ of corresponding sides, the _____ of their corresponding altitudes or the _____ of their perimeters.

   b. Corresponding sides, corresponding altitudes or the perimeters of similar polygons are to each other as the _____ of their areas.

2. Suppose that a triangle has been so enlarged that its sides are 2 times their original lengths.

   a. How many times has its altitude become enlarged? _____

   b. How many times has its perimeter become enlarged? _____

   c. How many times has its area become enlarged? _____

3. Suppose that a triangle has been so diminished in size that its area is 1/9 of its original area.

   a. To what part of its original length has its sides been diminished? _____

   b. To what part of its original length has its perimeter been diminished? _____

   c. To what part of its original length has each of its altitudes been diminished? _____

   Solve the following exercises.

4. The areas of two similar polygons are 100 and 196 respectively. If a side of the first is 5 in., what is the corresponding side of the second?

   Ans. _____

5. The area of a certain triangle is 63 sq. in. The dimensions of another triangle similar to the first are one-third as large as those of the first. What is the area of the second triangle?

   Ans. _____

6. The perimeters of two similar polygons are 80 and 20 respectively. The area of the first is 48. What is the area of the second?

   Ans. _____

7. The corresponding altitudes of two similar triangles are 2 and 5 respectively. The area of the second triangle is 200. What is the area of the first?

   Ans. _____

8. The base of a certain triangle is 10. What is the base of a similar triangle whose area is 3 times as great?

   Ans. _____

9. Accompanying solids A and B are *similar*. How is the ratio of their volumes related to the ratio of their corresponding sides?

   Ans. _____

10. How is the ratio of the total surface areas of solids A and B related to the ratio of their corresponding sides?

   Ans. _____

XVII.

REGULAR POLYGONS

A. INSCRIBED AND CIRCUMSCRIBED REGULAR POLYGONS

In order for a polygon to be REGULAR, it must meet these two conditions: 1. It must be equilateral. 2. It must be equiangular.

The common center of the circle circumscribed about a regular polygon and the circle inscribed within the polygon is called the *center of the polygon*. See point O in Fig. 1. The radius of the circle inscribed within a regular polygon is called the *apothem of the polygon*. See OM in Fig. 1. The radius of the circle circumscribed about a regular polygon is called the *radius of the polygon*. See OA in Fig. 1. All radii of the same regular polygon are equal. The angle formed by two adjacent radii of a regular polygon is known as the *central angle of the polygon*. See ∠ AOB in Fig. 1. The polygon in Fig. 2 is a *circumscribed polygon*; its sides are tangents to the circle appearing within it. The polygon in Fig 3 is an *inscribed polygon*, and its sides are chords of the circle appearing around it. In each of these polygons r is its radius and a its apothem.

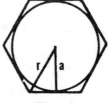

Fig. 1

POSTULATE 43: **An entire arc is equal to the sum of its parts.** (THE ARC-ADDITION POSTULATE)

Fig. 2   Fig. 3

PRELIMINARY EXERCISES A.

1. Name the two conditions which a polygon must meet in order to be *regular*. _____

_____

2. Fill the following answer-spaces correctly with either the word *always*, *sometimes* or *never*. Also make free-hand drawings in the space provided for illustrations to justify each answer.

ILLUSTRATIONS

   a. Equilateral polygons are _____ regular polygons.

   b. Equiangular polygons are _____ regular polygons.

   c. A square is _____ a regular polygon.

   d. An equilateral pentagon is _____ _____ a regular polygon.

   e. An equilateral pentagon is ____ _____ a regular polygon.

   f. A trapezoid is _____ a regular polygon.

3. Fill the following answer-spaces with correct answers:

The circle *circumscribed about* a _____ polygon and the circle *inscribed in* the same polygon have a common _____

4. Fill each of the following answer-spaces with the correct answer:

_____a. The common center of the circles circumscribed about and inscribed within a regular polygon.

_____b. The radius of the circle circumscribed about a regular polygon.

_____c. The radius of the circle inscribed within a regular polygon.

_____d. The angle formed by two adjacent radii of a regular polygon.

180

5. The polygons of Fig. 4 are regular. Refer to these polygons in filling the following answer spaces with the **correct answers.**

What term is applied to,

a. $\overline{OR}$? _____   d. $\overline{CM}$? _____

b. $\overline{OS}$? _____   e. $\overline{CA}$? _____

c. Point O? _____   f. ∠1? _____

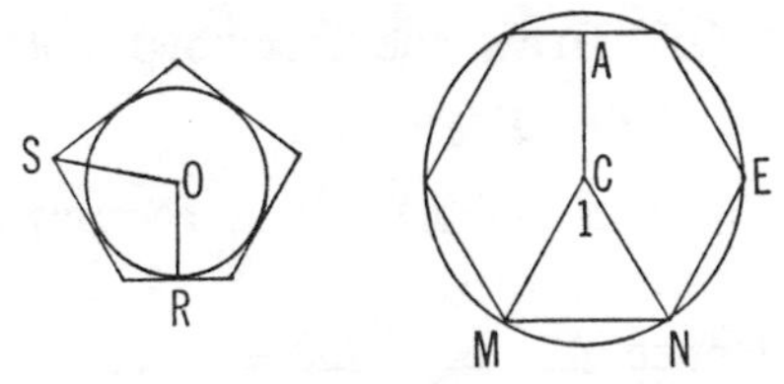

Fig. 4

THEOREM 117

An equilateral polygon inscribed in a circle is regular.

GIVEN: Equilateral polygon ABCDEF inscribed in ⊙ O.

TO PROVE: that polygon ABCDEF is regular.

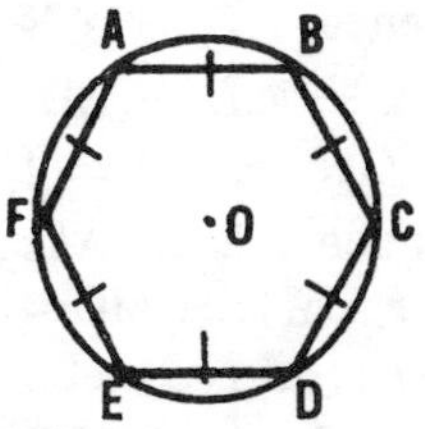

PROOF.   STATEMENTS

1. AB = BC = CD = DE etc.

2. $\overset{\frown}{AB} = \overset{\frown}{BC} = \overset{\frown}{CD} = \overset{\frown}{DE}$ etc.

3. ∠ A ≐ ½ arc BCDEF, ∠ B ≐ ½ arc CDEFA etc.

4. But arc BCDEF = arc CDEFA, etc.

5. Hence ∠A = ∠B = ∠C = ∠D etc.

6. ∴polygon ABCDEF is regular.

REASONS

1. _____

2. Unit 8, Th.? _____

3. Unit 10, Th.? _____

4. Arc - Add - Post. Applied to same no. of = arcs

5. _____ Prop. of Equality

6. _____

Therefore _____

THEOREM 118

If a circle is divided into equal arcs, the chords of these arcs form a regular inscribed polygon.

GIVEN: ⊙ O with $\overset{\frown}{AB} = \overset{\frown}{BC} = \overset{\frown}{CD} = \overset{\frown}{DE}$ etc. and corresponding chords

AB, BC, CD, DE etc., forming inscribed polygon ABCDEF.

TO PROVE: that polygon ABCDEF is a regular inscribed polygon.

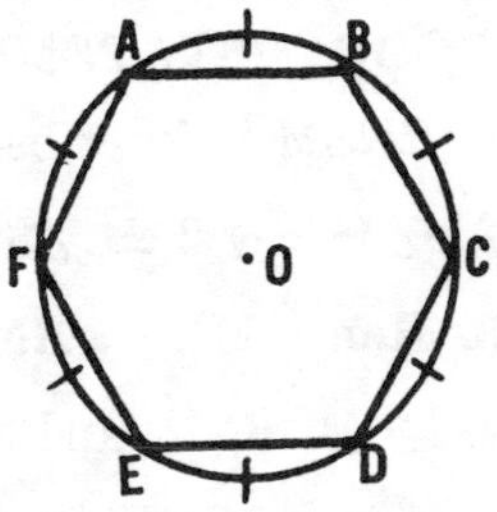

1.PROOF.   STATEMENTS

1. Polygon ABCDEF is an inscribed polygon

2. AB = BC = CD = DE = EF

3. ∴ polygon ABCDEF is regular.

Therefore _____ _____

REASONS

1. _____

2. Unit 8, Th.? _____

3. Th.? _____

THEOREM 119

If a circle is divided into equal arcs, the tangents drawn at the points of division form a regular circumscribed polygon.

GIVEN: ⊙ O' with $\overset{\frown}{AB} = \overset{\frown}{BC} = \overset{\frown}{CD} = \overset{\frown}{DE}$
and $\overline{KL}$, $\overline{LM}$, $\overline{MN}$, $\overline{NO}$ tangent at points A, B, C, D, and E, respectively.

TO PROVE: that polygon KLMNO is a regular circumscribed polygon.

PROOF. Draw the inscribed polygon ABCDE

STATEMENTS

1. Polygon ABCDE is a regular inscribed polygon.
2. Hence AB = ____ = ____ = ____ etc.
3. ∠1 = ∠2 = ∠3 = ∠4 = ∠5 = ∠6 = ∠7 etc.
4. Hence ▲ ABL, BMC, CND, DOE etc. are ≅
5. Hence ∠L = ∠M = ∠N = ∠O etc.
6. KA = AL = LB = BM = MC = CN = ND = DO etc.
7. Hence KA + AL, (or KL) = LB + BM (or LM) = MC + CN (or MN) = ND + DO, (or NO) etc.
8. ∴ polygon KLMNO is a regular circumscribed polygon
   Therefore _____

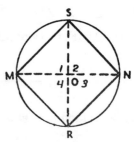

REASONS

1. Th.? ....
2. ....
3. Unit 10, Th.? and .... Prop. of Eq.
4. ....
5. ....
6. ....
7. .... and .... Properties of Eq.
8. ....

CONSTRUCTION 12

To inscribe a square in a circle.

GIVEN: ⊙ O.

REQUIRED: To inscribe a square in ⊙ O.

Construction: (1) Draw two diameters MN and RS ⊥ to each other. (2) Draw chords MR, RN, NS, and SM.

MRNS is an inscribed square.

PROOF.   STATEMENTS

1. RNSM is inscribed in ⊙ O.
2. ∠1 = ∠2 = ∠3 = ∠4
3. Hence MR = RN = NS = SM
4. ▲ M, R, N, and S are rt. ▲.
5. Hence MRNS is a square.
6. ∴ MRNS is a ▢ inscribed in ⊙ O.

REASONS

1. ....
2. Th.? ....
3. Unit 8, Th.? ....
4. Th. 69, Cor.? ....
5. ....
6. ....

CONSTRUCTION EXERCISES. A

Make the following constructions accurately with compass and straightedge.

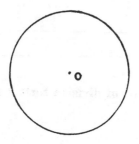

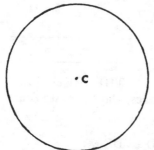

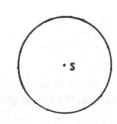

1. Inscribe a square in circle O. 2. Inscribe a regular octagon in circle C. 3. Circumscribe a square about circle S.

To inscribe a regular hexagon in a circle.

GIVEN: ⊙ O.

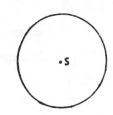

REQUIRED: To inscribe a regular hexagon in ⊙ O.

Construction: (1) Using the radius of the circle, mark off arc AB.
(2) Draw chord AB.   (3) Apply $\overline{AB}$ six times as a chord.

$\overline{AB}$ is the side of a regular inscribed hexagon ABCDEF.

PROOF. Draw radii OA and OB.

STATEMENTS	REASONS
1. ABCDEF is inscribed in ⊙ O.	1. Def. of a(n)? ....
2. △ AOB is equilateral.	2. Def. of a(n)? ....
3. Hence ∠ O = 60°	3. An equalateral △ is? ....
4. ∴ $\overset{\frown}{AB}$ = 60°, or 1/6 of a circle *	4. Converse of Post.? ....
5. ∴ Chord AB is one side of a regular hexagon	5. ....

CONSTRUCTION EXERCISES A′

Make the following constructions accurately with compass and straightedge.

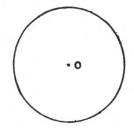

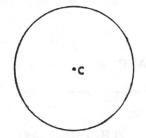

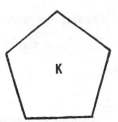

1. Inscribe a regular hexagon in circle O.

2. Inscribe an equilateral triangle in circle C.

3. Circumscribe a regular hexagon about circle S.

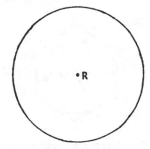

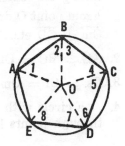

4. Inscribe a regular polygon of 12 sides in circle R.

5. Inscribe a circle within and circumscribe a circle about regular polygon K.

THEOREM 120

A circle can be circumscribed about any regular polygon.

GIVEN: Regular polygon ABCDE.

TO PROVE: that a circle can be circumscribed about ABCDE.

$$* \ \frac{60°}{360°} = \frac{1}{6}$$

PROOF.   STATEMENTS

1. Pass a circle through vertices A, B, and C, calling its center O. (why possible?)

2. ∠ B = ∠ C

3. BO = CO

4. Hence ∠ 3 = ∠ 4

5. ∠ 2 = ∠ 5

6. BA = CD

7. Hence △ AOB ≅ △ _____

8. AO = DO

9. ∴ D lies on ⊙ O

10. Similarly ∠ C = ∠ D

11. CO = DO

12. ∠ 5 = ∠ 6

13. Hence ∠ 4 = ∠ _____

14. CB = DE

15. Hence △ BOC ≅ △ _____

16. BO = EO

17. Finally E lies on ⊙ O

18. ∴ ⊙ O is circumscribed about ABCDE.

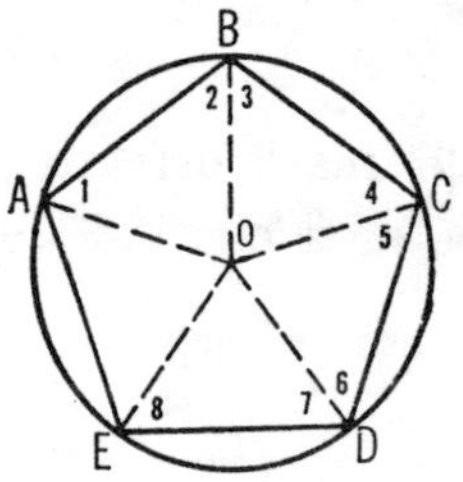

Therefore _____

REASONS

1. Unit. 9, Th.? _____

2. _____

3. Post.? _____

4. Unit 2, Th.? _____

5. _____ Prop. of Equality

6. _____

7. _____

8. _____

9. Post.? _____

10. _____

11. _____

12. _____

13. _____

14. _____

15. _____

16. _____

17. _____

18. _____

THEOREM 121

A circle can be inscribed in any regular polygon.

GIVEN: Regular polygon ABCDEF

TO PROVE: that a circle can be inscribed in ABCDEF.

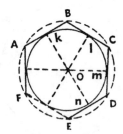

PROOF.   STATEMENTS

1. Circumscribe a circle about ABCDEF calling its center O
   From point O draw $\overline{Ok} \perp \overline{AB}$, $\overline{Ol} \perp \overline{BC}$, $\overline{Om} \perp \overline{CD}$ etc.

2. AB = BC = CD = DE etc.

3. Ok = Ol = Om = On etc.

4. ∴ a circle with center O can be passed through points k, l, m, n, etc.

REASONS

1. Th.? _____

2. Sides of a regular polygon are? _____

3. _____

4. _____

184

5. Hence AB, BC, CD, DE, etc. are tangent to the circle that passes through points k, l, m, n, etc.

5. _____

6. ∴ inner ⊙ O is inscribed in ABCDEF

6. _____

Therefore _____

THEOREM 122

Each central angle of a regular polygon of n sides equals $\dfrac{360°}{n}$.

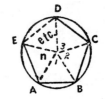

Since n central ∠ s = 360°, we have:

$$\frac{n \text{ central } \angle s}{n} = \frac{360°}{n}. \text{ Or each central } \angle = \frac{360°}{n} \quad \text{(Div. Prop. of Eq.)}$$

EXERCISES A

Fill the spaces in the following table with correct answers.

Kind of polygon	Sum of central angles	Value of each central engle	Sum of interior angles	Value of each interior angle	Value of each exterior angle
1. Regular Triangle					
2. Regular Quadrilateral					
3. Regular Pentagon					
4. Regular Octagon					

B. SIMILAR REGULAR POLYGONS

THEOREM 123

Any two regular polygons having the same number of sides are similar.

GIVEN: Regular polygons P and P′ with the same number of sides n.

TO PROVE: that polygon P ~ polygon P′.

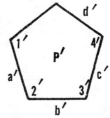

PROOF.   STATEMENTS

1. ∠1, ∠2, ∠3 . . . = $\dfrac{(n-2)\ 180°}{n}$ each, and

   ∠1′ ∠2′, ∠3′ . . . = $\dfrac{(n-2)\ 180°}{n}$ each

2. ∴ ∠1 = ∠1′, ∠2 = ∠2′, ∠3 = ∠3′ etc.

REASONS

1. Th. 43, Cor.? ....

2. ....

185

3. $a = b = c = d$ etc. and
$a' = b' = c' = d'$

3. Sides of a regular polygon are? ....

4. $\therefore \dfrac{a}{a'} = \dfrac{b}{b'} = \dfrac{c}{c'} = \dfrac{d}{d'}$ etc.

4. ....

5. $\therefore$ polygon P $\sim$ polygon P′

5. ....

Therefore _____

COR. 1. The areas of any two regular polygons having the same number of sides have the **same** ratio as the squares of any two sides.

GIVEN: Regular polygons R and R′ with the same number of sides in which s is a side of R and s′ is a side of R′

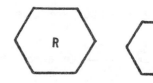

TO PROVE: that $\dfrac{A}{A'} = \dfrac{s^2}{s'^2}$.

PROOF. STATEMENTS

REASONS

1. _____ _____

1. Th. 123 ....

2. $\therefore$ _____

2. ....

Therefore _____

THEOREM 124

The perimeters of any two regular polygons having the same number of sides have the same ratio as their radii and as their apothems.

GIVEN: Regular polygons M and M′ with the same number of sides and with perimeters p and p′, radii r and r′, and apothems a and a′ respectively.

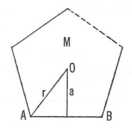

TO PROVE: (1) that $\dfrac{p}{p'} = \dfrac{r}{r'}$ and (2) that $\dfrac{p}{p'} = \dfrac{a}{a'}$.

PROOF. Draw $\overline{OB}$ and $\overline{O'B'}$. Post. _____

STATEMENTS

REASONS

1. Polygon M $\sim$ polygon M′

1. Th.? ....

2. Hence $\dfrac{p}{p'} = \dfrac{AB}{A'B'}$

2. Th.? ....

3. $\angle AOB = \dfrac{360°}{n}$ and $\angle A'O'B' = \dfrac{360°}{n}$

3. Th.? ....

4. Hence $\angle$ ___ $= \angle$ ___

4. ....

5. $AO = $ ___ and $A'O' = $ ___

5. ....

6. Hence $\dfrac{AO}{A'O'} = $ ___

6. .... Prop. of Equality

7. $\triangle AOB \sim \triangle A'O'B'$

7. Unit 14, Th.? ....

8. Hence $\dfrac{AB}{A'B'} = \dfrac{r}{r'}$

8. ....

186

9. And $\dfrac{AB}{A'B'} = \dfrac{a}{a'}$ 9. Th. 103, Cor.? ....

10. $\therefore \dfrac{p}{p'} = \dfrac{r}{r'}$ and $\dfrac{p}{p'} = \dfrac{a}{a'}$ 10. ....

Therefore ....

_____

COR. 1. The areas of any two regular polygons having the same number of sides are to each other as the squares of their radii and as the squares of their apothems.

GIVEN: Regular polygons N and N' with the same number of sides, with perimeters p and p', with radii r and r', and apothems a and a'.

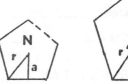

TO PROVE: (1) that $\dfrac{A}{A'} = \dfrac{r^2}{r'^2}$ and (2) that $\dfrac{A}{A'} = \dfrac{a^2}{a'^2}$.

PROOF.   STATEMENTS   REASONS

1. Polygon N ~ polygon N'   1.   Unit 16, Th.? ....

2. Hence $\dfrac{A}{A'} = \dfrac{p^2}{p'^2}$ 2.   ....

3. But $\dfrac{p}{p'} = \dfrac{r}{r'}$ and $\dfrac{p}{p'} = \dfrac{a}{a'}$ 3.   Th.? ....

4. Hence $\dfrac{p^2}{p'^2} = \dfrac{r^2}{r'^2}$ and $\dfrac{p^2}{p'^2} = \dfrac{a^2}{a'^2}$ 4.   .... Prop. of Equality

5. $\therefore \dfrac{A}{A'} = \dfrac{r^2}{r'^2}$ and $\dfrac{A}{A'} = \dfrac{a^2}{a'^2}$ 5.   ....

Therefore ....

_____

EXERCISES   B

Solve the following exercises.

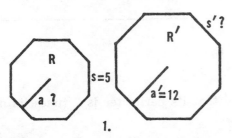

1.

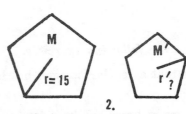

2.

Given: Regular octagons R and R' with area of R = 100 and area of R' = 400.

$s' = $ _____. $a = $ _____.

Given: Regular pentagons M and M' with perimeter of M = 60, perimeter of M' = 40, and area of M = 556.

Area of M' = _____. $r' = $ _____.

3. **What is the ratio of** the areas of an equilateral triangle inscribed in a circle and one circumscribed about a circle whose radius is 6 in.?

Ans. _____

4. A regular hexagon is circumscribed about a circle whose radius is 12 in. What is the perimeter of the hexagon?

Ans. _____

5. Two regular heptagons have areas of 400 sq. units and 900 sq. units respectively. Find the ratio of —

a. Their areas _____   c. Their radii _____   e. Their apothems

b. Their sides _____   d. Their perimeters _____   _____

C. AREAS OF REGULAR POLYGONS ● INSCRIBING REGULAR POLYGONS IN CIRCLES

THEOREM 125

The area of a regular polygon is equal to one-half the product of its apothem and perimeter.

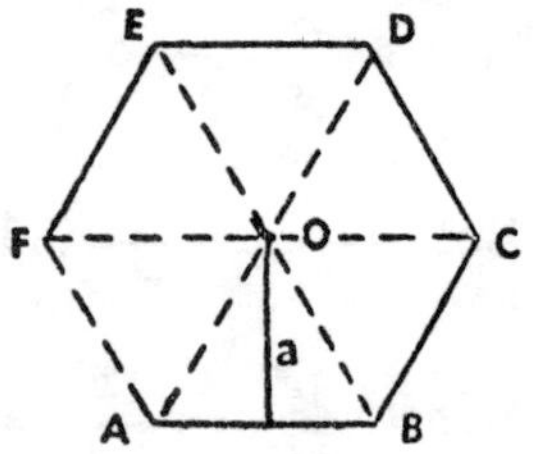

GIVEN: Regular polygon ABCDEF . . . with apothem a, perimeter p, and area A.

TO PROVE: that $A = \frac{1}{2} a \cdot p$.

PROOF. From center O draw all radii of the polygon, dividing it into triangles.

STATEMENTS	REASONS
1. $\triangle AOB = \frac{1}{2} a \cdot \overline{AB}$, $\triangle BOC = \frac{1}{2} a \cdot \overline{BC}$ etc.	1. _____
2. $\triangle AOB + \triangle BOC$ etc. $= \frac{1}{2} a \cdot \overline{AB} + \frac{1}{2} a \cdot \overline{BC}$ etc., or $\frac{1}{2} a (\overline{AB} + \overline{BC}$ etc.$)$	2. _____
3. But $\triangle AOB + \triangle BOC$ etc. $= A$	3. _____
4. Also $\overline{AB} + \overline{BC}$ etc. $= p$	4. _____
5. $\therefore A = \frac{1}{2} a \cdot p$	5. _____

Therefore _____

EXERCISES C.

Solve the following exercises.

1. Suppose that a regular octagon has been so enlarged that its perimeter is 7 times its original perimeter.

a. How many times has its sides been enlarged? _____; its apothem? _____; its radius? _____.

b. How many times has its area been enlarged? _____.

2. The side of a regular hexagon is 24. What is its area?

Ans. _____

3. The area of a regular polygon is 340, and its perimeter is 17. What is the radius of its inscribed circle?

Ans. _____

CONSTRUCTION 14

To inscribe a regular decagon in a circle.

GIVEN: ⊙ O.

REQUIRED: To inscribe a regular decagon in ⊙ O.

Construction: 1. Draw any radius $\overline{OA}$. 2. Divide $\overline{OA}$ into extreme and mean ratio so that AO:AP = AP:PO. 3. Mark off AB equal to AP, and apply $\overline{AB}$ 10 times as a chord.

$\overline{AB}$ is the side of the regular decagon.

PROOF. Measure $\overline{OP'}$ equal to $\overline{AP}$. Connect B and P', and O and B.

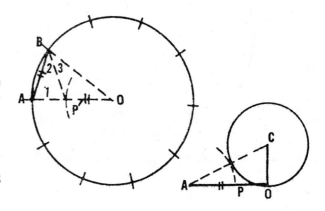

STATEMENTS	REASONS
1. AO:AP = AP:PO	1. Construction No.? ....
2. In ▲ AOB and ABP', AO:AB = AB:AP'	2. .... Principle
3. ∠ A = ∠ A	3. ....
4. Hence △ AOB ~ △ ABP'	4. Unit 14, Th.? ....
5. But △ AOB is isosceles	5. ....
6. Hence △ ABP' is isosceles	6. Def. of ~ ▲ ....
7. P'B = AB	7. Def. of ? ....
8. But OP' = AB	8. Construction ....
9. Hence OP' = P'B	9. ....
10. ∴ ∠ 3 = ∠ O	10. ....
11. ∠ 2 = ∠ O	11. What property of ~ ▲ ? ....
12. ∠ A = ∠ B	12. ....
13. But ∠ B = ∠ 2 + ∠ 3	13. Post.? ....
14. Hence ∠ B = 2 ∠ O and ∠ A = 2 ∠ ___	14. ....
15. ∠ A + ∠ B + ∠ O = 180°	15. Th.? ....
16. ∴ 2 ∠ O + 2 ∠ O + ∠ O, or 5 ∠ O = 180°	16. ....
17. ∠ O = 36°, or 1/10 of the central ∠ of circle O.	17. ....
18. ∴ ⌢AB = 36°, or 1/10 of the line circle.	18. Converse of Post.? ....
19. ∴ chord AB may be applied exactly 10 times around ⊙ O.	19. Definition of a (n)? ....

Make the following constructions accurately with compass and straightedge.

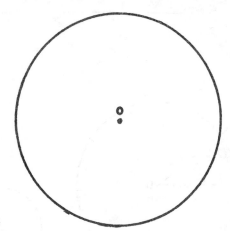

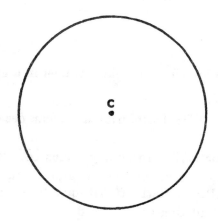

1. Inscribe a regular decagon in circle O.

2. Inscribe a regular pentagon in circle C.

CONTRUCTION 15

To inscribe a regular pentadecagon (a 15-sided polygon) in a circle.

GIVEN: Circle O.

REQUIRED: To inscribe a regular pentadecagon in ⊙ O.

Construction: 1. Draw chord AB = to the radius of the circle. 2. Draw $\overline{AC}$ = to the side of a regular inscribed decagon. 3. Draw $\overline{CB}$, and apply $\overline{CB}$ 15 times as a chord.

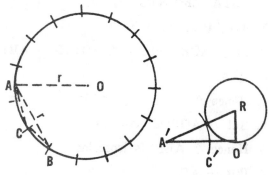

$\overline{CB}$ is the side of a regular pentadecagon.

PROOF.   STATEMENTS

1. $\overset{\frown}{AB}$ = 1/6 of a circle.
2. $\overset{\frown}{AC}$ = 1/10 of a circle.
3. ∴ $\overset{\frown}{AB}$ — $\overset{\frown}{AC}$ = 1/6 — 1/10 or 1/15 of ⊙ O.
4. ∴ $\overline{CB}$ is the side of a regular pentadecagon

REASONS

1. Construction No.? ....
2. ....
3. .... Prop. of Equality
4. Def. of a(n)? ....

EXERCISES C'

1. Name the regular polygon which one could construct to obtain each of the following angles as *central angles*.

   a. An ∠ of 24° _____
   b. An ∠ of 12° _____
   c. An ∠ of 90° _____

   d. An ∠ of 72° _____
   e. An ∠ of 36° _____
   f. An ∠ of 45° _____

Fill the corresponding answer-spaces provided below with the correct answers to the following questions.

Any .. 2 .. polygon inscribed in a circle is a regular polygon. A .. 3 .. may be .. 4 .. within or .. 5 .. about any .. 6 .. polygon. Regular polygons having the same number of sides are always .. 7 .., and their sides have the same ratio as either their .. 8 .., their .. 9 ..., or their .. 10. But their areas have the same ratio as the ratio of the .. 11 .. of any two of the above corresponding parts.

Chords which connect the points of division of equal arcs around a circle form a regular ... 12 .. polygon, whereas tangents connecting these points form a regular .. 13 .. polygon. Joining the *midpoints* of the arcs of any regular inscribed polygon to the extremities of its respective sides forms a (n) .. 14 .. polygon which has .. 15 .. times as many sides as the original polygon.

ANSWERS TO QUESTIONS 2-15

2. _____	6. _____	10. _____	14. _____
3. _____	7. _____	11. _____	15. _____
4. _____	8. _____	12. _____	
5. _____	9. _____	13. _____	

CONSTRUCTION EXERCISE C'

1. Construct a regular pentadecagon with its center at
   point C and with its radius
   equal to line-segment r.

r

·C

191

Unit XVIII

PRINCIPLES OF VARIABLES. MEASUREMENT OF THE CIRCLE
CYLINDERS ● CONES ● SPHERES

A. BASIC PRINCIPLES OF VARIABLES ● CIRCLES AS POLYGONS

We often deal with two kinds of mathematical quantities; namely, constants and variables. A *constant* is a quantity whose value remains fixed throughout a given discussion, whereas a *variable* is a quantity whose value changes during a discussion. For example, in algebra we have dealt with equations like this one: $y = x + 5$. As we assign various values to x as 1, 2, 3, etc., y assumes the corresponding values of 6, 7, 8, etc. But the term 5 does not change. Hence x and y in this discussion are variables, while 5 is a constant. A constant quantity such that the difference between it and a variable can be made to become and remain less than any given quantity is called the *limit of the variable*. For example, if v is the repeating decimal .666 ... etc., then v becomes a variable whose limit is 2/3. The expression $v \to 1$ is read: "v approaches 1 as a limit."

There are two basic PRINCIPLES OF VARIABLES, which may be regarded as *postulates*, that we are going to use in certain parts of this unit. These are:

1. If while approaching their limits two variables are always equal, then their limits are equal.

Or: If v always $= v'$ as $v \to 1$ and as $v' \to 1'$, then $1 = 1'$.

For example:
$$\begin{cases} \text{If } v \text{ changes from .3 to .33 to .333 etc. and} \\ \text{if } v' \text{ changes from .3 to .33 to .333 etc.,} \\ \text{then } v \text{ and } v' \text{ each} \to 1/3 \text{ as their limit.} \end{cases}$$

2. If a variable v approaches a limit 1 then (if c is a constant) cv approaches cl.

Or: If $v \to 1$, then $c. v \to c.1$

For example: If $v \to 1/3$ as a limit, then $2v \to 2/3$ as a limit.

EXERCISES A

1. Fill each of the following answer-spaces with the correct answer.

_____a. A quantity whose value changes during a given discussion.

_____b. A quantity whose value remains fixed throughout a given discussion.

_____c. A constant quantity such that the difference between it and a variable can be made to become and remain less than any given quantity.

_____d. The variable in the expression $x \to 7$

_____e. The constant in the expression of part d.

_____f. The limit in the expression of part d.

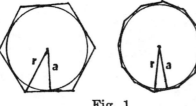

Fig. 1

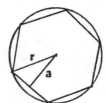

Fig. 2

2. Refer to Fig. 1 as you fill in the following answer-spaces with correct answers.

As the number of sides of a regular *circumscribed* polygon is increased infinitely,

192

a. Its radius r → _____

b. Its perimeter p → _____

c. Its area A → _____

d. What happens to its apothem a? _____

3. Refer to Fig. 2 as you fill the following answer-spaces with correct answers.

   As the number of sides of a regular *inscribed polygon* is increased infinitely,

a. Its apothem a → _____

b. Its perimeter p → _____

c. Its area A → _____

d. What happens to its radius r? _____

4. Fill the following answer-spaces with either the word *increases* or *decreases*.

   a. Increasing the number of sides of an *inscribed* polygon _____ its perimeter and

      _____ its area.

   b. Increasing the number of sides of a *circumscribed* polygon _____ its perimeter

      and _____ its area.

5. Given: m → n

   a. ∴ 3 m → 3n   Why? _____

   b. Also $\dfrac{m}{2} \to \dfrac{n}{2}$ Why? _____

6. Given: x = y, x → k, and y → c.

   a. ∴ k = c   Why? _____

   Now that we have studied **regular inscribed polygons** and **regular circumscribed polygons**, we are ready to accept these NEW postulates pertaining to circles:

44. **As the number of sides of a regular inscribed or circumscribed polygon is increased infinitely, its perimeter approaches the circumference of the circle as its limit.**

45. **As the number of sides of a regular inscribed or circumscribed polygon is increased infinitely, its area approaches the area of the circle as its limit.**

46. **As the number of sides of a regular inscribed polygon is increased infinitely, its apothem approaches the radius of the circle as its limit.**

   We may regard all circles as polygons having an infinite number of equal angles and an infinite number of equal sides. So the following postulate pertaining to circles is now acceptable too.

47. **All circles are REGULAR and SIMILAR polygons whose radii are the same as their apothems and whose circumferences are their perimeters.**

B. MEASUREMENT OF CIRCLES

We are going to prove Theorem 126 and Theorem 127 which follow by each of two methods, namely, METHOD I in which we regard circles as regular polygons and METHOD II in which we apply the theory of limits.

THEOREM 126

The circumferences of two circles have the same ratio as their radii and as their diameters.

GIVEN: ⊙ O and O′ with radii r and r′, diameters D and D′, and circumferences C and C′.

TO PROVE: that $\dfrac{C}{C'} = \dfrac{r}{r'} = \dfrac{D}{D'}$

PROOF (Method 1)   STATEMENTS

1. ⊙ O ~ ⊙ O′

2. ∴ $\dfrac{C}{C'} = \dfrac{r}{r'}$

3. $\dfrac{C}{C'} = \dfrac{2r}{2r'}$

4. ∴ $\dfrac{C}{C'} = \dfrac{D}{D'}$

Therefore _____

REASONS

1. Post.? .... and Th.? ....

2. Th.? ....

3. Converting r/r′ to an equivalent form

4. .... Principle

PROOF (Method 2)

STATEMENTS

1. Inscribe similar regular polygons in the circles with perimeters p and p′. (Why possible?)

2. $\dfrac{p}{p'} = \dfrac{r}{r'}$

3. So pr′ = p′r

4. But as the number of sides of each polygon is increased infinitely, p → C and p′ → C′

5. Hence pr′ → Cr′ and p′r → C′r

6. ∴ Cr′ = C′r

7. ∴ $\dfrac{C}{C'} = \dfrac{r}{r'}$

8. $\dfrac{C}{C'} = \dfrac{2r}{2r'}$

9. ∴ $\dfrac{C}{C'} = \dfrac{D}{D'}$

Therefore _____

REASONS

1. Th.? ....

2. Th.? ....

3. ....

4. Post. 43 ....

5. Prin.? about variables ....

6. Prin. I about variables ....

7. Th.? about proportions ....

8. ....

9. ....

COR. 1. The ratio of the circumference of a circle to its diameter is the same (or constant) for all circles.

GIVEN: ⊚ O and O′ with diameters D and D′, radii r and r′, and circumferences C and C′.

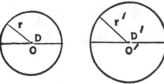

TO PROVE: that $\dfrac{C}{D} = \dfrac{C'}{D'}$, or $\dfrac{C}{D} =$ a constant.

PROOF.   STATEMENTS

REASONS

1. $\dfrac{C}{C'} = \dfrac{D}{D'}$

1. _____

2. ∴ $\dfrac{C}{D} = \dfrac{C'}{D'}$ or $\dfrac{C}{D} =$ a constant

2. _____

Therefore _____

The ratio of the circumference (C) of a circle to its diameter (D) is represented by the Greek letter π (called pī) Hence we have the Fundamental Formula $\dfrac{C}{D} = \pi$.

The numerical value of π is a non-ending decimal, which correct to 5 decimal places is 3.14159. We commonly use $\pi = 3.1416$. C and D are incommensurable, which makes π *irrational.* *

COR. 2. In any circle $C = \pi\,D$, or $C = 2\,\pi\,r$.

PROOF. Verify these formulas: _____

COR. 3. The length of an arc having a central angle of n degrees is $\dfrac{n}{360} \cdot 2\,\pi\,r$.

PROOF. Verify this expression. : _____

CONSTRUCTION 16

To find the side of a regular inscribed polygon having twice the number of sides of a given inscribed polygon.

GIVEN: ⊙ O having radius r, with $\overline{MN}$ (or s) as one side of a regular inscribed polygon, and $\overline{MR}$ (or s′) as the side of a regular inscribed polygon having twice the number of sides.

REQUIRED: To find, in terms of r and s, the side s′ of a regular inscribed polygon of twice the number of sides.

Construction: Draw $\overline{OM}$. Also draw $\overline{OR} \perp$ to $\overline{MN}$.

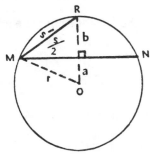

REASONS

SOLUTION.   STATEMENTS

1. $a^2 = r^2 - \dfrac{s^2}{4}$ or $\dfrac{4r^2 - s^2}{4}$

1. _____

2. Hence $a = \frac{1}{2}\sqrt{4r^2 - s^2}$

2. _____

3. $b + a = r$

3. _____

4. $b = r - a$

4. _____

* This means that C and D are never both integers in a particular circle. Otherwise, the ratio C/D would be a rational number.

195

5. $b = r - \frac{1}{2} \sqrt{4r^2 - s^2}$ 5. _____

6. $b^2 = (r - \frac{1}{2} \sqrt{4r^2 - s^2})^2 =$ 6. _____

   $r^2 - r \sqrt{4r^2 - s^2} + \frac{1}{4}(4r^2 - s^2) =$

   $2r^2 - r \sqrt{4r^2 - s^2} - \frac{s^2}{4}$

7. $s'^2 = b^2 + \frac{s^2}{4}$ 7. _____

8. Hence $s'^2 = 2r^2 - r \sqrt{4r^2 - s^2} - \frac{s^2}{4} + \frac{s^2}{4}$ 8. _____

   $= 2r^2 - r \sqrt{4r^2 - s^2}$

9. $\therefore\ s' = \sqrt{2r^2 - r\sqrt{4r^2 - s^2}}$ 9. _____

EXERCISES B

1. A regular hexagon is inscribed within a circle whose radius is 1.

  a. What is the value of one of its sides s ? _____ Its perimeter p? _____ The ratio of its perimeter p to its diameter d ? _____

  b. What is the value of s, one of the sides of a regular 12-sided polygon inscribed within the above circle _____ Its perimeter p? _____ The ratio of p to d? _____

  c. As the number of sides of a regular polygon inscribed within the above circle is increased infinitely, what value does the ratio $p \div d$ approach? _____

2. We may regard all circles as regular _____ polygons.

3. An open tube (a cylinder) has a diameter of 4 in. and a height of 5 in.

  a. If we cut open the *curved surface* along line l and then open and flatten out this surface, what familiar geometric polygon do we get?

    _____

  b. What is the *lateral area* (the area of the curved surface) of the tube?

    _____

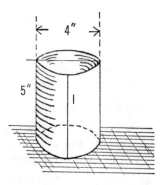

THEOREM 127

The area of a circle is equal to one-half the product of its radius and circumference.

GIVEN: $\odot$ O with radius r, circumference C, and area A.

TO PROVE: that $A = \frac{1}{2} rC$.

PROOF (Method 1)   STATEMENTS   REASONS

1. $\odot$ O is a regular polygon   1. Post.? ....

2. In regular polygons $A = \frac{1}{2} a \cdot p$ 2. Th.? ....

3. In circles, $r = a$ and $C = p$ 3. Post.? ....

4. $\therefore A = \frac{1}{2} rC$ 4. ....

  Therefore _____

THEOREM 127

The area of a circle is equal to one-half the product of its radius and circumference.

GIVEN: ⊙ O with radius r, circumference C, and area A.

TO PROVE: that A = ½ rC.

PROOF (Method 2) Circumscribe a regular polygon about circle C. Call its perimeter p and its area A′. Let the number of its sides be increased infinitely. (Th. 119)

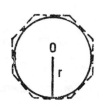

STATEMENTS	REASONS
1. A′ = ½ rp	1. Th. 125 ....
2. p → C	2. Post.? ....
3. ½ r·p → ½ r·C	3. Principle? about variables ....
4. A′ → A	4. Post.? ....
5. ∴ A = ½ rC	5. ....

Therefore _____

COR. 1. The area of a circle is equal to πr².

GIVEN: ⊙ O with radius r, circumference C, and area A.

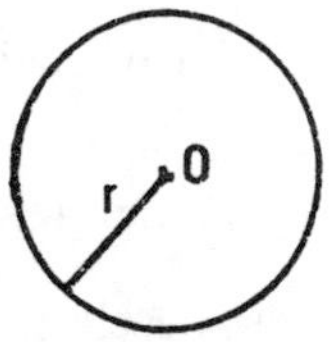

TO PROVE: that A = πr².

PROOF. STATEMENTS   REASONS

STATEMENTS	REASONS
1. A. = ½ rC	1. ....
2. But C = _____	2. Th. 126, Cor.? ....
3. ∴ A = _____ or π r²	3. ....

Therefore _____

COR. 2. The areas of two circles are to each other as the squares of their radii (or diameters).

GIVEN: ⊙ O and O′ with radii r and r′, and areas A and A′ respectively.

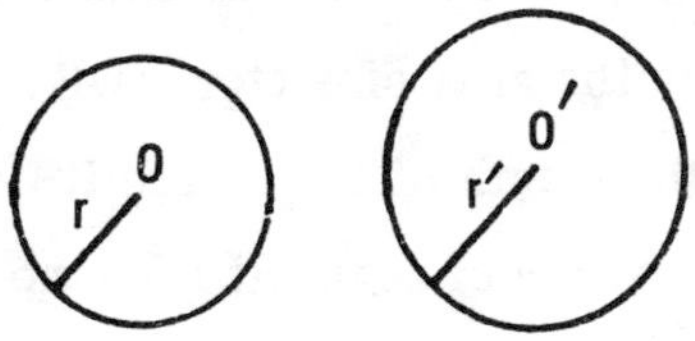

TO PROVE: that $\frac{A}{A'}$ = _____ = _____

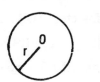

PROOF. STATEMENTS

1. A = _____ and A′ = _____   REASONS

2. ∴ $\frac{A}{A'}$ = _____ = _____

REASONS
1. ....
2. ....

Therefore _____

_____

COR. 3. The area of a sector having a central angle of n degrees is $\frac{n}{360°} \cdot \pi r^2$.

PROOF. Verify this expression: _____

Fill each of the following answer-spaces with the correct answer.

1. The diameters of two circles have the same ratio as their _____ and as their

_____

2. The areas of any two circles have the same ratio as the _____ of either their

_____, or their _____, or their _____

Solve the following exercises. Use π = 3.1416 *in exercises that require the use of pi in their solutions.*

3. Fill the answer-spaces in the table below with the correct answers.

	Circle	Radius	Diameter	Circumference	Area
a.	O	5a		6n	
b.	O'	3			
c.	C				314.16

4. The ratio of the radii of two pipes is 2 to 5. The cross-sectional area of the smaller pipe is 800 sq. in.

   a. What is the ratio of their cross-sectional areas? _____

   b. What is the cross sectional area of the larger pipe? _____

   c. If the smaller pipe can fill a given tank in 40 minutes, how long will it take the larger pipe to fill the tank? _____

5. The ratio of the areas of two circles is 4 to 25. The radius of the smaller circle is 5 ft. What is the circumference of the larger circle?

   Ans. _____

6. Given: In Fig. 1 ⊙ O with its radius = 10 in. and $\overset{\frown}{AB}$ = 45°.

   a. How long is $\overset{\frown}{AB}$? _____
   b. What is the area of sector AOB? _____

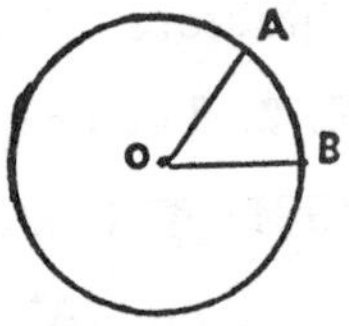

7. What is the length of major arc RS of circle O in Fig. 2? _____

8. What is the area of segment RS (the shaded part) in Fig. 2? _____

9. The height of a tin can (a cyclinder) is 10 in. and its diameter is 6 in.
   a. What is its *lateral area*? _____
   b. What is its *total area*? _____
   c. What is its *volume*?* _____

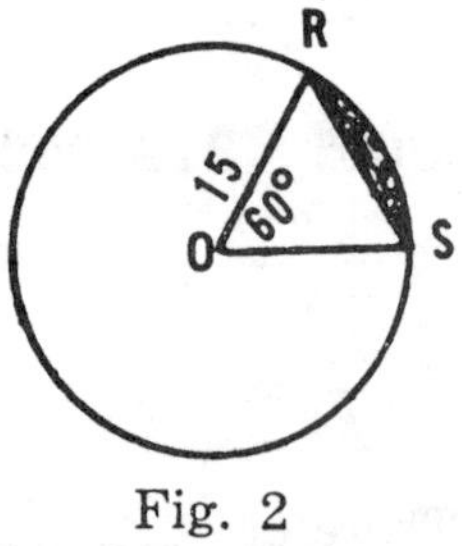

Fig. 1

Fig. 2

CONSTRUCTION EXERCISE B

1. Construct a circle whose area will be twice the area of circle O.

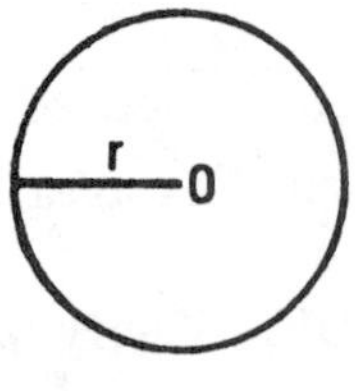

* Vol. of cylinder = area of base × height, or A = πr² · h.

C. AREAS AND VOLUMES OF CONES

A cone may be regarded as a PYRAMID with a circular base and a smooth, uniformly curved lateral surface. The uniform curvature of its lateral surface and its circular base may be attributed to the shape that a pyramid takes when it is composed of an INFINITE number of very tiny, flat needle-like congruent isosceles, triangles resting upon an INFINITE number of correspondingly tiny sides to form its base. See Fig. 1.

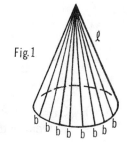

Fig. 1

Under these conditions, the perimeter (P) of the pyramid becomes equal to the circumference (C) of the base. Therefore, we may *substitute C for P* in the formula for the lateral area of a pyramid (which is: $A_1 = \frac{1}{2} lP$) and get a SPECIAL formula for the lateral area of a **cone**:

$$A_1 = \frac{1}{2} l\,C$$

Now if we substitute $2\pi r$ for C in the above formula, the formula becomes:

$$A_1 = \frac{1}{2} l\,(2\pi r) = l\,\pi\,r$$

The *total area* of a cone = its lateral area + the area of its base, or:

$$A_t = \frac{1}{2} l\,C + \pi r^2 \quad \text{Or:} \quad A_t = l\,\pi\,r + \pi\,r^2$$

We may discover the formula for finding the volume of a cone by performing the following experiment:

1. EQUIPMENT: An empty water-tight circular can (a cylinder) and a water-tight cone with equal circular bases and equal altitudes (or depths). A container of water or sand.

2. PROCEDURE: Determine the number of cones of water (or sand) that it takes to fill the can. See Fig. 2.

Fig. 2

3. CONCLUSION: It takes _____ cones of water (or sand) to fill the cyclinder. So the volume of the cone, expressed in terms of the volume of the cylinder (which is: $V = B\,h$ or $V = \pi r^2 h$) becomes:

$$V_c = \text{_____} B\,h \quad \text{or} \quad V_c = \text{_____} \pi r^2 h$$

EXERCISES C.

1. In Fig. 3, the radius of the base of the cone is 5″, the slant height is 13″, and

   the altitude is 12″.

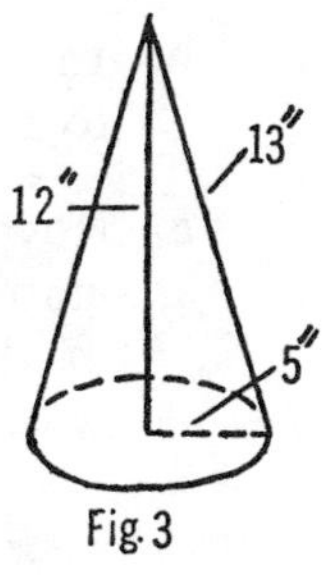

   a. What is its *lateral area*? _____

   b. What is its *total area*? _____

   c. What is its volume? _____

Fig. 3

2. The volume of a *can* is 450 cu. in. What is the volume of a CONE whose base and whose altitude are equal to the base and altitude of the can?

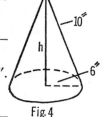
Fig. 4

_____

3. In Fig. 4, the radius of the base of the cone is 6″ and the slant height is 10″. Find the volume of the cone.

_____

D. AREAS AND VOLUMES OF SPHERES

We may derive the formula for determining the *surface area* of a sphere by experiment in this manner:

1. EQUIPMENT: A very THIN metal or plastic sphere of uniform thickness. A number of flat, circular discs having the same material, diameter, and thickness as the sphere. A sensitive balance.

2. PROCEDURE: Place the sphere on one side of the balance and on the other side, place the number of the discs needed to balance the sphere. Since the weight of ONE SQUARE INCH of a *disc* equals the weight of one square inch of the sphere, the weight of the sphere and the combined weights of the discs required to balance the sphere represent equal surface areas. See Fig. 5

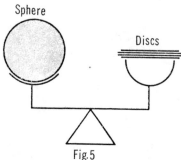
Fig. 5

3. CONCLUSION: It requires _____ of the discs to balance the sphere. So the surface area of the sphere is the same as the surface area of _____ of the discs. Since the surface area of ONE of the discs (expressed in terms of its radius r and π) is πr^2, the formula for the *total surface area* of the sphere becomes:

$$A_s = \text{_____} \pi r^2$$

We may experimentally derive the formula for finding the volume of a sphere in this manner:

1. EQUIPMENT: A closed water-tight sphere. A cylinder whose diameter and altitude are each equal to the diameter of the sphere. A graduated measuring vessel. A funnel; a container of water.

2. PROCEDURE: a. Fill the cylinder (shown at A) with water and then pour the water from the cylinder into the measuring vessel (shown at B) to determine the volume of the cylinder. In taking readings, sight horizontally along the *bottom* of the meniscus of the water in B and in D. Record the volume of the cylinder here:

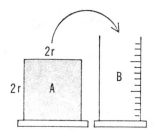

_____

b. Insert the sphere into the empty cylinder, and add enough water to fill the cylinder as shown at C.

c. Now pour the water from the cylinder (shown at C) into the empty measuring vessel (shown at D), to determine how much of the cylinder is being occupied by water. Record the volume of water that the cylinder had contained with the sphere in it here:

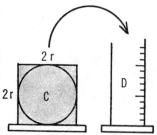

_____

d. From the volume of the water recorded in step *a* subtract the volume of the water recorded in step *c*, to determine the volume of the sphere. Record the volume of the sphere here: _____

e. From steps *a* and *d*, determine what fractional part the volume of the sphere is of the volume of cylinder A. Record the fractional part of cylinder A that was occupied by the sphere here: .... _____

3. CONCLUSION: Since the formula for the volume of the cylinder (expressed in terms of its radius *r* and its height 2 *r*) is: $V = B \cdot h = \pi r^2 \cdot 2 r = 2 \pi r^3$, the formula for the volume of the sphere becomes:

$$V_s = \underline{\qquad} \pi r^3$$

EXERCISES D.

1. In Fig. 4, the radius of the sphere is 5″. What is its surface area?

   _____

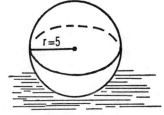

2. What is the surface area of a sphere if the surface area of one of its great circles is 60 s. i.?

   _____

Fig. 4

3. What part of the volume of a cylinder is a sphere which (when placed in the cylinder) snugly fits the curved surface of the cylinder and just touches the top and bottom?

   _____

4. In Fig. 4, find the volume of the sphere.

   _____

5. A cylinder whose height is equal to its diameter has a volume of 750 cu. in. What is the volume of a sphere whose diameter is equal to the diameter of the cylinder? (Hint: You need not find the radius.)

Modern Geometry — Unit Test 1.

Answer the following questions.

1. How many planes are determined by three points which are not in alignment? .... 1. _____

2. In how many points can two straight lines intersect? .... 2. _____

3. How many straight lines can be drawn through two points? .... 3. _____

4. What is the shortest distance between two points? .... 4. _____

5. What is the shortest distance from a point to a straight line? .... 5. _____

6. How many lines can be drawn parallel to a given line through a given point that is not on the given line? .... 6. _____

7. How many points does a line contain? .... 7. _____

8. How many points does a line-segment contain? .... 8. _____

9. How many points does space contain? .... 9. _____

10. How many points does a ray contain? .... 10. _____

11. How many lines can be drawn through a given outside point perpendicular to a given line? .... 11. _____

12. Is a plane determined by two points? .... 12. _____

13. Is a plane determined by two intersecting straight lines? .... 13. _____

14. Is a plane determined by two parallel lines? .... 14. _____

15. Is a plane determined by a line and a point outside that line? .... 15. _____

16. Are two points *always*, *sometimes*, or *never* collinear? .... 16. _____

17. What is the minimum number of distinct points required to form a "particle of space"? .... 17. _____

18. Which one of the following items represents the distance between two points: a. $\overrightarrow{RS}$ b. $\overline{RS}$ c. $\overleftrightarrow{RS}$ d. RS? .... 18. _____

19. What is the plane surface between the sides of an angle called? .... 19. _____

20. What is that type of reasoning called which involves the arrival at general conclusions from a study of specific supporting facts? .... 20. _____

21. What is that type of reasoning called which involves the arrival at specific conclusions on the basis of generally established supporting principles? .... 21. _____

22. GIVEN: Points A, B, and X with AX = XB. Must A, X, and B be collinear? .... 22. _____

23. GIVEN: Points A, B, and X with AX + XB = AB. Must X lie between A and B? .... 23. _____

What term is applied to each of the following expressions?

24. An angle that is greater than 90° but less than 180° .... 24. _____

25. Two angles that have a common vertex and a common side between them .... 25. _____

26. A definite part of a line .... 26. _____

27. A ray which passes through the vertex of an angle and separates the angle into halves .... 27. _____

28. The geometry which deals with space figures .... 28. _____

29. An angle whose sides are perpendicular to each other .... 29. _____

30. An angle whose sides form a straight line and also lie on opposite sides of its vertex .... 30. _____

31. Another commonly accepted name for the center of a line-segment .. 31. _____

32. Two angles whose sum is 90° .... 32. _____

33. A geometric figure formed by the union of two distinct rays that have the same end-point .... 33. _____

Solve the following exercises.

34. What is the complement of an angle of 85°? .... 34. _____

35. What is the supplement of an angle of 85°? .... 35. _____

36. A certain angle is three times as large as its COMPLEMENT. How many degrees are there in its COMPLEMENT? .... 36. _____

37. A certain angle is twice as large as its SUPPLEMENT. How many degrees are there in the ANGLE? .... 37. _____

38. How many degrees are there in ∠x in Fig. 1? $3X°+20$ ⌐$x°$⌐ $160°$ .... 38. _____

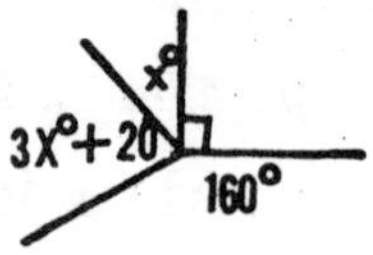

Fig. 1

39. In Fig. 2, $\overleftrightarrow{AB}$ and $\overleftrightarrow{CD}$ are intersecting straight lines. How many degrees are there in ∠ AOC? .... 39. _____

40. In Fig. 2, how many degrees are there in ∠1? .... 40. _____

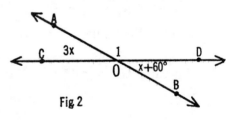

Fig 2

2

Modern Geometry — Unit Test 2.

What is the best term that may be applied to each of the following expressions?

1. The name for a closed geometric figure formed by the union of three or more coplanar line-segments .... 1. _____

2. The name for a closed coplanar geometric figure with five sides. .... 2. _____

3. The name for a closed coplanar geometric figure with eight sides. .... 3. _____

4. The name for a triangle with each side different in length .... 4. _____

5. The name for a triangle with at least two sides equal in length .... 5. _____

6. The name for a triangle with all three sides equal in length .... 6. _____

7. The name for the sum of the lengths of the sides of a polygon .... 7. _____

8. The name for a line-segment that joins any two non-consecutive vertices of a polygon. .... 8. _____

9. The name for the surface inclosed within a polygon .... 9. _____

10. The name for the perpendicular distance from a vertex of a triangle to the opposite side (or to its extension) .... 10. _____

11. How many axes of symmetry does a square have? .... 11. _____

12. How many axes of symmetry does a circle have? .... 12. _____

LIST OF REASONS

1. Associative Property of Multiplication
2. Symmetric Property of Equality
3. Associative Property of Addition
4. Commutative Property of Multiplication
5. Transitive Property of Equality
6. Comutative Property of Addition
7. Distributive Prop. of Multiplication over Add.
8. Reflexive Property of Equality
9. Addition Property of Equality
10. Closure Property
11. Multiplication Property of Inequality
12. Transitive Property of Inequality
13. Real numbers
14. Substitution
15. None of these

Fill each of the following answer-spaces with the NUMBER of the correct answer selected from the LIST OF REASONS.   REASONS

13. $5 + 3 = 3 + 5$ .... 13. _____
14. $5(3) = 3(5)$ .... 14. _____
15. $(5 + 3) + 2 = 5 + (3 + 2)$ .... 15. _____
16. $(5 \times 3)2 = 5(3 \times 2)$ .... 16. _____
17. $6(5 + 3) = 6(5) + 6(3)$ .... 17. _____
18. $7 = 7$ .... 18. _____
19. If $x = 3$, then $3 = x$ .... 19. _____
20. If $x = 3$ and $y = 5$, then $x + y = 8$ .... 20. _____
21. If $x > a$ and $a > 5$, then $x > 5$ .... 21. _____
22. If $x > 10$, then $3x > 30$ .... 22. _____

3

Fill each of the following answer-forms with the abbreviated form of the correct answer.
(For example: ASA, vert. ∠ are =, and the like)

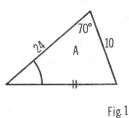

Fig. 1

23. In Fig. 1 △A ≅ △B. How many degrees
are there in ∠1 of △B? .... 23. _____

24. In Fig. 1, how long is side m of △B?

24. _____

GIVEN: Quadrilateral LMNO with LM = ON and LO = MN. Also $\overline{BC}$ is drawn through A, the midpoint of diagonal LN. TO PROVE: that AB = AC.

PROOF.   STATEMENTS   REASONS

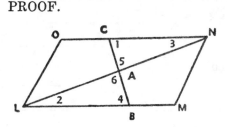

25. △ LMN ≅ △ LON .... 25. _____

26. Hence ∠2 = ∠3 .... 26. _____

27. ∠5 = ∠6 .... 27. _____

28. Hence △LBA ≅ △NCA .... 28. _____

29. ∴ AB = AC .... 29. _____

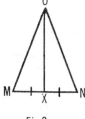

Fig. 2

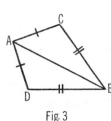

Fig. 3

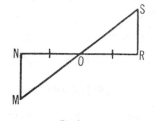

Fig. 4

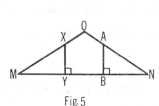

Fig. 5

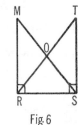

Fig. 6

30. In Fig. 2 $\overline{OX}$ ⊥ to $\overline{MN}$ and MX = NX. ∴ △MXO ≅ △NXO .... 30. _____

31. In Fig. 3 AC = AD and BC = BD. ∴ △ADB ≅ △ACB .... 31. _____

32. In Fig. 4 NO = RO and ∠N = a rt. ∠ and ∠R = a rt. ∠.
∴ △MON ≅ △RSO .... 32. _____

33. In Fig. 5 XO = AO and MO = NO. Also $\overline{XY}$ and $\overline{AB}$ are each ⊥ to $\overline{MN}$.
∴ △MYX ≅ △NBA .... 33. _____

34. In Fig. 6 RT = SM. Also $\overline{MR}$ and $\overline{TS}$ are ⊥ to $\overline{RS}$. ∴ △RST ≅ △SRM .... 34. _____

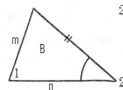

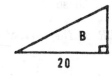

35. △A ≅ △B .... 35. _____

36. In △ C ∠ R = ?° .... 36. _____

37. In △ D side m = ? .... 37. _____

GIVEN: △RST with RT = ST and RA = SB.   TO PROVE: that AT = BT and ∠1 = ∠2.
PROOF.   STATEMENTS   REASONS

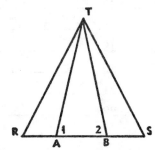

38. △ RAT ≅ △ SBT .... 38. _____

39. Hence AT = BT .... 39. _____

40. ∴ ∠1 = ∠2 .... 40. _____

4

Modern Geometry — Unit Test 3.

Make the following constructions accurately with compass and straightedge. Leave all construction lines.

1. In Fig. 1 bisect line-segment MN. Draw all auxiliary lines required for the proof.

Fig. 1: M ●————————● N

QUESTIONS FOR FIG. 1:

2. Why are the two △ which extend across MN congruent? .... _____

3. Why are the other two △ congruent? _____ _____

4. Why are the two line-segments into which $\overline{MN}$ is divided equal? .... _____

5. Why are the adjacent angles formed at the point of division of $\overline{MN}$ equal? .... _____

6. Why is the vertical line-segment (dividing $\overline{MN}$ into two equal parts) perpendicular to MN? _____ _____

7. In Fig. 2 bisect ∠ ABC. Draw all auxiliary lines required for the proof.

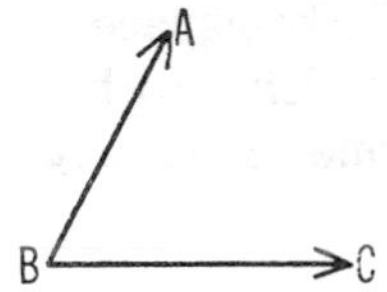

Fig 2

QUESTIONS FOR FIG. 2:

8. Why are the two △ congruent? _____ _____

9. Why are the ∠ at B equal? _____ _____

10. In Fig. 3 construct a perpendicular to $\overline{XY}$ from point C. Draw all auxiliary lines required for the proof.

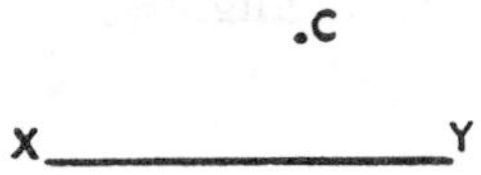

Fig. 3: X————————Y   .C

QUESTIONS FOR FIG. 3:

11. Why are the two △ which extend across $\overline{XY}$ congruent? .... _____

12. Why are the two △ above $\overline{XY}$ congruent? _____ _____

13. Why are the adjacent ∠ formed by $\overline{XY}$ and the vertical line-segment drawn through point C equal? _____ _____

14. Why is the vertical line-segment drawn through point C perpendicular to $\overline{XY}$? _____ _____

15. In Fig. 4 construct a perpendicular to $\overline{RS}$ at point P. Draw all auxiliary lines required for the proof.

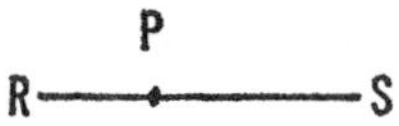

Fig. 4: R————●————S   P

QUESTIONS FOR FIG 4:

16. Why are the two △ (necessary for proof) congruent? .... _____

17. Why are the ∠ formed at P equal? _____ _____

18. Why is the vertical line-segment through P perpendicular to $\overline{RS}$? _____

19. In Fig. 5 construct an angle with its vertex at K that will
    equal ∠O. Draw all auxiliary lines required for the proof.

Fig. 5: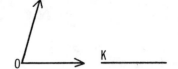

QUESTIONS FOR FIG. 5:

20. Why are the △ congruent? .... _____

21. Why does ∠K = ∠O? .... _____

22. In the space at the right, construct a △ which will have line-segments **m, n,** and **r** as its sides.

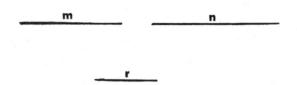

23. In the space at the right construct a right △
    which will have **h** as its hypotenuse and **s** as
    one of its sides.

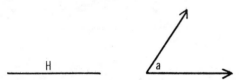

24. In the space at the right construct a right △ which will have **H** as its hypotenuse and ∠**a** as
    one of its angles.

25. In the space at the right construct a △ that will have ∠x and ∠y and line-segment **c** as the
    side between these two angles.

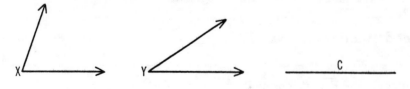

6

Modern Geometry — Unit Test 4.

Answer each of the following questions which is always true with an A, each which is some-times true with an S, and each which is never true with an N. (SPACE relations as well as plane relationships are to be considered in answering these questions.)

1. Do three parallel lines lie in the same plane? .... 1. _____

2. Do two intersecting lines determine a plane? .... 2. _____

3. If a line is perpendicular to one of two parallel lines, is it perpendicular to the other? .... 3. _____

4. Are two lines parallel, if each is parallel to a third line? .... 4. _____

5. Are two straight lines in the same plane cut by a transversal parallel, if the alternate exterior angles are equal? .... 5. _____

6. Are two straight lines in the same plane cut by a transversal parallel, if the corresponding angles are supplementary? .... 6. _____

7. Are straight lines which never meet parallel? .... 7. _____

8. Can two lines be drawn through a given point parallel to a given line? .... 8. _____

9. Can two lines in the same plane be drawn through a given point perpendicular to a given line? .... 9. _____

10. Are two straight lines in the same plane parallel, if they are perpendicular to the same line? .... 10. _____

11. If two angles have their sides parallel, right (initial) side to left (terminal) side and left (terminal) side to right (initial) side, are the angles equal? .... 11. _____

12. If two parallel lines are cut by a transversal, are the corresponding angles equal? .... 12. _____

13. Are two straight lines in the same plane cut by a transversal parallel, if the consecutive interior angles are equal? .... 13. _____

14. Are two straight lines in the same plane cut by a transversal parallel, if the consecutive interior angles are supplementary? .... 14. _____

15. If two angles have their sides parallel, right (initial) side to right (initial) side and left (terminal) side to left (terminal) side, are the angles equal? .... 15. _____

16. Will two lines that are not parallel intersect? .... 16. _____

Make the following construction accurately with compass and straightedge. Leave all con-struction lines and arcs.

17. Through point O construct a line-segment parallel to $\overline{AB}$.

.O

A_____B

In Fig. 1 what term is applied to each of the following combinations of angles?

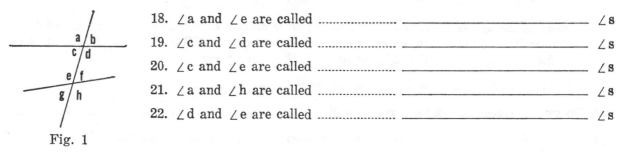

18. ∠a and ∠e are called .... _____ ∠s

19. ∠c and ∠d are called .... _____ ∠s

20. ∠c and ∠e are called .... _____ ∠s

21. ∠a and ∠h are called .... _____ ∠s

22. ∠d and ∠e are called .... _____ ∠s

Fig. 1

Fill each of the following answer-spaces with the NUMBER of the correct answer selected from the LIST OF REASONS.

LIST OF REASONS

1. HA	5. Vertical ∠ are =	9. c.p.c.t.e.
2. HS (HL)	6. ∠ opposite = sides of a △ are =	10. SSS
3. Construction	7. Substitution Principle	11. SAS
4. Given	8. A line ⊥ to one of 2 ∥s is ⊥ to the other.	12. ASA

THEOREM. If two parallel lines are cut by a transversal, the alternate interior angles are equal.

GIVEN: Two ∥ lines AB and CD cut by transversal $\overleftrightarrow{MN}$.

TO PROVE: that ∠1 = ∠2.

PROOF. Draw $\overline{XY}$ through O, the midpoint of $\overline{RS}$, ⊥ to $\overleftrightarrow{CD}$.

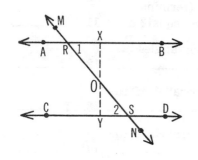

STATEMENTS	REASONS
23. ∠ROX = ∠SOY	23. _____
24. ∠Y is a rt. ∠	24. _____
25. Hence ∠X is a rt. ∠	25. _____
26. RO = SO	26. _____
27. Hence △ ROX ≅ △ SOY	27. _____
28. ∴ ∠1 = ∠2	28. _____

Solve the following exercises.

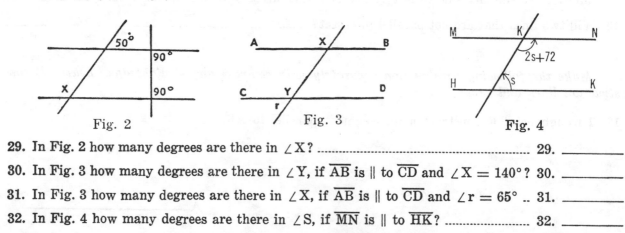

Fig. 2　　　　　Fig. 3　　　　　Fig. 4

29. In Fig. 2 how many degrees are there in ∠X? .... 29. _____

30. In Fig. 3 how many degrees are there in ∠Y, if $\overline{AB}$ is ∥ to $\overline{CD}$ and ∠X = 140°? 30. _____

31. In Fig. 3 how many degrees are there in ∠X, if $\overline{AB}$ is ∥ to $\overline{CD}$ and ∠r = 65° .. 31. _____

32. In Fig. 4 how many degrees are there in ∠S, if $\overline{MN}$ is ∥ to $\overline{HK}$? .... 32. _____

33. In Fig. 4 how many degrees are there in ∠K, if $\overline{MN}$ is ∥ to $\overline{HK}$? .... 33. _____

8

Modern Geometry — Unit Test 5.

Answer each of the following questions which is always true with an A, each which is some-times true with an S, and each which is never true with an N.

1. Can a triangle have more than one obtuse angle? .... 1. _____

2. Are two lines which are perpendicular respectively to two intersecting lines parallel? .... 2. _____

3. Are two right triangles congruent, if they have a leg and an acute angle of one equal respectively to a leg and the corresponding acute angle of the other? .... 3. _____

4. Are two triangles congruent, if they have two angles and a side of one equal re-spectively to the two angles and corresponding side of the other? .... 4. _____

5. Is the sum of two angles of a triangle greater than the third angle? .... 5. _____

6. If two angles have their sides perpendicular right (initial) side to left (terminal) side and left (terminal) side to right (initial) side, are the angles equal? .... 6. _____

7. Are the bisectors of two angles of a triangle parallel? .... 7. _____

8. If two triangles have two angles of one equal to the two angles of the other, are the third angles equal? .... 8. _____

9. If two angles have their sides perpendicular right (initial) side to right (initial) side and left (terminal) side to left (terminal) side, are the angles equal? .... 9. _____

10. If two angles have their sides perpendicular right (initial) side to right (initial) side and left (terminal) side to left (terminal) side, are the angles supplementary?
10. _____

11. If two angles have their sides perpendicular right (initial) side to left (terminal) side and left (terminal) side to right (initial) side, are the angles supplementary? 11. _____

12. Are two isosceles triangles congruent, if they have the vertex angle and the base of one equal to the vertex angle and the base of the other? .... 12. _____

Make the following construction accurately with compass and straightedge.

Leave all construction lines and arcs.

13. Construct △ ABC having given ∠A, ∠C, and side AB.

A————————————B

Fill each of the following answer-spaces with the number of the correct answer selected from the LIST OF REASONS.

LIST OF REASONS

1. Vertical ∡ are =
2. Substitution principle
3. Add. prop. of equality
4. Div. prop. of equality
5. Substraction prop. of equality
6. Given
7. Sides opposite = ∡ of a △ are =
8. All right ∡ are =
9. ∡ opposite = sides of a △ are =
10. The sum of the ∡ of a △ = a straight ∠
11. Angle-Addition Postulate
12. Definition of a straight ∠
13. AŠA
14. SAS
15. SSS
16. AAA
17. HS(HL)
18. HA
20. None of these

GIVEN: △ ABC with AD = DC = BD.

TO PROVE: that ∠B is a rt. ∠.

PROOF.   STATEMENTS   REASONS

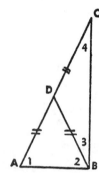

14. ∠1 = ∠2 .... 14. _____

15. ∠3 = ∠4 .... 15. _____

16. ∠1 + ∠2 + ∠3 + ∠4 = 180° .... 16. _____

17. Hence 2 ∠2 + 2 ∠3 = 180° .... 17. _____

18. ∴ ∠2 + ∠3, or ∠B, = 90°, or a rt ∠ .... 18. _____

Solve the following exercises.

19. How many degrees are there in each base angle of an isosceles right triangle? .... 19. _____

20. One angle of a triangle is twice the smallest, and the third angle exceeds the smallest angle by 48°. How many degrees are there in the smallest angle? .... 20. _____

21. How many degrees are there in each angle of an equilateral triangle? .... 21. _____

22. One of the acute angles of a right triangle is 72°. How many degrees are there in the other acute angle? .... 22. _____

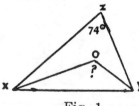

Fig. 1

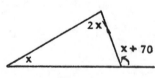

Fig. 2

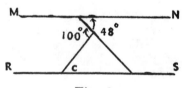

Fig. 3

23. In Fig. 1 $\overline{XO}$ bisects ∠X and $\overline{YO}$ bisects ∠Y. How many degrees are there in ∠XOY? ....

.... 23. _____

24. In Fig. 2 how many degrees are there in ∠x? .... 24. _____

25. In Fig. 3 how many degrees are there in ∠c, if $\overline{MN}$ and $\overline{RS}$ are ∥? .... 25. _____

10

Modern Geometry — Unit Test 6.

Answer each of the following questions correctly with ALWAYS, SOMETIMES, *or* NEVER.

1. Are two consecutive angles of a parallelogram equal? .... 1. _____

2. Are the diagonals of a rhombus perpendicular to each other? .... 2. _____

3. If a number of parallels intercept equal distances on one of two transversals, will they intercept equal distances on the other? .... 3. _____

4. If the diagonals of a quadrilateral are equal, is the quadrilateral a square? .... 4. _____

5. Are the opposite angles of a parallelogram equal? .... 5. _____

6. Are segments of parallel lines included between parallel lines equal? .... 6. _____

7. Is a trapezoid a parallelogram? .... 7. _____

8. Is a rectangle a parallelogram? .... 8. _____

9. Is a quadrilateral whose opposite sides are parallel a parallelogram? .... 9. _____

10. Is a quadrilateral whose four angles are right angles a square? .... 10. _____

11. If a pair of opposite sides of a quadrilateral are equal, is the figure a parallelogram? .... 11. _____

12. If the opposite sides of a quadrilateral are equal, is the figure a parallelogram? 12. _____

13. If two sides of a quadrilateral are equal and parallel, is the figure a parallelogram? .... 13. _____

14. If the diagonals of a quadrilateral bisect each other, is the quadrilateral a parallelogram? .... 14. _____

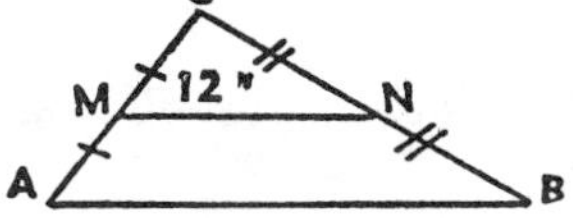

Fig. 1   Fig. 2 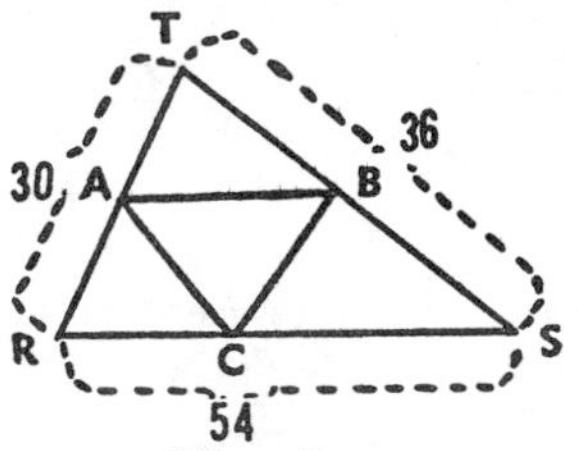   Fig. 3 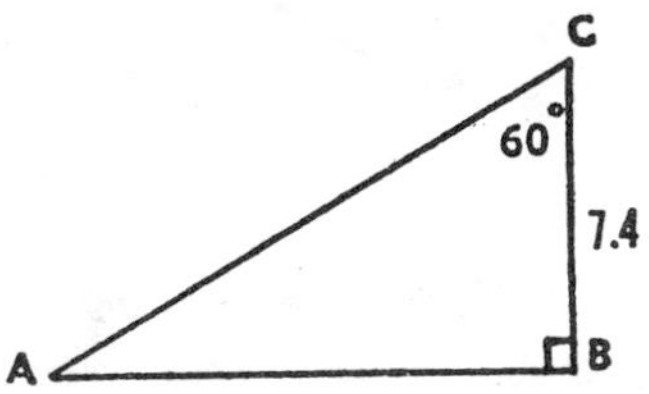   Fig. 4

Solve the following exercises and answer the questions.

15. In Fig. 1 $\overline{MN}$ is 12 inches long and joins the midpoints of $\overline{AC}$ and $\overline{BC}$ of △ ABC. How long is $\overline{AB}$? .... 15. _____

16. In Fig. 2 ∠R of ▱ RSTW is 48°. How many degrees are there in ∠S? .... 16. _____

17. In Fig. 3 RT = 30, RS = 54, and ST = 36. A, B, and C are the midpoints of the sides of △ RST. What are the lengths of the sides of △ ABC? .... 17. _____

18. In Fig. 4 what is the length of $\overline{AC}$ in △ ABC? .... 18. _____

19. All native Americans are *born* free. Mr. Jones was born in America. Therefore, Mr. Jones was *?* .... 19. _____

20. The type of deductive reasoning involved in statement 19 is called a(n) *?* 20. _____

11

STATEMENT A: If two △ can be made to coincide, they are congruent.

21. "If two △ are congruent, they can be made to coincide" is called the *?* of STATEMENT A .... 21. _____

22. "If two △ cannot be made to coincide, they are not congruent" is called the *?* of STATEMENT A. .... 22. _____

23. "If two △ are not congruent, they cannot be made to coincide" is called the *?* of STATEMENT A .... 23. _____

24. Is statement 21 true or false? .... 24. _____

25. Is statement 22 true or false? .... 25. _____

26. Is statement 23 true or false? .... 26. _____

LIST OF REASONS

Fill each of the following answer-spaces with the NUMBER of the correct answer selected from the LIST OF REASONS.

1. Lines cut by a transv. forming = alt. int. △ are ∥

2. ∥ lines cut by a transv. form = alt. int. △

3. Opposite sides of a ▱ are =

4. SSS

5. cpcte

6. SAS

7. ASA

8. Def. of ▱

9. Vert. △ are =

GIVEN: ▱ MSRN with diagonals MR and SN.

TO PROVE: that MA = RA and SA = NA.

PROOF.

STATEMENTS	REASONS
27. MN is ∥ to SR	27. _____
28. Hence ∠1 = ∠2 and ∠3 = ∠4	28. _____
29. MN = SR	29. _____
30. Hence △MAN ≅ △SAR	30. _____
31. ∴ MA = RA and SA = NA	31. _____

Make the following constructions accurately with compass and straightedge. Leave all construction lines and arcs.

32. Divide line-segment AB into three equal parts.

A ————————————————— B

33. Construct a parallelogram having side MN, side NR, and diagonal MR.

M—————————N

N————————R

M————————————R

12

Modern Geometry — Unit Test 7.

Answer each of the following questions correctly with YES or NO.

1. Is it possible for a REGULAR polygon to have an exterior angle of 24°? .... 1. _____

2. Is it possible for a REGULAR polygon to have an exterior angle of 80°? .... 2. _____

3. Is it possible for a polygon to have an interior angle of 17°? .... 3. _____

4. Is it possible for a polygon to have an interior angle of 180°? .... 4. _____

5. Is it possible for a polygon to have an exterior angle of 180°? .... 5. _____

6. In $\triangle ABC$ $\angle A = 80°$ and $\angle B = 30°$. Which side in the longest? .... 6. _____

Answer each of the following questions which is always true with an A, each which is sometimes true with an S, and each which is never true with an N.

7. Is the sum of the exterior angles of a triangle (made by extending the sides of the triangle in succession) the same as the sum of the exterior angles of a hexagon (made by extending its sides in succession)? .... 7. _____

8. Does each interior angle of a REGULAR polygon decrease as the number of sides of the polygon increases? .... 8. _____

9. Are an exterior angle of a polygon and an adjacent interior angle suppplementary? .... 9. _____

10. Is the sum of the interior angles of a regular polygon of 15 sides the same as the sum of the interior angles of an irregular polygon of 15 sides? .... 10. _____

11. Is an equiangular polygon a regular polygon? .... 11. _____

Solve the following exercises.

12. A polygon is composed of 34 triangles formed by drawing all possible diagonals from a single vertex. How many sides does the polygon have? .... 12. _____

13. How many sides does a polygon have, if the sum of its interior angles is equal to the sum of its exterior angles (made by extending its sides in succession)? .... 13. _____

14. Four interior angles of a pentagon are 100°, 140°, 110°, and 120° respectively. How many degrees are there in the remaining angle? .... 14. _____

15. How many degrees are there in the total sum of the exterior angles of a polygon (made by extending its sides in succession) and its interior angles, if the polygon has 20 sides? .... 15. _____

16. How many degrees are there in each interior angle of a regular polygon of twelve sides? .... 16. _____

17. How many sides does a polygon have, if the sum of its interior angles is 1980° 17. _____

18. How many sides does a regular polygon have, if each of its interior angles contains 150° .... 18. _____

19. How many degrees are there in each exterior angle of a regular octagon? .... 19. _____

Fill each of the following answer-spaces with the NUMBER of the correct answer selected from the LIST OF REASONS.

LIST OF REASONS

1. Given

2. Substitution Principle

3. Add. Prop. of equality

4. ∡ opposite = sides of a △ are =

5. The sum of 2 sides of a △ is greater than the third one.

6. Construction.

7. The entire length of a line-segment is greater than the length of any one of its parts.

8. If 2 ▲ have 2 sides of the one = to 2 sides of the other but the included ∠ of the first △ > the included ∠ of the second △, then the third side of the first △ > the third side of the second △.

9. If 2 sides of a △ are unequal, the ∠ opposite the greater side is the greater.

10. If 2 ▲ have 2 sides of the one = to the 2 sides of the other but the third side of the first △ > the third side of the second △, then the ∠ opposite the third side of the first △ > the ∠ opposite the third side of the second △.

11. Transitive Property of equality

12. Transitive Property of inequality

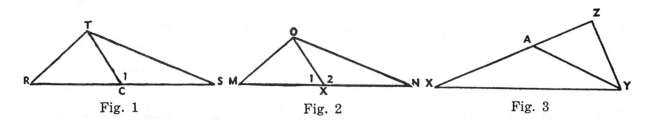

Fig. 1   Fig. 2   Fig. 3

GIVEN: In Fig. 1 △RST with RC = SC. Also ∠ 1 is obtuse.

20. ST > RT. Why? .... 20. _____

21. Hence ∠R > ∠S. Why? .... 21. _____

GIVEN: In Fig. 2 △MNO with MX = NX and NO > MO.

22. ∠2 > ∠1. Why? .... 22. _____

GIVEN: In Fig. 3 △XYZ with AZ = YZ.

23. XZ > AZ. Why? .... 23. _____

24. Hence XZ > YZ. Why? .... 24. _____

25. ∴ ∠Y > ∠X. Why? .... 25. _____

Modern Geometry — Unit Test 8.

Fill each of the following answer-spaces with the NUMBER of the correct answer selected from the LIST OF REASONS.

LIST OF REASONS

1. Sides opposite equal ∡ of a △ are =
2. ∡ opposite equal sides of a △ are =
3. Corresponding ∡ of ∥ lines are =
4. Complements of equal ∡ are =
5. Substitution Principle
6. Any quantity is either =, >, or < a like quantity. (Trichotomy)
7. In equal ⊚, the greater of 2 central ∡ has the greater chord.
8. In equal ⊚, the greater of 2 arcs has the greater chord.
9. Alternate interior ∡ of ∥ lines are equal.
10. Elimination of all possibilities except one.
11. In the same ⊙ or in equal ⊚, equal central ∡ have equal chords.
12. In the same ⊙ or in equal ⊚, equal central ∡ have equal arcs.
13. Contradiction of hypothesis
14. c.p.c.t.e.
15. Vertical ∡ are =
16. The whole = the sum of its parts
17. SSS
18. ASA
19. SAS
20. HS (HL)
21. HA
22. Reflex. prop. of equality
23. None of these

GIVEN: Equal ⊚ O and O′ with chord MN > chord M′N′ and having central ∡ O and O′ respectively.

TO PROVE: that ∠O > O′.

PROOF.

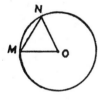

STATEMENTS	REASONS
1. Either ∠O = ∠O′, or ∠O < ∠O′, or ∠O > ∠O′	1. _____
2. If ∠O = ∠O′, then chord MN must = chord M′N′	2. _____
3. But $\overline{MN}$ cannot = $\overline{M'N'}$ (Why?), and hence ∠O cannot = ∠O′	3. _____
4. If ∠O < ∠O′, then chord MN must be < chord M′N′	4. _____
5. But $\overline{MN}$ cannot be < $\overline{M'N'}$ (Why?) and hence ∠O cannot be < ∠O′	5. _____
6. ∴ ∠O must be > ∠O′	6. _____

GIVEN: ⊙ C with radius CB ∥ to chord MA.

TO PROVE: that $\overarc{AB} = \overarc{NB}$.

PROOF. Draw $\overline{AC}$.

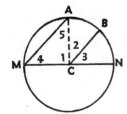

STATEMENTS	REASONS
7. ∠4 = ∠5	7. _____
8. ∠3 = ∠4	8. _____
9. ∠2 = ∠5	9. _____
10. Hence ∠2 = ∠3	10. _____
11. ∴ $\overarc{AB} = \overarc{NB}$	11. _____

15

Refer to the corresponding figures in answering the following questions.

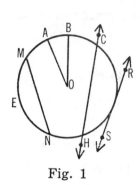

Fig. 1

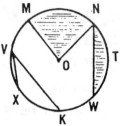

Fig. 2

12. In Fig. 1, what kind of angle is acute ∠AOB called? .... 12. _____

13. In Fig. 1, what is $\overline{MN}$ called? .... 13. _____

14. In Fig. 1, what is $\overline{OB}$ called? .... 14. _____

15. In Fig. 1, what is $\overleftrightarrow{RS}$ called? .... 15. _____

16. In Fig. 1, what is $\overleftrightarrow{CH}$ called? .... 16. _____

17. In Fig. 1, what is curved line-segment MEN called? .... 17. _____

18. In Fig. 2, what is shaded area MON called? .... 18. _____

19. Ln Fig. 2, what is shaded area NWT called? .... 19. _____

20. In Fig. 2, what kind of angle is acute ∠XVK called? .... 20. _____

21. A circle has a radius of 4.5 in. What is the length of its longest chord? 21. _____

22. What term is applied to a figure consisting of all those points and only those points which fulfill a given condition? .... 22. _____

23. Construct the locus of points which are equidistant from points M and N.

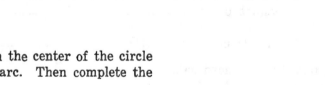

23.

24. Draw the locus of a point which is ¼ in. from line-segment RS.

24.

25. Find by construction the center of the circle of which AB is an arc. Then complete the circle.

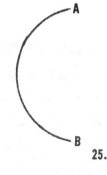

25.

16

Modern Geometry — Unit Test 9.

Answer each of the following questions which is always true with an A, each which is some-times true with an S, and each which is never true with an N.

1. Is it possible to inscribe a circle in any rectangle which is not a square? .... 1. _____

2. Is it possible to circumscribe a circle about any rectangle which is not a square? 2. _____

3. Is it possible to inscribe a circle in any triangle? .... 3. _____

4. Is it possible to circumscribe a circle about any triangle? .... 4. _____

5. Is it possible to inscribe a circle in any rhombus? .... 5. _____

6. Is it possible for the bisectors of the sides of a triangle to meet at the same point as that of the bisectors of its angles? .... 6. _____

Fill each of the following answer-spaces with the number of the correct answer selected from the LIST OF REASONS.

LIST OF REASONS

1. Given

2. SSS

3. c.p.c.t.e.

4. SAS

5. HA

6. HS(HL)

7. Construction

8. Substitution Principle

9. Add. Prop. of equality

10. Multiplication Prop. of equality

11. Reflex. Prop. of equality

12. A diameter ⊥ to a chord bisects its arcs.

13. A line ⊥ to one of 2 ∥s is ⊥ to the other.

14. A tangent is ⊥ to a radius drawn to the point of contact.

15. The greater of 2 central ∡ has the greater arc.

16. Equal central ∡ in equal circles have equal arcs.

GIVEN: ⊙O with diameter CD ⊥ to chord AB.

TO PROVE: that AX = BX and that $\overset{\frown}{AD} = \overset{\frown}{BD}$.

PROOF. Draw $\overline{AO}$ and $\overline{BO}$.

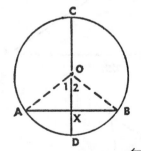

STATEMENTS	REASONS
7. △AXO ≅ △BXO	7. _____
8. ∴ AX = BX	8. _____
9. ∠1 = ∠2	9. _____
10. ∴ $\overset{\frown}{AD} = \overset{\frown}{BD}$	10. _____

GIVEN: ⊙O′ with $\overleftrightarrow{MN}$ tangent to ⊙O at X and ∥ to $\overline{RS}$.

TO PROVE: that $\overset{\frown}{RX} = \overset{\frown}{SX}$.

PROOF. Draw diameter XY.

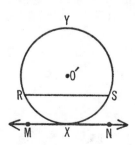

STATEMENTS	REASONS
11. $\overline{XY}$ is ⊥ to $\overleftrightarrow{MN}$	11. _____
12. Hence $\overline{XY}$ is ⊥ to $\overline{RS}$	12. _____
13. ∴ $\overset{\frown}{RX} = \overset{\frown}{SX}$	13. _____

What geometric term is applied to each of the following expressions?

14. The point of intersection of the medians of a triangle .... 14. _____

15. A line passing through the centers of two circles .... 15. _____

16. The point of intersection of the perpendicular bisectors of the sides of a triangle .... 16. _____

17. The point of intersection of the bisectors of the angles of a triangle 17. _____

18. The point of intersection of the altitudes of a triangle .... 18. _____

Solve the following exercises.

19. An equilateral triangle is inscribed in a circle whose radius is 18. How long is its altitude? .... 19. _____

20. The altitude of an equilateral triangle is 15 in. long. How long is the radius of the circle circumscribed about the triangle? .... 20. _____

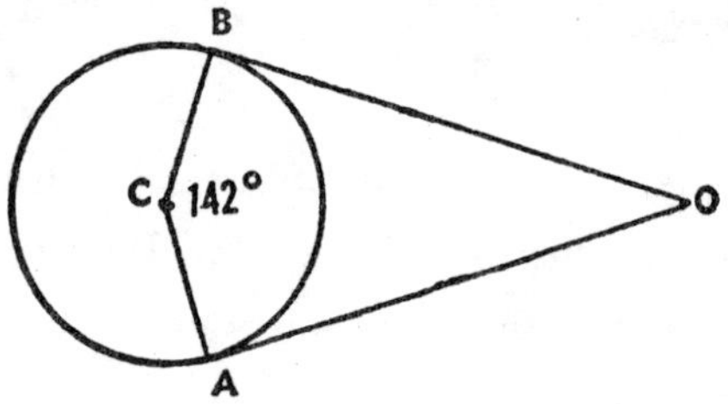

Fig. 1

21. In Fig. 1 $\overline{AO}$ and $\overline{BO}$ are tangent to $\odot C$. $\angle ACB$ = 142°. How many degrees are there in $\angle O$? ...... 21. _____

Make the following constructions accurately with compass and straightedge. Leave all construction lines and arcs.

22. Bisect arc AB.

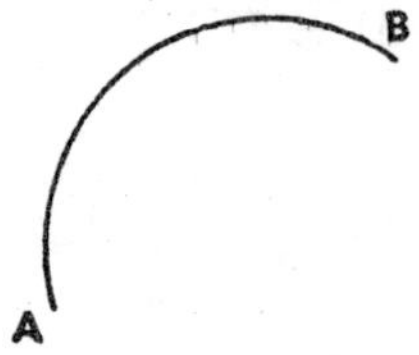

22.

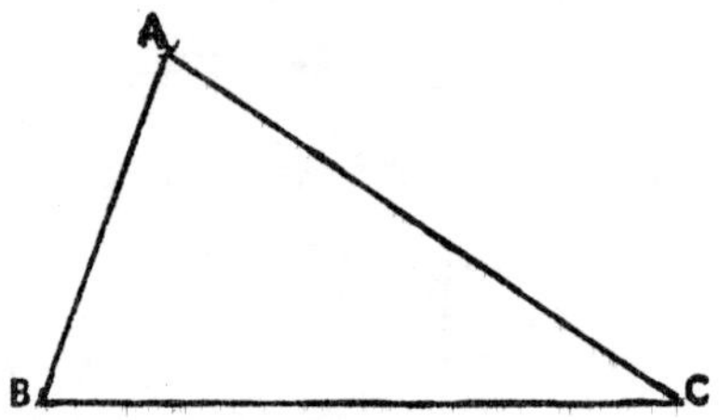

23.

23. Inscribe a circle in △ABC.

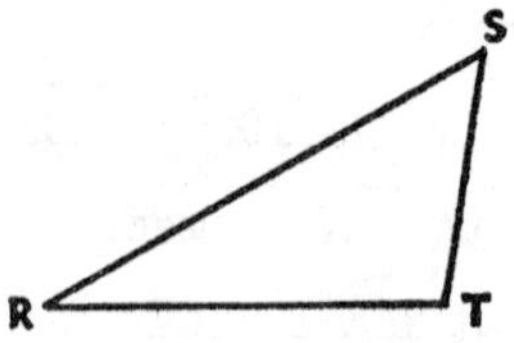

24. Circumscribe a circle about △RST.

24.

A•

•C

25. Pass a circle through points A, B, and C.

B •

25.

18

Modern Geometry — Unit Test 10.

Complete each of the following statements with the correct answer.

1.-2. Angles inscribed in arcs *less* than a semicircle intercept arcs which are .. 1 .. than 180° and hence are always .. 2 .. angles.

3. Angles inscribed in semicircles are always .. 3 .. angles.

4.-5. In equal circles, chords *nearest* the center are .. 4 .. in length, and those *farthest* from the center are .. 5 .. in length.

6.-7. A (n) .. 6 .. angle always equals its intercepted arc, whereas a (n) .. 7 .. angle always equals one-half its intercepted arc.

8. In *unequal* circles, arcs containing the same number of degrees have .. 8 .. central angles.

9.-11. In equal circles, equal chords are always .. 9 .. from .. 10 .., and they always contain .. 11 .. arcs.

1. _____

2. _____

3. _____

4. _____

5. _____

6. _____

7. _____

8. _____

9. _____

10. _____

11. _____

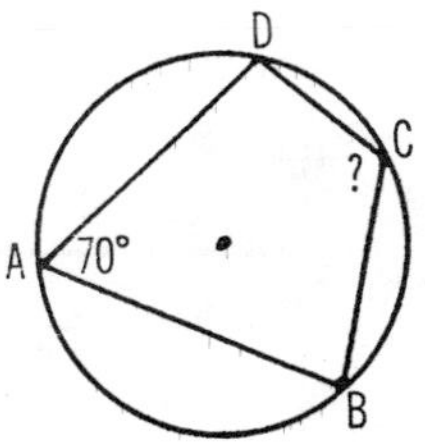

Fig.1

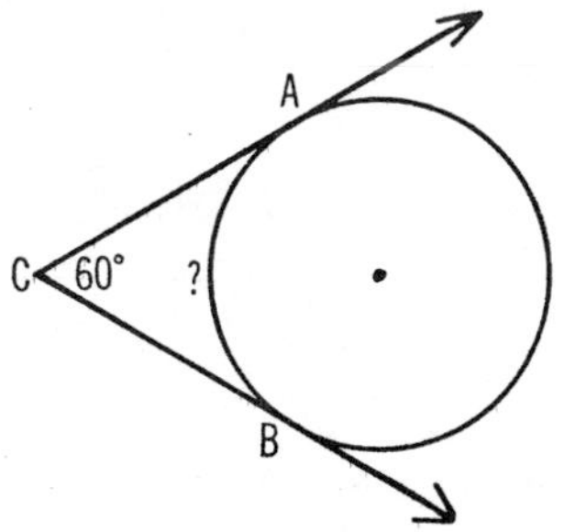

Fig. 2

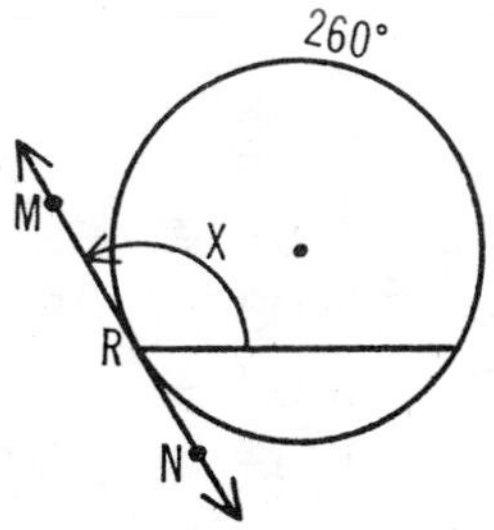

Fig.3

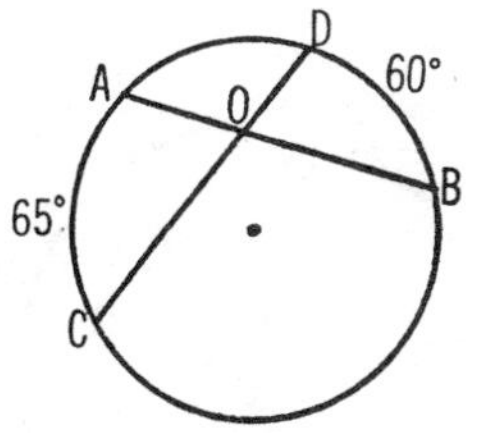

Fig 4

Solve the following exercises.

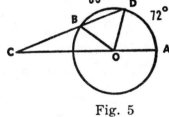

Fig. 5

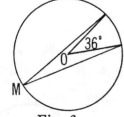

Fig. 6

12. In Fig. 1 how many degrees are there in ∠C? .... 12. _____

13. In Fig. 1 how many degrees are there in arc BAD? 13. _____

14. In Fig. 2 how many degrees are there in minor $\widehat{AB}$? 14. _____

15. In Fig. 3 how many degrees are there in ∠x? .... 15. _____

16. In Fig. 4 how many degrees are there in ∠AOC? .... 16. _____

17. In Fig. 5 AC passes through O, the center of the circle. How many degrees are there in ∠C? .... 17. _____

18. In Fig. 5 how many degrees are there in ∠ COB? .... 18. _____

19. In Fig. 5 how many degrees are there in ∠ CBO? .... 19. _____

20. In Fig. 6 ∠O is a central angle. How many degrees are there in ∠M? .... 20. _____

19

Fill each of the following answer-spaces with the number of the correct answer selected from the LIST OF REASONS.

LIST OF REASONS

1. ASA
2. SSS
3. HA
4. SAS

8. Alternate interior ∠ of ∥ lines are =.
9. An inscribed ∠ is measured by ½ its intercepted arc.
10. A central ∠ is measured by its intercepted arc, and conversely.
11. ∠ opposite equal sides of a △ are =.
12. An exterior ∠ of a △ = the sum of the 2 non-adjacent interior ∠.

5. Arcs between ∥s are =.
6. Radii of the same ⊙ are =.
7. Transitive property of equality

14. Subtraction property of equality
15. Multiplication property of equality
16. Division property of equality
13. Powers property of equality
17. Substitution Principle

18. Vertical ∠ are =
19. Addition property of equality
20. Definition of an ∠
21. None of these

GIVEN: ∠R inscribed in ⊙O.   TO PROVE: that ∠R ≐ ½ ⌢MS.

PROOF. Draw $\overline{SO}$.

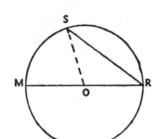

STATEMENTS	REASONS
21. RO = SO	21. _____
22. ∠R = ∠S	22. _____
23. ∠MOS ≐ ⌢MS	23. _____
24. ∠MOS = ∠R + ∠S	24. _____
25. ∠MOS = 2∠R	25. _____
26. ∠R = ½ ∠MOS	26. _____
27. ½ ∠MOS ≐ ½ ⌢MS	27. _____
28. ∴ ∠R ≐ ½ ⌢MS	28. _____

GIVEN: ⊙C with tangent AB and chord MN, making ∠X at point of contact M.

TO PROVE: that ∠X ≐ ½ ⌢MN.

PROOF. Through N draw chord NS ∥ to $\overline{AB}$.

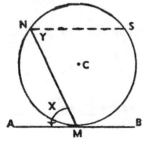

STATEMENTS	REASONS
29. ∠X = ∠Y	29. _____
30. ⌢MN = ⌢MS	30. _____
31. ∠Y ≐ ½ ⌢MS	31. _____
32. ∴ ∠X ≐ ½ ⌢MN	32. _____

Make the following construction accurately with compass and straightedge. Leave all construction lines and arcs.

33. Construct a tangent to ⊙O from point P.

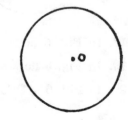

P.

20

Modern Geometry — Unit Test 11.

What term is applied to each of the following expressions?

1. Polygons that have equal areas .... 1. _____

2. The number of square units of measure contained in a surface .... 2. _____

3. Quantities that have a common unit of measure which is contained in each of them a whole number of times .... 3. _____

4. A line-segment which joins the midpoints of the non-parallel sides of a trapezoid .... 4. _____

Answer each of the following questions which is always true with an A, each which is sometimes true with an S, and each which is never true with an N.

5. Are parallelograms which have equal bases and altitudes equal in area? .... 5. _____

6. Are triangles that have equal bases and altitudes equal in area? .... 6. _____

7. Is the area of a parallelogram equal to the product of its two adjacent sides? .... 7. _____

8. Is the area of a square equal to the square of one of its sides? .... 8. _____

9. Is the area of a triangle one-half the area of a parallelogram whose base and altitude is the same as the base and altitude of the triangle? 9. _____

10. Is $\frac{3}{4}$ a rational number? .... 10. _____

11. Is the $\sqrt{3}$ a rational number? .... 11. _____

Solve the following exercises.

12. What is the area of a rectangle 15 ft. long and 10 in. wide? .... 12. _____

13. What is the area of triangle having a base of 7.35 ft. and an altitude of 20 ft? .... 13. _____

14. What is the area of a trapezoid whose bases are 12 and 20 and whose altitude is 6? .... 14. _____

15. What is the area of a trapezoid whose median is 10 and whose altitude is 50? .... 15. _____

16. What is the volume of a rectangular solid 5 in. long, 3 in. wide, and 8 in. high? .... 16. _____

17. The base of pyramid P is a 16 x 16 square. Its altitude is 15. Find its lateral area. .... 17. _____

18. What is the volume of pyramid P? 18. _____

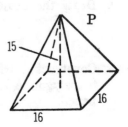

19. What is the side of a square which has the same area as a rectangle whose dimensions are 5 by 80? .... 19. _____

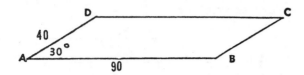 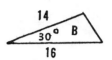

20. What is the area of parallelogram ABCD? .... 20. _____

21. What is the area of △A? .... 21. _____

22. What is the length of W in △A? .... 22. _____

23. What is the area of △B? .... 23. _____

24. What is the area of an isosceles trapezoid whose bases are 20 and 36 and whose non-parallel sides are 17 each? .... 24. _____

25. In trapezoid ABCD base AB = 40, base CD = 20, non-parallel side AD = 8, and ∠A = 60°. What is the area of the trapezoid? .... 25. _____

26. What is the area of a triangle whose sides are 15, 10, and 7? .... 26. _____

27. What is the area of a square whose diagonal is 14? .... 27. _____

28. What is the value of x in rt. △C? .... 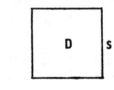 .... 28. _____

29. What is the area of rt. △C? .... 29. _____

Make the following constructions accurately with compass and straightedge, leaving all construction lines and arcs.

30. Construct a square whose area will be twice the area of square D.

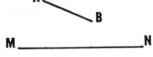

31. Upon $\overline{RS}$ as its base, construct a parallelogram which will be equivalent to △ RST. Shade the parallelogram with pencil.

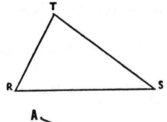

32. Draw the projection of $\overline{AB}$ upon $\overline{MN}$.

33. Construct a triangle that will be equivalent to polygon ABCDE. Shade the triangle with pencil.

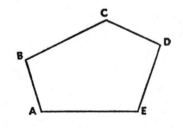

22

Modern Geometry — Unit Test 12.

Give the correct answer to each of the following questions.

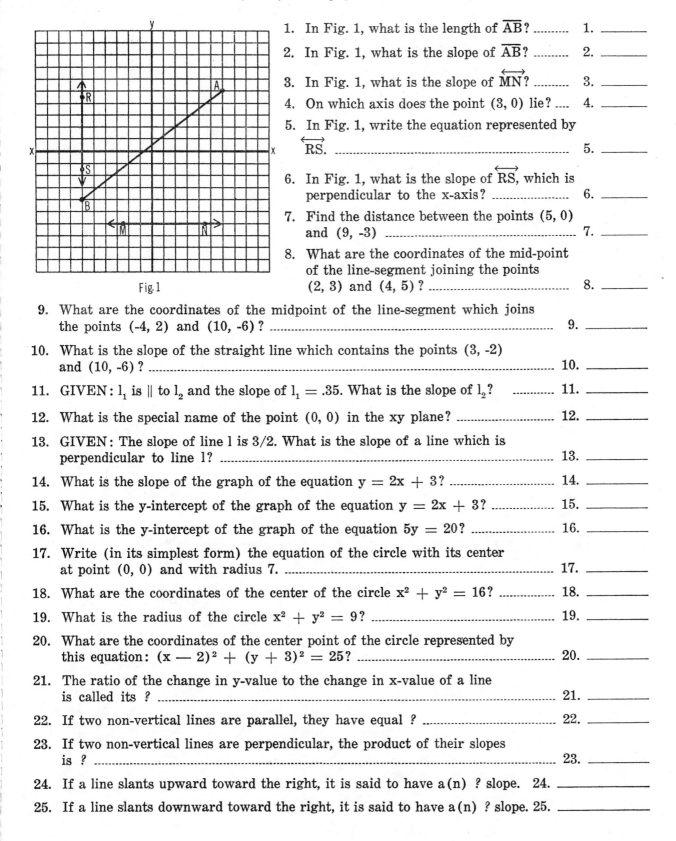

Fig. 1

1. In Fig. 1, what is the length of $\overline{AB}$? .... 1. _____
2. In Fig. 1, what is the slope of $\overline{AB}$? .... 2. _____
3. In Fig. 1, what is the slope of $\overleftrightarrow{MN}$? .... 3. _____
4. On which axis does the point (3, 0) lie? .... 4. _____
5. In Fig. 1, write the equation represented by $\overleftrightarrow{RS}$. .... 5. _____
6. In Fig. 1, what is the slope of $\overleftrightarrow{RS}$, which is perpendicular to the x-axis? .... 6. _____
7. Find the distance between the points (5, 0) and (9, -3) .... 7. _____
8. What are the coordinates of the mid-point of the line-segment joining the points (2, 3) and (4, 5)? .... 8. _____

9. What are the coordinates of the midpoint of the line-segment which joins the points (-4, 2) and (10, -6)? .... 9. _____

10. What is the slope of the straight line which contains the points (3, -2) and (10, -6)? .... 10. _____

11. GIVEN: l_1 is ∥ to l_2 and the slope of l_1 = .35. What is the slope of l_2? .... 11. _____

12. What is the special name of the point (0, 0) in the xy plane? .... 12. _____

13. GIVEN: The slope of line l is 3/2. What is the slope of a line which is perpendicular to line l? .... 13. _____

14. What is the slope of the graph of the equation y = 2x + 3? .... 14. _____

15. What is the y-intercept of the graph of the equation y = 2x + 3? .... 15. _____

16. What is the y-intercept of the graph of the equation 5y = 20? .... 16. _____

17. Write (in its simplest form) the equation of the circle with its center at point (0, 0) and with radius 7. .... 17. _____

18. What are the coordinates of the center of the circle $x^2 + y^2 = 16$? .... 18. _____

19. What is the radius of the circle $x^2 + y^2 = 9$? .... 19. _____

20. What are the coordinates of the center point of the circle represented by this equation: $(x - 2)^2 + (y + 3)^2 = 25$? .... 20. _____

21. The ratio of the change in y-value to the change in x-value of a line is called its ? .... 21. _____

22. If two non-vertical lines are parallel, they have equal ? .... 22. _____

23. If two non-vertical lines are perpendicular, the product of their slopes is ? .... 23. _____

24. If a line slants upward toward the right, it is said to have a(n) ? slope. 24. _____

25. If a line slants downward toward the right, it is said to have a(n) ? slope. 25. _____

23

Modern Geometry — Unit Test 13.

Complete each of the following statements with the correct answer.

1. A single fraction, like "3:4," which expresses the comparison of two numbers of like kind, is called a (n) . . 1 . ... 1. _____

2. An expression like "3:5 = 6:10", which expresses the equality of two fractions, is called a (n) . . 2 . ... 2. _____

3. A line which divides two sides of a triangle proportionally is . . 3 . . to the third side. .... 3. _____

4. If two line-segments are divided in such a way that any two parts of the one have the same ratio as the corresponding parts of the other, the line-segments are said to be divided . . 4 . ... 4. _____

5. If the point of division of a line-segment lies upon its extension, the line-segment is said to be divided . . 5 . ... 5. _____

6. If the point of division of a line-segment lies between its end points, the line-segment is said to be divided . . 6 . ... 6. _____

In the expression 5 : 10 = x : y,

7. Which terms are the means? .... 7. _____

8. Which terms are the extremes? .... 8. _____

9. Which terms are the antecedents? .... 9. _____

10. Which terms are the consequents? .... 10. _____

Fill correctly the answer-space of each of the following questions with YES or NO.

11. If m:n = r:s, then is m:r = n:s? .... 11. _____

12. If a:x = b:y, then is x:a = y:b? .... 12. _____

13. If a:b = c:x, then is a:c = x:b? .... 13. _____

14. If 1:7 = x:y, then is 8:7 = (x + y) : y? .... 14. _____

15. If mb = nc, then is m:n = c:b? .... 15. _____

16. If r:a = x:y, then is (r — a) : a = (x .... y) : y? .... 16. _____

17. If a:m = r:x, then is ax = mr? .... 17. _____

18. If $\dfrac{h}{c} = \dfrac{x}{b}$, then is $\dfrac{h + x}{c + b} = \dfrac{x}{b}$? .... 18. _____

Solve the following exercises.

19. 5 : 3 = x : 6 $\qquad$ x = ... 19. _____

20. $\dfrac{x + 5}{7} = \dfrac{3}{4}$ $\qquad$ x = ... 20. _____

21. What is the third proportional to 4 and 12? .... 21. _____

22. What is the fourth proportional to 3, 5, and 12? .... 22. _____

23. What is the mean proportional between 15 and 60? .... 23. _____

24. The ratio of two complementary angles is 3 to 7. How many degrees are there in the smaller angle? .... 24. _____

25. The ratio of two supplementary angles is 4 to 5. How many degrees are there in the larger angle? .... 25. _____

26. A line-segment 45 in. long is divided into two parts whose ratio is 2 to 7. How long is the shorter part? .... 26. _____

27. r : 5 = s : m and a : x = b : c. If r = a, s = b and m = c, what is x? .... 27. _____

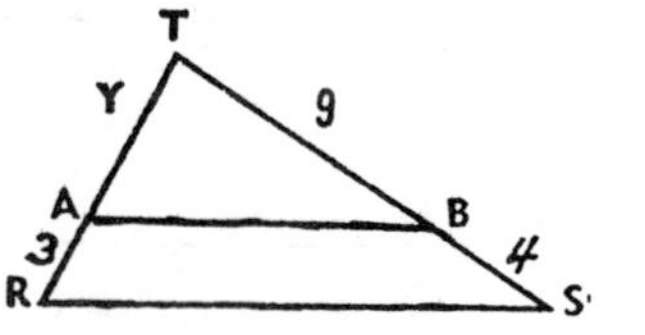

Fig. 1 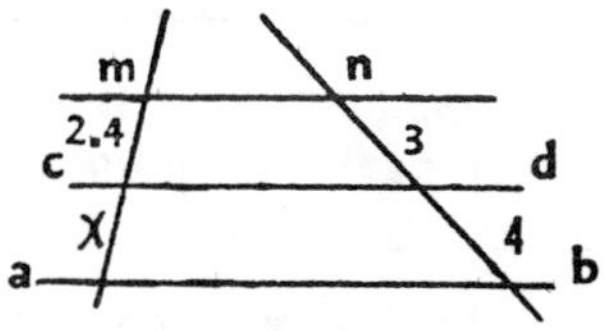   Fig. 2 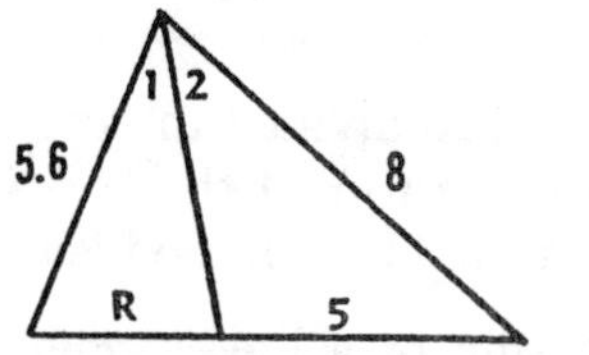   Fig. 3 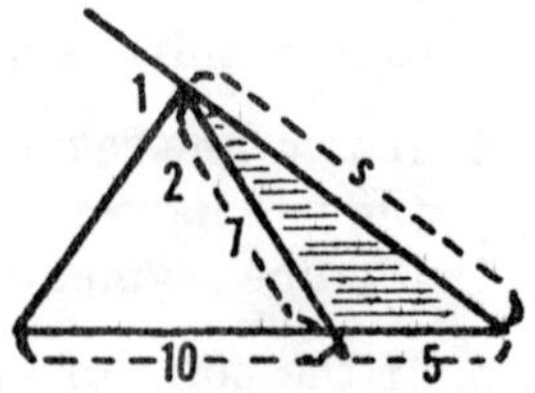   Fig. 4

28. In Fig. 1 $\overline{AB}$ is ‖ to $\overline{RS}$. How long is Y? .... 28. _____

29. In Fig. 2 ab, cd, and mn are ‖. How long is x? .... 29. _____

30. In Fig. 3 if ∠1 = ∠2, how long is R? .... 30. _____

31. In Fig. 4 if ∠1 = ∠2, how long is s? .... 31. _____

Make the following constructions with compass and straightedge, leaving all construction lines and arcs.

32. Divide line-segment MN into three parts which are proportional to line-segments m, n, and r.

M_____N

_____ m _____   _____ n _____   _____ r _____

33. Construct a rectangle whose length is l and that will be equivalent to square N.

_____ l _____   N | s

Modern Geometry — Unit Test 14.

Answer each of the following questions which is always true with an A, each which is sometimes true with an S, and each which is never true with an N.

1. Are triangles that are similar to the same triangle similar to each other? .... 1. _____

2. Are congruent triangles similar? .... 2. _____

3. Are similar triangles congruent? .... 3. _____

4. Are rectangles similar, if their corresponding sides are proportional? .... 4. _____

5. Are quadrilaterals similar, if their corresponding angles are equal? .... 5. _____

6. Are two triangles similar, if the sides of one are 5, 7, 9 and the sides of the other 15, 21, 18? .... 6. _____

7. Are two polygons similar, if they have the same shape? .... 7. _____

8. Are two triangles similar, if their sides are parallel, respectively? .... 8. _____

9. Are two triangles similar, if they have two angles of one equal to two angles of the other? .... 9. _____

10. Are equivalent triangles similar? .... 10. _____

11. Are right triangles similar? .... 11. _____

12. Are equilateral triangles similar? .... 12. _____

13. Are squares similar? .... 13. _____

14. Are isosceles right triangles similar? .... 14. _____

15. Is an obtuse triangle similar to a right triangle? .... 15. _____

16. Do corresponding sides of similar polygons have the same ratio as their perimeters? .... 16. _____

17. Can two similar polygons be divided into the same number of triangles which are similar each to each? .... 17. _____

18. Are two polygons similar if they are composed of the same number of triangles which are similar each to each and similarly placed? .... 18. _____

19. Do the corresponding diagonals of two similar polygons have the same ratio as a pair of corresponding sides? .... 19. _____

20. In $\triangle ABC$ $\angle B = 75°$, $AB = 4$, and $AC = 5$. In $\triangle A'B'C'$ $\angle B' = 75°$, $A'B' = 9$, and $A'C' = 10$. Are the triangles similar? .... 20. _____

Solve the following exercises.

21. The three sides of a certain triangle are 30 in., 45 in., and 60 in. respectively. If the triangle is diminished in size but not in shape until the 30 in. side becomes 8 in., what will be the lengths of the other *two* sides of the diminished triangle? 21. _____

22. The perimeters of two similar hexagons are 35 in. and 70 in. respectively. If one side of the first is 10 in., find the corresponding side of the second. .... 22. _____

23. What is the width of a sheet of paper 16 in. long such that, when folded in fourths crosswise, each fourth will have the same shape as the original sheet? .. 23. _____

27

24. The perimeters of two similar polygons are 24.8 and 124. What is the ratio of similitude of these triangles? .... 24. _____

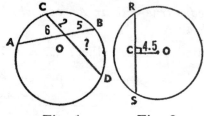

Fig. 1   Fig. 2

25. In Fig. 1 AO = 6, CO = 2, and BO = 5. How long is OD? .... 25. _____

26. In Fig. 2 the radius of ⊙O is 7.5. CO = 4.5. How long is $\overline{RC}$? 26. _____

27. How long is $\overline{RS}$.? .... 27. _____

Fill each of the following answer-spaces with the NUMBER of the correct answer selected from the LIST OF REASONS.

LIST OF REASONS

1. Dividing the numerator and the denominator of a fraction by the same number does not change the value of the fraction.

2. Corresponding sides of ~ polygons are proportional.

3. If 2 △ have an ∠ of the one equal to an ∠ of the other and the including sides proportional, the △ are similar.

4. Corresponding ∡ of ~ polygons are =

5. △ that are mutually equiangular are ~

6. Proportion by alternation.

7. Substitution Principle

8. Given

9. c.p.c.t.e.

10. SSS

11. SAS

12. ASA

13. None of these

GIVEN: △RST ~ △R'S'T' with medians MT and M'T' respectively.

TO PROVE: △RMT ~ △R'M'T'.

PROOF.

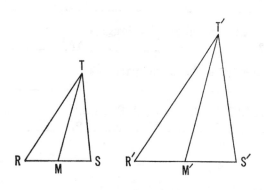

STATEMENTS	REASONS
28. ∠R = ∠R'	28. _____
29. $\dfrac{RT}{R'T'} = \dfrac{RS}{R'S'}$	29. _____
30. $\dfrac{RM}{R'M'} = \dfrac{RS}{R'S'}$	30. _____
31. $\dfrac{RT}{R'T'} = \dfrac{RM}{R'M'}$	31. _____
32. ∴ △RMT ~ △R'M'T'	32. _____

33. Upon $\overline{XY}$ as the base corresponding to side MN of △MNO, construct a triangle that will be similar to △MNO.

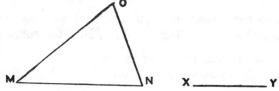

28

Modern Geometry — Unit Test 15.

Complete each of the following statements with the correct answer.

1-4. If a tangent and a secant are drawn to a circle from an external point, the . . 1 . . becomes the . . 2 . . between the whole . . 3 . . and its . . 4 . . part ....

5-6. A perpendicular drawn from any point on a circle to its diameter is the . . 5 . . between the segments of the . . 6 . ...

7-10. The altitude drawn from the vertex of the . . 7 . . angle of a right △ to the hypotenuse forms two . . 8 . . which are . . 9 . . to each other and to the given . . 10 . . ..

11-12. A line-segment is said to be divided into extreme and mean ratio if the . . 11 . . part becomes the mean proportional between the whole line-segment and the . . 12 . . part. ....

1. _____

2. _____

3. _____

4. _____

5. _____

6. _____

7. _____

8. _____

9. _____

10. _____

11. _____

12. _____

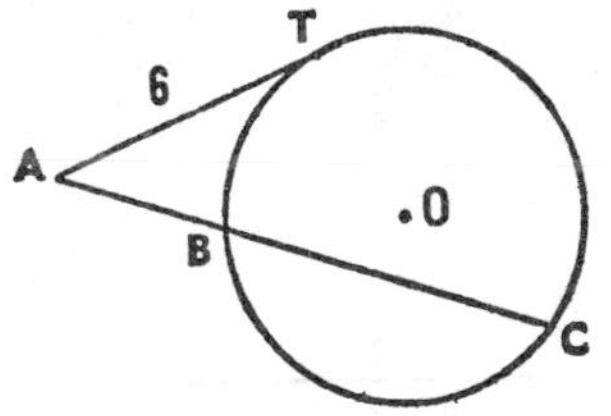

Fig. 1

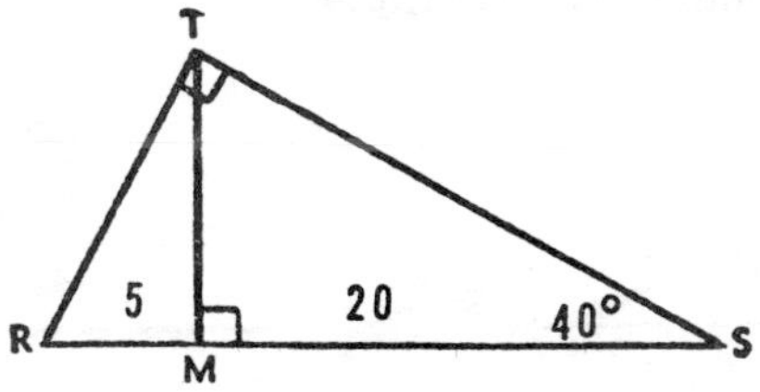

Fig. 2

13. In Fig. 1 $\overline{AT}$ is tangent to circle O and $\overline{BC}$ is 3 times as long as $\overline{AB}$. How long is $\overline{AC}$? ....

13. _____

In the triangle of Fig. 2, what is the value of —

14. ∠RTM? ....

14. _____

15. ∠R ? ....

15. _____

16. ∠MTS? ....

16. _____

17. $\overline{MT}$? ....

17. _____

18. $\overline{RT}$? ....

18. _____

19. $\overline{ST}$? ....

19. _____

20. In Fig. 2, how many similar triangles are present? ....

20. _____

21. A line-segment is 12 inches long. What is the length of the longer part if the line-segment is divided into extreme and mean ratio? ....

21. _____

Make each of the following constructions geometrically, leaving all construction lines and arcs.

22. Upon line-segment **c** construct a mean proportional, **x**, between **a** and **b**.

a —————— b —————— c ————————————————

23. Upon line-segment **d** construct a rectangle, whose length and width is $\overline{RS}$ that will be equivalent to square A. Shade the rectangle with pencil.

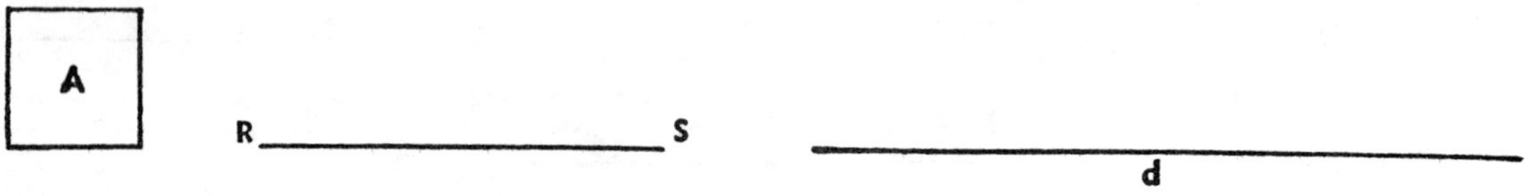

A

R —————————— S   d ————————————————

24. Upon line-segment **e** construct a line-segment, **m**, which will be $\sqrt{6}$ times line-segment **r**.

r ——————   e ————————————————

25. Divide line segment MN into extreme and mean ratio. Indicate the point of division with the letter P.

M ———————————— N

Modern Geometry — Unit Test 16.

Answer each of the following questions which is always true with an A, each which is some-times true with an S, and each which is never true with an N.

1. Do the areas of two triangles have the same ratio as their altitudes? .... 1. _____

2. Do the areas of two triangles have the same ratio as the products of their bases and altitudes? .... 2. _____

3. Do the perimeters of two *similar* triangles have the same ratio as their areas? 3. _____

4. Do the areas of two parallelograms have the same ratio as the products of their altitudes and bases? .... 4. _____

5. Do the areas of parallelograms with equal altitudes have the same ratio as the square roots of their bases? .... 5. _____

6. Do the areas of two rectangles have the same ratio as the squares of their bases? 6. _____

7. Do the areas of two similar polygons have the same ratio as the squares of any two corresponding sides? .... 7. _____

8. Do the areas of two similar parallelograms have the same ratio as the squares of a pair of diagonals? .... 8. _____

9. Do the squares of a pair of corresponding altitudes of similar triangles have the same ratio as the squares of a pair of corresponding sides? .... 9. _____

10. Are two rectangles that have equal perimeters equivalent in area? .... 10. _____

Complete each of the following statements with the correct answer.

11. If the perimeter of the first of two similar triangles is one-third that of the the second, then the area of the first triangle is . . 11 . . that of the second .... 11. _____

12. If the areas of two triangles (with equal altitudes) have a ratio of 4 to 9, then their bases have a ratio of . . 12 . ... 12. _____

13. Any . . 13 . . of any triangle will divide the triangle into two equivalent parts 13. _____

14. If a polygon is diminished in size until each of its sides becomes 2/5 its original length, then its area will become . . 14 . . its original area. .... 14. _____

15. If a polygon is magnified until its area becomes 100 times its original area, then its sides will become . . 15 . . times their original lengths. .... 15. _____

Solve the following numerical exercises.

16. The areas of two similar polygons are 25 and 625 respectively. If a side of the first is 6, what is the corresponding side of the second? .... 16. _____

17. The area of a certain polygon is 80 sq. in. What is the area of a similar polygon whose dimensions are one-fourth as large as those of the given polygon? .... 17. _____

18. The perimeters of two similar triangles are 60 in. and 40 in. respectively. The area of the larger is 72 sq. in. What is the area of the smaller? .... 18. _____

19. The corresponding altitudes of two similar triangles are 2 in. and 3 in. respectively. The area of the larger triangle is 36 sq. in. What is the area of the smaller? .... 19. _____

20. A, B, and C are three regular polygons with the same number of sides. Each side of A is 5 and its area is 100. Each side of B is 4 and its area is 64. What is the area of C if each of its sides is 3? .... 20. _____

21. The base of a certain triangle is 4. What is the corresponding base of a similar triangle whose area is 10 times as great? .... 21. _____

22. In △ABC ∠A = 50°, AB = 16, and AC = 20. In △MON ∠M = 50°, MO = 40, and MN = 24. The area of △MON = 75. What is area of △ABC? .... 22. _____

Fill each of the following answer-spaces with the number of the correct answer selected from the LIST OF REASONS.

LIST OF REASONS

1. The areas of similar △ are proportional to the squares of any 2 corresponding sides.
2. Similar polygons can be divided into the same number of similar △ similar each to each.
3. In any proportion the sum of the antecedents (numerators) is to the sum of the consequents (denominators) as any antecedent (numerator) is to its consequent (denominator).
4. Transitive property of equality.
5. Addition property of equality   6. The area — Addition postulate   7. Substitution principle
8. None of these.

GIVEN: Polygon P ~ polygon P' with respective areas a and a'.

TO PROVE: that $\dfrac{a}{a'} = \dfrac{s^2}{s'^2}$.

PROOF. From corresponding vertices O and O' draw diagonals OR and OK, and O'R' and O'K' respectively.

STATEMENTS   REASONS

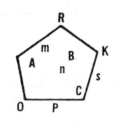

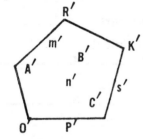

23. △A ~ △A', △B ~ △B' and △C ~ △C'   .... 23. _____

24. $\dfrac{\triangle A}{\triangle A'} = \dfrac{m^2}{m'^2}$ and $\dfrac{\triangle B}{\triangle B'} = \dfrac{m^2}{m'^2}$ .... 24. _____

25. $\dfrac{\triangle A}{\triangle A'} = \dfrac{\triangle B}{\triangle B'}$ .... 25. _____

26. $\dfrac{\triangle B}{\triangle B'} = \dfrac{n^2}{n'^2}$ and $\dfrac{\triangle C}{\triangle C'} = \dfrac{n^2}{n'^2}$ .... 26. _____

27. $\dfrac{\triangle B}{\triangle B'} = \dfrac{\triangle C}{\triangle C'}$ .... 27. _____

28. Hence $\dfrac{\triangle A}{\triangle A'} = \dfrac{\triangle B}{\triangle B'} = \dfrac{\triangle C}{\triangle C'}$ .... 28. _____

29. $\dfrac{\triangle A + \triangle B + \triangle C}{\triangle A' + \triangle B' + \triangle C'} = \dfrac{\triangle C}{\triangle C'}$ .... 29. _____

30. However, a = △A + △B + △ C and a' = △A' + △B' + △C' .... 30. _____

31. $\dfrac{\triangle C}{\triangle C'} = \dfrac{s^2}{s'^2}$ .... 31. _____

32. ∴ $\dfrac{a}{a'} = \dfrac{s^2}{s'^2}$ .... 32. _____

33. Construct a △ A'B'C' that will be similar to △ ABC and that will have *four* times the area of △ ABC.

32

Modern Geometry – Unit Test 17.

Answer each of the following questions which is always true with an A, each which is some-times true with an S, and each which is never true with an N.

1. Are equiangular polygons regular? .... 1. _____

2. Is it possible to inscribe a circle in any regular polygon? .... 2. _____

3. Are two regular polygons having the same number of sides similar? .... 3. _____

4. Are the areas of two regular polygons having the same number of sides propor-tional to their sides? .... 4. _____

5. Are the perimeters of two regular polygons having the same number of sides proportional to their apothems? .... 5. _____

6. Is an equilateral polygon inscribed in a circle regular? .... 6. _____

7. Is an equiangular polygon inscribed in a circle regular? .... 7. _____

8. Are equilateral polygons regular? .... 8. _____

9. Is it possible to circumscribe a circle about a regular polygon? .... 9. _____

10. Is it possible to inscribe a circle in a triangle? .... 10. _____

Refer to the corresponding figure in answering the following questions.

Fig. 1

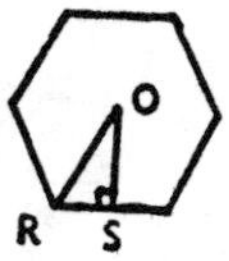

11. In Fig. 1 what is ∠AOB called? .... 11. _____

12. In Fig. 2 what is $\overline{OR}$ called? .... 12. _____

13. In Fig. 2 what is $\overline{OS}$ called? .... 13. _____

Fig. 2

Solve the following numerical exercises.

14. How many degrees are there in the central angle of a regular pentagon?
.... 14. _____

15. How many degrees are there in each interior angle of a regular octagon? .... 15. _____

16. What is the perimeter of a regular hexagon circumscribed about a circle whose radius is 5? .... 16. _____

17. The areas of two similar polygons are 40 and 10 respectively. If the perimeter of the first is 24, what is the perimeter of the second? .... 17. _____

18. The side of a regular hexagon is 40. What is its area? .... 18. _____

19. What is the ratio of the area of the equilateral triangle inscribed in a circle whose radius is 6 to the area of the one circumscribed about the circle? .... 19. _____

20. The area of a regular polygon is 75 sq. in., and its perimeter is 40 in. What is the radius of the inscribed circle? .... 20. _____

21. How many sides does a regular polygon have if each of its central angles contains 15 degrees? .... 21. _____

Make the following constructions accurately with compass and straightedge. Leave all construction lines and arcs.

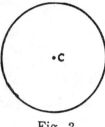

Fig. 3

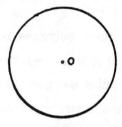

Fig. 4

22. Inscribe an equilateral △ in ⊙ C (Fig. 3).

23. Inscribe a regular octagon in ⊙O (Fig. 4).

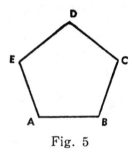

Fig. 5

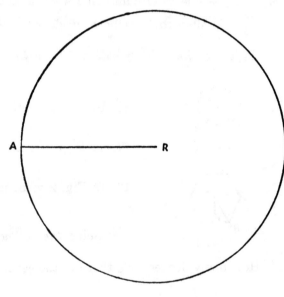

Fig. 6

24. Circumscribe a circle about regular polygon ABCDE (Fig. 5).

25. Inscribe a regular pentagon in ⊙R (Fig. 6).

Modern Geometry — Unit Test 18.

Complete each of the following statements with the correct answer.

1. A mathematical quantity (or number) which may change in value in a given situation (or problem) is called a (n) . . 1 . .

   1. _____

2. A mathematical quantity (or number) whose value remains fixed throughout a given discussion is called a (n) . . 2 . .

   2. _____

3. If variable $x \rightarrow 7$, then $5x \rightarrow$ . . 3 . .

   3. _____

4. If variable x always $=$ variable y, and $x \rightarrow$ m as $y \rightarrow$ n, then m $=$ . . 4 . .

   4. _____

5. The ratio of the circumference of a circle to its . . 5 . . is π.

   5. _____

6. If the radius of a circle is doubled, its area will become . . 6 . . times as great.

   6. _____

   7. _____

7-8. The value of the sum of the angles of a triangle is an example of a (n) . . 7 . . quantity. The value of any one of the three angles of a triangle is an example of a (n) . . 8 . . quantity.

   8. _____

   9. _____

9-13. As the number of sides of a regular polygon inscribed within a circle is increased infinitely, its . . 9 . . will approach the radius of the circle, its . . 10 . . will approach the circumference of the circle, its . . 11 . . will approach the . . 12 . . of the circle, and its . . 13 . . will remain constant.

   10. _____

   11. _____

   12. _____

   13. _____

14-18. As the number of sides of a regular polygon circumscribed about a circle is increased infinitely, its area will approach the area of the . . 14 . ., its . . 15 . . will approach the radius of the circle, its . . 16 . . will approach the . . 17 . . of the circle, and its . . 18 . . will remain constant.

   14. _____

   15. _____

   16. _____

   17. _____

   18. _____

19. Has the exact numerical value of π ever been determined?

   19. _____

Solve the following exercises. (Use $\pi = 3.14$ in those exercises which require the use of π.)

20. A regular polygon is inscribed in a circle whose radius is 3 in. What will be the limit of the *area* of the polygon as the number of its sides is increased infinitely? (Express the answer in square inches.)

   20. _____

21. What will be the limit of the *perimeter* of the polygon in problem 20 expressed in inches?

   21. _____

22. What will be the limit of the length of the apothem of the polygon in problem 20? (Express the answer in inches.)

   22. _____

23. Circle A has a radius of $\sqrt{5}$ and circle B has a radius of 3. What is the ratio of the area of circle A to the area of circle B?

   23. _____

24. What is the area of a circle whose radius is 1 in.? (Express the answer in square inches.)

   24. _____

25. What is the **circumference** of a circle whose diameter is **5 in.?** (Express the answer in inches.) .... 25. _____

26. The radius of a circle is 9 in. Find the length of an arc of 80°. (Express the answer in inches.) .... 26. _____

27. The radius of a circle is 3m and its circumference is 4n. What is the area of the circle in terms of m and n? (Do not use π.) .... 27. _____

28. The ratio of the circumference of two circles is 25 : 4. What is the ratio of their areas? .... 28. _____

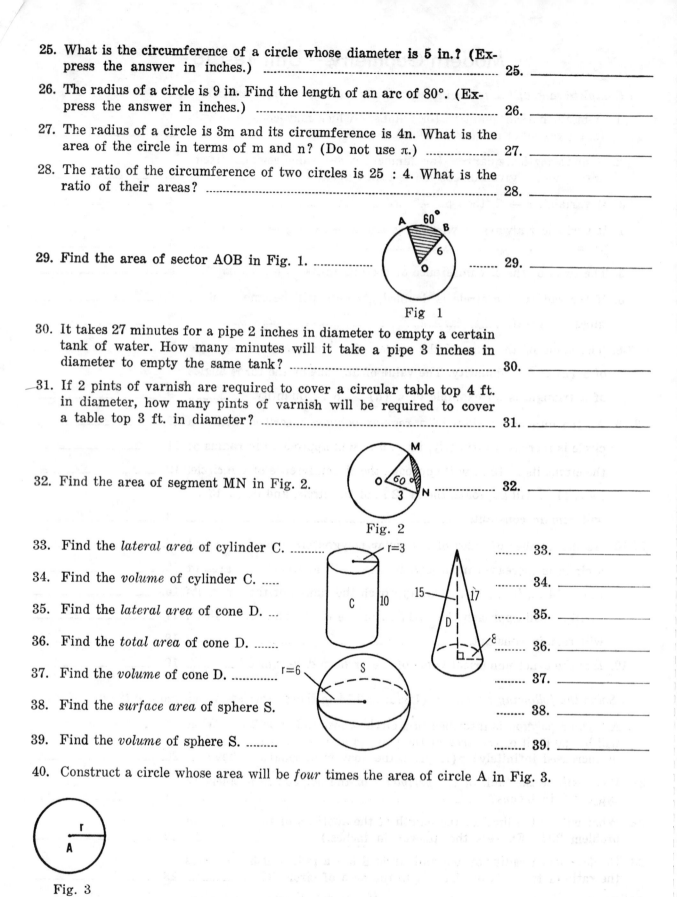

29. Find the area of sector AOB in Fig. 1. .... 29. _____

Fig 1

30. It takes 27 minutes for a pipe 2 inches in diameter to empty a certain tank of water. How many minutes will it take a pipe 3 inches in diameter to empty the same tank? .... 30. _____

31. If 2 pints of varnish are required to cover a circular table top 4 ft. in diameter, how many pints of varnish will be required to cover a table top 3 ft. in diameter? .... 31. _____

32. Find the area of segment MN in Fig. 2. .... 32. _____

Fig. 2

33. Find the *lateral area* of cylinder C. .... 33. _____

34. Find the *volume* of cylinder C. ..... 34. _____

35. Find the *lateral area* of cone D. ... 35. _____

36. Find the *total area* of cone D. .... 36. _____

37. Find the *volume* of cone D. .... 37. _____

38. Find the *surface area* of sphere S. 38. _____

39. Find the *volume* of sphere S. .... 39. _____

40. Construct a circle whose area will be *four* times the area of circle A in Fig. 3.

Fig. 3